DISCOURSE ON METHOD, OPTICS,

GEOMETRY, and METEOROLOGY

D1344912

The Library of Liberal Arts

OSKAR PIEST, FOUNDER

DISCOURSE ON METHOD, OPTICS, GEOMETRY, and METEOROLOGY

René Descartes

Translated, with an Introduction, by
Paul J. Olscamp
Assistant Professor of Philosophy, The Ohio State University

The Library of Liberal Arts

published by

THE BOBBS-MERRILL COMPANY, INC.
A SUBSIDIARY OF HOWARD W. SAMS & CO., INC.
Publishers • Indianapolis • New York • Kansas City

René Descartes: 1596–1650

The *Discourse on Method, Optics, Geometry,*
and *Meteorology* were first published
together in 1637.

TRANSLATOR'S PREFACE

*But I have not been able to understand your objection
concerning the title "Discourse on Method"; for I did not
call it* Treatise on Method, *but* Discourse on Method,
*which is the same as Preface or Advice concerning Method,
in order to show that I do not intend to teach it, but only
to speak about it. For as you can see from what I say of it,
it consists more in Practice than in Theory, and I called
the treatises following the Discourse* Essays *in this Method,
because I hold that the things that they contain could
not have been discovered without the method, and that
through them you can know its value.*

—DESCARTES TO MERSENNE

So much has been written about Descartes that it would not,
I believe, be amiss to mention here three facts which justify
the present volume. First, two of Descartes' works, the *Dioptrique* and the *Météores* (here called *Optics* and *Meteorology*),
have never before been translated fully into English. Descartes
is indisputably one of the greatest figures in Western philosophy, and it would seem desirable to have all of his works
available in English translation.

Moreover, Descartes himself intended the *Discourse on
Method* to be a preface to the *Optics, Geometry,* and *Meteorology;* it was so published in 1637. It is therefore evident that
the relations among all these works are important to the study
of Descartes; yet contrary to his original intention, the *Discourse* has been studied for hundreds of years apart from the
other three works.

Finally, it is in fact true that new light is shed on the Cartesian method when the works in this volume are considered as a unit; I have tried to sketch the implications of this in my Introduction, hoping that it will spur a re-evaluation of the traditional interpretations of the works of this soldier, scientist, and philosopher.

The works in this book have been translated from the *Œuvres de Descartes,* edited by Charles Adam and Paul Tannery.

I have received a good deal of help in the preparation of this book, and I trust that those who aided me will realize the depth of my gratitude. The original idea for the volume was given to me by Professor Colin Murray Turbayne of the University of Rochester, and he has remained steadfast in his active support of the venture ever since its inception. Not only has he given me valuable aid in criticizing the Introduction, but it will be evident to the readers of his own book, *The Myth of Metaphor,* that I owe much to him concerning my own ideas about the Cartesian method. My colleagues in the Department of Philosophy at the Ohio State University, especially Dr. Andrew Oldenquist and Dr. Wallace Anderson, have contributed welcome suggestions to the Introduction. Finally, a special word of thanks to my dearest friend, Gilles Matte, who has given his time without reservation to the checking and revision of the translations; without his assistance it would not have been possible for this book to appear. The fact that this volume is dedicated to him is an inadequate measure of my gratitude for his aid, and my esteem for the man.

CONTENTS

INTRODUCTION

I

In 1637 René Descartes published the *Discourse on the Method for Rightly Directing One's Reason and Searching for Truth in the Sciences* as an introduction to three other essays—the *Geometry*, the *Optics*, and the *Meteorology*—in which he intended to give an actual illustration of the method described in the *Discourse*. But at the time the three scientific treatises proved to be more interesting to the intellectual public, and the introduction was ignored. Ironically, history has completely reversed this sequence: today the *Discourse* is studied, and the works in science are not only ignored but virtually forgotten. If any attention at all is given to them, it usually takes the form of a posthumous bow to the inventor of analytic geometry; aside from this formality, modern scholars direct their notice for the most part to the method of doing philosophy and science described by Descartes in such works as the *Rules for the Direction of the Mind,* the *Meditations,* and, of course, the *Discourse*. But to study either Descartes' method or its implementation in isolation from one another is contrary to his intention, and I believe that it is time for us to reconsider the Cartesian method in the light of what he did in the three works to which the *Discourse* is an introduction.

One reason for doing this is that we have a different picture of the intention and meaning of the *Discourse* when we consider it as an introduction to the three following works. Previous attempts to describe the Cartesian method have largely ignored Descartes' actual works in science, and as a result such traditional interpretations often come up with versions of this method that are substantially different from the one he actually uses in his scientific work. Therefore, either the traditional versions are mistaken, or else Descartes did something in practice other than what he said he was going to do. I shall try to show that the traditional versions *are* mistaken, and that Descartes did do what he said he was going to do. I shall also try to describe exactly what method Descartes used, and how it is related to the methods of modern-day science.

Descartes' ostensible purpose was to achieve a system of philosophical truth through the use of reason, to develop a system of true statements that would assume nothing to be true which was not known to be so indubitably and self-evidently. He used the word "philosophy" in a much broader sense than we do now. In the prefatory letter to the *Principles of Philosophy* he says:

> Philosophy means the study of wisdom, and by wisdom we understand not only prudence in affairs but also a perfect knowledge of all things that man can know both for the conduct of his life and for the conservation of his health and the invention of all the arts.[1]

= physics

Within the study of human wisdom, therefore, were included not only metaphysics but natural philosophy—that is, physics—and all of the other sciences insofar as they are related to physics; for no discipline can *be* a science for Descartes unless it is related to physics in certain specifiable ways. One of the defining features of any science is a universally applicable way in which we can conduct our thought within its framework. Descartes calls this method of investigation and procedure in the sciences the "Universal Mathematics." In the fourth of the *Rules for the Direction of the Mind*, he notes that "Mathematics" properly speaking means the same thing as "scientific study," and he goes on to talk about what is studied in a mathematical investigation, and what may be so studied:

> But as I considered this more attentively, it finally became clear that only those subjects in which order or measure are considered are regarded as mathematical, and it makes

1 *Œuvres de Descartes*, ed. Charles Adam and Paul Tannery. 13 vols. (Paris: Léopold Cerf, 1897–1913), IX, 2.

no difference whether such measure is sought in numbers, or figures, or stars, or sounds, or any other object whatever. It then follows that there must be a certain general science which explains everything which can be asked about order and measure, and which is concerned with special subject matter and that this very thing called "pure mathematics. . . ." [2]

Philosophy, therefore, is certain knowledge attained through the use of pure mathematics. It should be evident that the key to understanding the Cartesian method is this method of investigation, and the way Descartes applied it, or thought it could be applied, in all fields of human endeavor. For it is through the use of this method that the principles of physics, and thus of all the other sciences, are discovered and justified.

Descartes actually did try to apply his mathematical method in several fields, among them geometry, optics, and meteorology; he also tried to use it to discover the foundations of his physics. In this latter endeavor, which he calls his metaphysics, and which is exemplified by his *Meditations of First Philosophy*, he also describes his method as "analysis":

. . . I have used in my Meditations only analysis. . . . [3]

and he distinguishes between analysis and synthesis. [4] It therefore appears that the universal mathematics is primarily involved in analysis, which is the method of the discovery and justification of the principles of knowledge in all fields. It should not be thought, however, that analysis is exclusively confined to metaphysics, for Descartes uses it in all fields of investigation.

Just as the geometers of old could claim that their theorems were true if and only if they knew that the principles from which they followed were true, so Descartes has been under-

2 Descartes, *Philosophical Essays*, tr. Laurence J. Lafleur, "The Library of Liberal Arts," No. 99 (New York: The Liberal Arts Press, Inc., 1964), p. 161.

3 "Reply to Objections II." *Philosophical Works of Descartes*, tr. E. S. Haldane and G. R. T. Ross. 2 vols. (New York: Dover Publications, Inc., 1955), II, 49.

4 *Ibid.*

stood to believe that the same was true of his physics. This is a misleading interpretation of Descartes' system, as I shall show; but in these first pages I am merely attempting to outline what a plausible first reading of Descartes would lead one to believe. Indeed, the sketch given in this first section is the usual interpretation of the Cartesian system. Thus, physics could not be shown to be an organic part of human wisdom unless and until its principles could be known to be true. This is the cardinal place of intuition in the Cartesian system: the clear and distinct apprehension of propositions seen to be self-evidently true. Intuition occurs either after or concomitantly with analysis, and I shall say more of it later on. The other sciences are included in human wisdom or philosophy only insofar as their laws are deductively related to the principles of physics, and hence indirectly related to metaphysics, since it is the latter science through which the principles of physics are justified.

But although Descartes often speaks as if the laws of physics were directly deducible from metaphysics, he realized that such a priori proceedings could never give us knowledge of the actual applicability of physical laws to this particular world. At best, he thought that we could deduce all the physical laws applicable to *any* possible world, since through the use of analysis he believed that he could arrive at an intuitive knowledge of the simple natures of such components of any possible material world as extension and motion, and thence arrive at a knowledge of the general laws applicable to these in any universe.[5] But the only way that it could be shown which of these laws are actually in force here is to guarantee the veracity of our perceptions of this world, and this Descartes tries to do by proving the existence of a good God who would not deceive us. (As we shall see, he also uses physical experimentation for this purpose.) God thus guarantees the objectivity of our clear and distinct perceptions of things.

The six *Meditations* are the core of Descartes' attempt to

[5] *Discourse on Method*, V (pp. 35–36).

provide a metaphysical foundation for his physics. In a letter to Mersenne in 1638 he remarks that demonstration—that is, synthesis in physics—was impossible unless the principles of physics could be metaphysically justified, and in another letter to the same man in 1641 he states that "these six meditations contain the entire foundations of my physics. . . ." [6]

In 1640, also in a letter to Mersenne, he claims that he has reduced the laws of physics dealing with extension to the laws of mathematics, or more precisely, to the laws of solid geometry; and he claims that as a result of this momentous achievement, "the demonstration [of physics] is now possible." [7] The *Meditations* must therefore provide the metaphysical justification for the claim that the principles of physics dealing with extended bodies are certainly true. Moreover, since these principles will be the laws of solid geometry, Descartes must have believed that he had discovered the secret of the ancient geometers, analysis, and that he had used it successfully. Now if the proofs of God's existence in the *Meditations* are sound and valid, then our clear and distinct perceptions are veridical, and what we perceive clearly and distinctly are objects extended in length, breadth, and depth. But these are nothing other than the objects of solid geometry, and Descartes thought that he had reduced the laws of theoretical physics to the laws of this science plus the laws of motion. It follows that in order to gain knowledge of this world, all we would have to do was to deduce from our self-evident perceptions necessarily true statements about these objects of solid geometry and about motion, in order to know the physical principles of the real world.

But at least two things remain unclear at this point: one is the exact nature of the analysis and synthesis used by Descartes, and the other is the precise role of physical experimentation in his method. In the second and fourth parts of this Introduction, I shall speak at some length about

[6] Adam and Tannery, II, 141.
[7] *Ibid.*, p. 268.

both of these problems. Here, however, it might be noted that in most of the traditional interpretations of the Cartesian method, the most important function of experimentation is to attempt to bridge the gap between the a priori justification and derivation of physical principles, and their actual application in the real world. As we shall see, however, the real significance of experimentation has thus been vastly underrated, and the first step in re-evaluating it must be a closer examination of analysis and syntheses.

II

Method consists in a set of rules or procedures for using the natural capacities and operations of the mind correctly; there are only two of these operations, which Descartes calls "intuition" and "deduction." Actually, they are so closely related that it is perhaps difficult to conceive of them as two operations at all, since deduction is distinguishable from intuition only by the fact that it involves "a certain movement or succession" and that "present evidence is not necessary to [it], as it is to intuition, but rather, in a certain measure, it derives its certainty from memory." The first principles of knowledge alone are known by intuition, and the conclusions from them are known by deduction.[8]

The method for using these two faculties of the mind is a very old one, invented by the Greek philosophers and mathematicians; its two parts, analysis and synthesis, are used for the discovery of truth and its demonstration, respectively. Analysis is the way we discover truth and synthesis is the way we demonstrate it; the traditional interpretations of Descartes preserve this rigid separation between the two. Analysis has often been called the inductive method, and Aristotle gives Socrates credit for having invented it. It is the means by which general principles or axioms are derived from particular facts or sets of facts. Synthesis, or the axio-

---

[8] *Rules for the Direction of the mind*, Rule III, Lafleur, p. 155.

matic method, is used to present or exhibit what has already been discovered or justified through analysis, by showing how what we have discovered is deducible from axioms or principles that are already known to be true in virtue of prior analysis. As we have seen, Descartes says that his *Meditations* are an illustration of the analytic part of the method, and much of his *Principles of Philosophy* is an example of the synthetic or deductive method. He also appends to his *Reply to the Second Set of Objections* [9] an illustration "in the synthetic style" of some of his arguments in the *Meditations*. Just prior to this example of the synthetic mode of argumentation, Descartes makes a statement about analysis and synthesis which is, I think, important enough to quote at length:

> . . . there are two things that I distinguish in the geometrical mode of writing, viz. the *order* and the *method* of proof.
> The order consists merely in putting forward those things first that should be known without the aid of what comes subsequently, and arranging all other matters so that their proof depends solely on what precedes them. I certainly tried to follow this order as accurately as possible in my *Meditations;*. . .
> Further, *the method of proof is two-fold,* one being analytic, the other synthetic.
> *Analysis* shows the true way by which a thing was methodically *discovered* and *derived,* as it were *effect from cause.* . . .
> *Synthesis* contrariwise employs an *opposite* procedure, one in which the *search* goes as it were from effect to cause (though often here the *proof* itself is from cause to effect to a greater extent than in the former case). It does indeed clearly demonstrate its conclusions, and it employs a long series of definitions, postulates, axioms, theorems and problems, so that if one of the conclusions that follow is denied, it may at once be shown to be contained in what has gone before. . . . Yet this method . . . does not show the way in which the matter taught was discovered.
> It was this synthesis alone that the ancient Geometers

9 Haldane and Ross, II, 52–59.

employed in their writings, not because they were wholly
ignorant of the analytic method, but, in my opinion,
because they set so high a value on it that they wished
to keep it to themselves as an important secret.[10]

I have italicized certain portions of these quotations because
their true significance is often overlooked. Thus, the method
of proof contains *both* analysis and synthesis; analysis is how
we discover and derive the explanation of a thing by showing how it is an effect of one certain cause rather than of
another; since the *search* (not the proof) in synthesis goes
"from effect to cause," the search in analysis must go from
cause to effect; the proof exhibits what has been discovered
and derived "in synthetic style" to show how conclusions
are logically related to their principles or causes, but such
proof does not show *how* the principles and their relations
to their effects were discovered; if the proof is adequate, each
statement in it will depend upon the truth of preceding
statements in the proof. What I should like to emphasize
is that synthesis is involved here in the *search* for truth as
well as in its demonstration, a fact which has been largely
overlooked by the traditional interpretations of Descartes.

The vindication of principles demands that we know them
to be true if we are going to claim indubitable truth for
what follows from them, and the problem for analysis is how
to achieve the certain knowledge that these principles are
true. Plato said that in using analysis we treat our starting
assumptions as hypotheses until we have intuitively grasped
their truth. Descartes calls these assumptions "complex and
obscure propositions" in the *Rules for the Direction of the
Mind*,[11] and there is evidence to suggest that these obscure
propositions are identical with what he elsewhere calls "suppositions" and "hypotheses." Plato also used a metaphor to
characterize the entire process of "analysis–intuition–synthesis," and this was the metaphor of the stepped arch, in
which intuition was the coping stone that held the two

10 "Reply to Objections II." Haldane and Ross, II, 48–49.
11 Rule V. Lafleur, p. 163.

sides of the arch, analysis and synthesis, together.[12] Aristotle too, in the *Nicomachean Ethics*, spoke of this method in terms of a metaphor, which in his case was a race course, where the principles or *archai* were apprehended intuitively at the halfway mark of the course. Plato, Aristotle, the ancient geometers, and Descartes realized that there could be no viable synthesis without analysis, and that both analysis and synthesis seemed to need intuition for their ultimate justification. Insofar as scientific knowledge is demonstrative, that is, synthetic, it follows that it must depend upon analysis and intuititon.

Descartes gives us the method for using intuition and deduction in several works, the most important of which are the *Rules for the Direction of the Mind* and the *Discourse on Method;* in these works, the fifth, sixth, and twelfth rules and the second and sixth parts of the *Discourse* are the most important sources of information about how to use these faculties. Analysis, the process through which we use intuition and deduction to discover our principles, is regarded by Descartes as far more important than synthesis. Speaking of it in a letter to Clerselier, he says:

> For it is certain that in order to discover the truth we should always start with particular notions, in order to arrive at general conceptions subsequently, though we may also in the reverse way, after having discovered the universals, deduce other particulars from them.[13]

This has usually been taken as additional support for the thesis that synthesis plays little or no part in analysis, and occurs only *after* analysis, in the method.

It is also usually claimed that analysis justifies the principles of physics in two ways: it makes clear in a systematic manner how they are reached, and why they are asserted, that is, because they are clearly and distinctly seen to be true. The actual use of analysis in the Cartesian system begins in

[12] Colin Murray Turbayne, *The Myth of Metaphor* (New Haven: Yale University Press, 1962).
[13] Haldane and Ross, II, 127.

the *Meditations* with the advent of methodological doubt, through which we reject for purposes of discovery every proposition which it is possible to doubt. Eventually, at the end of that part of analysis described in the *Rules* as the "descent," we arrive at what is impossible to doubt, and these are what Descartes calls "simple natures," or at other times, "simple propositions"; it is impossible to doubt these because they are clearly and distinctly known through intuition. Then, still using analysis, we "ascend" through a series of intuitions to the knowledge of such truths as the laws of motion. Another way of describing the journey is to say that we begin with complex and obscure propositions (Plato's "hypotheses") and after having methodologically doubted them wherever possible, broken them down into their simple natures, and apprehended these in the light of "an unclouded and attentive mind," we come to know through a series of intuitions the principles, laws, causes, or universals which stand at their foundations—that is, we come to know their explanations. When this has happened, we have finished our analysis and are ready to demonstrate "in the synthetic style" what we have discovered. Thus, we begin with complex and obscure propositions, and end up with complex but clear propositions.

III

Traditionally, then, the principles which underlie the simple natures or propositions that are the final results of analysis are the first principles of synthesis. Euclid's geometry is a traditional and outstanding example of the synthetic method, wherein what is already known is demonstrated. Descartes was brief in his treatment of synthesis or demonstration; it is a pity that he did not give it more attention, for his neglect of synthesis is partially responsible for raising some very important logical and philosophical hurdles, which many have felt to be insurmountable. For example, on some occasions he speaks of the final products of analysis as simple natures or essences, and on others he speaks of them as simple propositions. Yet he never explains how simple natures or essences can be simple propositions, or how, in a synthetic system, simple natures can be principles. Indeed, what he *does* use as principles in his syntheses are neither simple natures nor simple propositions, but general laws, and he never explains these discrepancies. Moreover, Descartes begins with what might be called the order of knowledge rather than the order of being; that is, he begins with propositions known to be true independently of experience, and not known to be true *of* the world of experience. As a result, many of his critics have held that his simple natures remain forever in this ideal realm, and that it is impossible to deduce existential propositions from them. In a letter to Clerselier, Descartes denies that he ever deduces existential propositions from logical or mathematical ones,[14] yet in his *Meditations* he claims that the existential proposition "Cogito, ergo sum" is the fundamental principle in the order of *knowledge,* and only then does he go on to deduce, in the fifth and sixth meditations, the existence of God and the real world.

He was careless not only in his consideration of synthesis, but also in his remarks about the place of experiment in both analysis and synthesis. This problem is especially acute in his attempts to relate his a priori deductions concerning the principles of physics to the actual world in which we live. So far as the usual versions of his theory are concerned, there would seem to be two fundamental roles of experiment, or experience.[15] The first is based on the theory of innate ideas. In the sixth part of the *Discourse,* Descartes

14 Adam and Tannery, IV, 445.

15 It should be noted that these two words are extremely important in the translation of Descartes' works. The French word *expérience* can be translated as either "experience" or "experiment"; by and large, we must look to the context in order to choose between the two. When an experience is especially designed to confirm or disconfirm the existence or explanation of certain objects corresponding to our ideas, we might better call it an "experiment."

says that we can derive the first causes or principles of
anything which is or can be in the real world simply from
". . . certain germs of truth which are naturally in our souls."
Similar remarks are to be found in the *Principles of Philosophy*. These germs of truth are the innate ideas implanted
in our minds by "nature," or God. All of our clear and
distinct ideas are innate, and all scientific knowledge is
therefore either of or by means of such ideas. Our minds
produce these innate ideas upon the occasion of some experience—that is, sense experience provides the impetus for
forming ideas which prior to this experience are only poten-
tially or dispositionally in our minds. Such experience alone,
however, cannot enable us to derive the universal and indubitable laws and principles of physics, for all sense experience is of the particular, whereas laws and principles are
general or universal. Therefore, according to this interpretation, the first role of experience is to serve as the occasion
for formulating the ideas of universal laws that are already
dispositionally in our minds; the second role is to enable us,
by the grace of an honest God, to confirm to ourselves that
there are external objects which correspond to, or are explained by, our ideas.[16]

Another possible interpretation of the role of experiment
or experience, which is also based upon the sixth part of the
Discourse, but on the twelfth of the *Rules for the Direction
of the Mind* rather than on the *Principles* and the *Notes
Against a Programme,* might be as follows. Before we can
apply the Cartesian method to the real world, we must have
empirical data, provided by experience or experiment or
perhaps both. Then through analysis we arrive at an intuitive
knowledge of the principles underlying the simple natures
of these particulars. Next, by reversing the process, so to
speak, and starting with the simple natures, or the principles
or causes which explain them and from which we can deduce
them as effects, we ought to end up with the same particulars
with which we started, except that their true natures are

[16] Adam and Tannery, 13, VIII, 358–359.

now understood. That is, we begin with complex and obscure propositions about the particulars provided us by experience or experiment, and we end up with complex but clear propositions about these same particulars. According to this version, therefore, the first role of experience is to provide us with the data for analysis. The second role, in common with the previous suggestion concerning the verification of the existence of the objects that our innate ideas explain or indicate, hinges on the fact that from the first principles or causes which we uncover in analysis, an indefinite number of primary or general effects can be deduced. We must somehow be able to distinguish, among these general effects, the ones which actually occur in our world; the only way we are able to do this is through observation and experiment.

In spite of the fact that Descartes himself thus realized that more than the mathematical method alone was needed in the verification and confirmation of scientific truths, experimentation is still usually considered to play only a minor role in his system. It is said to be necessary merely to make up for the natural limits of our human understanding, but certainly not to be as important as it is in our present-day sciences. The traditional view of the Cartesian method is that of a system wherein the ideal of science remains that of a purely deductive schema.

If this is an accurate picture, however, then surely Descartes was uncertain that such an ideal could ever be achieved. He indicates on numerous occasions that he considers physical experimentation indispensable to the search for knowledge. He himself practiced numerous experiments in physics, optics, meteorology, and anatomy, as the essays in this volume prove; his letter to Mersenne, in which he claims that the geometrical demonstration of matters which depend on physics is impossible,[17] shows that he did not believe that the principles of physics could be proven without experimentation. These remarks seem to indicate that Descartes paid much more attention to experimentation than

[17] *Ibid.*, V, 112 and II, 141.

he has hitherto been interpreted to pay. Yet in the face of this suggestion there flies his letter of 1638 to Mersenne, in which he states that ". . . my physics is nothing else but geometry . . . ," [18] which seems to be an outright contradiction of his previous assertion that the geometrical demonstration of physical matters is impossible.

In view of these conflicting statements, a closer examination of what he said and what he did is warranted.

IV

Probably the clearest summary of his actual procedure in the sciences is to be found in the sixth part of the *Discourse on Method*. There he says:

> First, I tried to discover the general principles, or first causes, of all that is or can be in the world, without for this purpose considering anything but God alone, its Creator, and without deriving these principles from anything but certain seeds of truth which are naturally in our souls. After that, I examined what were the first and most ordinary effects that we could infer from these causes. And it seems to me that thereby I discovered the skies, the stars, an earth, and even, on the earth, water, air, fire, minerals, and certain other such things, which are the commonest and simplest of all, and thus the easiest to understand.
>
> Then, when I wanted to descend to those effects that were more particular, so many diverse ones presented themselves to me that I did not believe it possible for the human mind to distinguish between the forms or species of objects that are on the earth, and an infinity of other ones which could have been, if it had been the will of God to put them there. Nor, as a result of this, *did I believe it possible to direct them to our use, unless it be by arriving at the causes through their effects, and by using many particular experiments.* Following this, I reflected upon all the objects that presented themselves to my senses, and I venture to say that I have never noticed a single thing about them which I could not explain quite conveniently through the

[18] *Ibid.*, II, 268, and III, 39.

principles I had discovered. But I must also confess
that the power of nature is so ample and so vast,
and these principles so simple and so general, that I
never noticed any particular effect such that I did not
see right away that it can be derived from these principles in many different ways and *my greatest difficulty is
usually to discover in which of these ways the effect depends upon the principle or cause. And to do that I
know no other expedient than again to search for certain
experiments which are such that their result is not the
same when we explain the effect by one hypothesis, as
when we explain it by another.*[19]

I have italicized what are, I believe, the most important words in this quotation, which tell us that in order to discover the causes, principles, or laws governing a particular
effect or class of effects, we should examine the effect, and
discover which among a number of possible explanations
posited as hypotheses is the correct one. We can do this only
through experimentation, and this is what Descartes actually
does. But if he had followed the method usually ascribed to
him, he would have performed an analysis of the complex
and obscure propositions in the relevant sciences, and only
then—after having reached an intuitive knowledge of the
truth of the scientific principles involved—would he have
deduced conclusions from them. Then he would have performed experiments to see which of the conclusions actually
applied to this world.

He does not do this. He discovered that the universal
mathematics alone would not enable him to derive laws in
the sciences which he knew to be directly applicable to this
world. Because of this, there is a definite change in his method.
He uses synthesis *as a part of* analysis, as the reader will see
in the *Optics, Meteorology* and *Geometry.* The consequences of
this are quite clear: since we cannot reach an intuitive knowledge of the principles of science except through analysis, and
since any propositions deduced from these principles can
be known to be certainly true only if the principles from
which they are deduced are so known, then if we deduce

[19] *Discourse on Method,* VI (p. 52).

propositions from principles which a complete analysis has not yet shown to be true, such principles can only be hypotheses, and the propositions drawn from them only hypothetically true. If Descartes uses syntheses as elements in the method of discovery, analysis, then the principles of such syntheses must be hypotheses; and indeed, this is exactly how he treats them, as I shall show, and as the reader may confirm for himself by reading the three scientific essays. He formulates various possible explanations of a given phenomenon—that is, hypotheses—and chooses among them on the basis of critical experiments. In more modern language, he confirms his hypotheses by means of inductive testing. Today, the method by which Descartes selects hypotheses, derives subsidiary propositions or laws from them, and then indirectly tests the hypotheses by confirming or disconfirming their effects through critical experiments is called the hypothetico-deductive method; in its more sophisticated form, it is the method of twentieth-century science.

There is a great amount of evidence that it was Descartes' intention to use this procedure, rather than that of analysis –intuition–synthesis–testing, and that it was not something he merely fell into using through oversight. First of all, if it is mere oversight, then it is alarmingly consistent. Second, interpreting Descartes' method thus, one can not only describe what he actually does, but one has the added advantage of reconciling what are otherwise inconsistent passages from his works. Most important, Descartes himself tells us in many places that he uses this method. In the third part of the *Principles* he says:

> I shall put forward all that I am going to write just as an hypothesis. Even if this be thought false, I shall think my achievement worth while if all the inferences from it agree with experience.

The hypothesis of which he is speaking here is that the universe is composed of small particles of matter of the same shape, each one of which revolves around its own center.

Again, when speaking of the causes or principles of natural phenomena, he says:

> . . . I yet merely desire to assert that those principles I set forth are to be regarded as hypotheses.[20]

In the fourth part of the same book he makes it abundantly clear that in the first three parts he has been speaking hypothetically:

> . . . I have described the earth, and all the visible world, as if it were simply a machine in which there was nothing to consider but [the] figure and movements [of its parts]. . . .[21]

In the sixth part of the *Discourse on Method*, he calls the matters with which he deals in the *Optics* and *Meteorology* "hypotheses," and then goes on to state how these hypotheses are confirmed:

> . . . For it seems to me that the arguments there follow from each other in such a way that, *just as the last ones are proven by the first, which are their causes, so those first [principles or causes] are reciprocally proven by the last, which are their effects.* And you must not think that I commit in this the fallacy that the logicians call arguing in a circle; for *as experimentation makes most of these effects very certain, the causes from which I derive them serve not so much to prove these effects as to explain them; but, on the contrary, the [hypothetical] principles or causes are proven by their effects.*[22]

What exactly is Descartes describing here? Consider the following:

> . . . when I wanted to descend to those effects that were more particular, so many diverse ones presented themselves to me, that I did not believe it possible for the human mind to distinguish between the forms or species of objects that are on the earth, and an infinity of other ones which could have been, if it had been the will of

20 *Principles of Philosophy*, III, XLIV.
21 *Ibid.*, IV, CLXXXVIII. Haldane and Ross, p. 289.
22 *Discourse on Method*, pp. 50–61.

God to put them there. Nor, as a result of this, did I believe it possible to direct them to our use, *unless it be by arriving at the causes through their effects,* and *by using many particular experiments.* . . . But . . . these principles [are] so simple and so general that I almost never noticed any particular effect such that I did not see right away that it can be derived from these principles in many different ways; and my greatest difficulty is usually to discover in which of these ways the effect depends upon the principle or cause. And to do that I know no other expedient than again to search for certain *experiments which are such that their result is not the same when we explain the effect by one hypothesis, as when we explain it by another.*[23]

In short, we learn the causes of particular effects by examining these effects, which involves performing many experiments. But an effect can depend upon a cause in many different ways; and the only way we can decide *how* it depends upon a particular cause is to perform still more experiments. But exactly how Descartes uses these experiments, and exactly what he conceives to be an experiment, remain unclear. Perhaps some examples of his own will help. Consider then his use of the "hypothetical world" and the "hypothetical man" in the *Discourse on Method.* In the fifth part, in order to avoid, he says, disputes with the learned over this world, he resolves

. . . to speak only of what would happen in a new world, if God were now to create somewhere, in imaginary space, enough matter to compose it, and if He agitated the parts of this matter diversely and without order, so that He made of it a chaos as confused as the poets can imagine, and if afterwards He did nothing else except lend his ordinary support to nature, and left it to act according to the laws which He established.[24]

He then goes on to show that the laws which apply to this hypothetical world must apply to any world, and how, given these laws and the nature of the matter, he can explain all

[23] *Ibid.,* p. 52 (my italics).
[24] *Ibid.,* p. 35.

the effects in this world. Then, after speaking about this hypothetical world, he says:

> I thought I had said enough about it to make it known that there is nothing to be seen in the phenomena of this [actual] world which would not, or at least which could not, appear in the same way in the phenomena of the world I was describing.[25]

Thus, it would appear that he uses the hypothetical world as a model to explain the actual one.

Having done this with the world, he moves to man, and again speaks hypothetically of the body of a man, which God formed "entirely similar to one of ours" except that it has no rational soul, but only "one of those fires without light." Using this hypothetical man, he proceeds to explain how, given this hypothesis, we can explain all the bodily events in man, including the circulation of the blood, as effects of this fire. To do this, he asks the reader to perform an experiment using the heart of a large animal, ". . . for it is in every respect quite similar to the heart of a man. . .";[26] and with the hypothesis and the experiments, he compares the human body to "a machine which, having been made by the hands of God, is incomparably better designed, and has in itself more admirable movements, than any of those which can be invented by men."[27] Again, what he has done is to posit an hypothesis, test it by experiment, and conclude that it is the proper explanation of the effects pertinent to it, *because* it does explain them.

This account of Descartes' procedure is consistent with his own definitions of his method. Consider the third rule of the second part of the *Discourse*:

> . . . to direct my thinking in an orderly way, by beginning with the simplest and easiest objects to understand, in order to climb little by little, gradually, to the knowl-

---

25 *Ibid.*, p. 36.
26 *Ibid.*, p. 38.
27 *Ibid.*, p. 45.

edge of the most complex; *and even assuming an order among those objects which do not naturally precede each other.*[28]

That is, there are some cases where the order of causal dependency is not apparent, and in these cases it is necessary to *assume* such an order, by positing a hypothetical explanation, and then testing to see if it is the correct one. Another example of Descartes' actual practice of this rule is found in the twelfth of the *Rules*, where he is attempting to explain the nature of sense perception. He states that the senses are passive in perception, and that they receive their stimuli "... in the same way that wax receives an impression from a seal." He goes on to say:

> Nor must it be thought that this is said as an analogy; it must be understood that the external shape of the perceiving body is really changed by the object, just as the shape of the surface of the wax is changed by the seal. ...
> It is exceedingly helpful to conceive all those matters thus, for nothing falls more readily under sense than figure, which can be touched and seen.

In the same place he goes on to suggest another hypothesis as a model for the explanation of the relations between different colors, in this case picturing different colors as different lines with various relations to one another, and he says that the same procedure is permissible in all cases of this sort.[29]

Another famous example of the Cartesian method in application is his examination of the magnet, also in the twelfth rule. There he says that the way to proceed in answer to the question "What is the nature of the magnet?" is as follows:

> He ... will first diligently collect all the information he can obtain about this stone, from which he will then try to deduce what combination of simple natures is necessary to produce all those effects which are discovered in the magnet. Once he has discovered this, he can boldly assert

[28] *Ibid.*, p. 16 (my italics).
[29] Lafleur, p. 189.

that he has found the true nature of the magnet, in so far as it can be discovered by man on the basis of the available information.[30]

It is clear what Descartes is doing here: he is making an attempt to discover the relationships between the parts of the magnet which are necessary in order to produce its effects, and he is doing this partly through the use of experiments. It seems obvious as a result of the other quotations included here that the way he would proceed is to set up an hypothesis, even assuming, if necessary, an order among the parts of the magnet which he did not know to exist, and then test the hypothesis by seeing whether or not it did explain the effects of a magnet. Remember that he is looking for the proportions, the relations between the elements of a thing which account for its effects, and that to know this we must discover the order of dependency, causal dependency, which will explain a thing. As he says in the sixth rule:

In order to distinguish the simplest things from complex ones, and to put them in order, we should observe in every series of propositions in which we have directly deduced some truths from others, which one is the simplest of all, and how far from this one each of the others is removed, either more or less, or equally.[31]

With regard to their dependence upon one another, all elements of an object or event can be said to be either absolute or relative, and the simplest element—the one not dependent upon the others, and upon which all others depend—is the absolute one. Descartes says the term "absolute" is applicable

[to] all which is considered as independent, causal, simple, universal, unitary, equal, similar, straight. . . .

Whereas the term "relative" applies to what is

dependent, resultant, compound, particular, multiple, unequal, dissimilar, oblique. . . .[32]

30 *Ibid.*, p. 201.
31 *Ibid.*, p. 164.
32 *Ibid.*

Throughout the *Optics* and the *Meteorology*, there are numerous confirming instances of the theory of Descartes' method in science that I have developed. He affirms his faith in the procedure of formulating hypotheses or "assumptions" based upon empirical observation near the beginning of the *Optics*, when he says that he is going to use two or three comparisons in order to conceive the nature of light ". . . in the manner which to me seems the most convenient to explain all those of its properties that experience acquaints us with, and to deduce afterwards all the others which cannot be so easily observed; . . ." and he says that in so doing he is

> . . . imitating . . . the Astronomers, who, although their assumptions are almost all false or uncertain, nevertheless, because these assumptions refer to different observations which they have made, never cease to draw many very true and well-assured conclusions from them.[33]

Immediately after this, he asks us to consider light as

> a certain movement or action, very rapid and very lively, which passes towards our eyes through the medium of the air and other transparent bodies, in the same manner that the movement or resistance of the bodies that this blind man encounters is transmitted to his hand through the medium of his stick.[34]

Given this hypothesis—that light is a movement transmitted to our eyes much in the same way that resistance is transmitted through a blind man's cane to his hand—he then goes on to explain the phenomena of sight, making use of yet other hypotheses on the way. One of these other hypotheses is that rays of light are deflected, that is, refracted and reflected, much as is a ball striking surfaces of various consistencies at different angles, and he then continues, as with the "blind man" hypothesis, to test this hypothesis empirically, and confirm it.[35] The most important confirming experiment in the *Optics* involves the use of the eye of a

[33] *Optics*, pp. 66–67.
[34] *Optics*, p. 67.
[35] *Optics*, pp. 70–74.

dead animal, through the use of which he confirms that the causes of the image on the base of the eye of the animal, in this case an ox, may be given in terms of the hypotheses he has used. He concludes:

> . . . having thus seen this picture in the eye of a dead animal, and having considered the reasons or causes, you cannot doubt that quite a similar one is formed in the eye of a live man, on the interior membrane for which we have substituted the white body *RST;* . . .[36]

It is clear then that Descartes took the experimental confirmation of his hypotheses as confirmation for the same explanation in the case of human sight.

At the beginning of the *Meteorology,* he confirms that in the *Optics* he has been using hypotheses, and that he is going to do the same thing in the *Meteorology.* He says:

> It is true that since the knowledge of these matters depends on general principles of nature which have not yet, to my knowledge, been accurately explained, I must make use of certain hypotheses at the outset, as I did in the *Optics.*[37]

He then goes on to specify the hypotheses, which include the assumptions that all bodies are composed of minute, differently shaped particles which, however carefully joined, still have tiny spaces between them that are filled with a "fine material" moving at great speeds which vary under different circumstances. Given these assumptions, as well as the explanation of the nature and behavior of light given in the *Optics,* we can explain the sensations of heat and cold, and heat and cold themselves, as well as most meteorological phenomena. As final confirmation of these hypotheses, he describes in great detail a series of observations he made, beginning February 4, 1635, and lasting for three days. These observations concerned the shapes and sizes of snow and ice crystals, and the types of clouds from which they came, as

[36] *Optics,* p. 97.
[37] *Meteorology,* p. 264.

well as the wind and temperature which gave birth to them. Descartes has previously tried to explain what conditions would have to hold in order for such crystals to fall, and having verified his hypothetical explanation through these observations, he concludes that "I confirmed my belief in all that I had imagined concerning this matter." [38] He pursues exactly the same procedure later in the *Meteorology*, when he attempts to explain the causes of the rainbow. Using the comparison between rolling, rotating balls and the movement of light which he had used earlier in the *Optics* in order to explain the action of various light rays in the rainbow, he says that the explanation "enabled me to solve the most important of all the difficulties that I had in this matter," [39] the most important difficulty here being the explanation of the relations between the colors of the rainbow, which he explains by the speed of the rotation of the particles "of the fine substance which transmits the action of the light." He concludes:

> And in all of this, the explanation accords so perfectly with experience, that I do not believe it possible, after having carefully studied both, to doubt that the matter is such as I have just explained. [40]

Finally, let us consider once more his remarks about analysis and synthesis, quoted above at length. [41] The order consists in organizing things according to their dependence upon one another; analysis shows how we discover the order; synthesis demonstrates the order in propositional form. But having taken into account what has been said herein, we know that Descartes uses hypotheses to discover the order of dependency and performs experiments to test for the correct hypothesis or explanation, and that synthesis is used in analysis in the formulation of these hypothetical explanations. This is not

[38] *Meteorology*, p. 319.
[39] *Meteorology*, p. 337.
[40] *Meteorology*, p. 338.
[41] Pp. xi, xvi.

only what Descartes says, it is what he does—in the examples I have given, in the *Optics,* in the *Meteorology,* in his experiments in anatomy, and to some extent in the *Geometry.* It would seem, therefore, that even at this late date in the history of Cartesian studies, a re-examination of his writings is necessary. Among the purposes of such an investigation should be an attempt to answer the following questions:

1) Given that Descartes used different methods in his metaphysics and in the particular sciences, how, if at all, are they related?

2) Since the Cartesian method of doing metaphysics, as well as the theory of innate ideas and the doctrine of intuition, firmly place Descartes among the ranks of the rationalists, how, if at all, does the rationalist's method of *doing* science differ from that of the empiricist?

3) If my claims about the way Descartes did science are well founded, ought we to give him a more prominent place among the founders of modern scientific method?

An introduction of this scope and nature cannot be expected to undertake the detailed investigation necessary to answer these questions. But purely in the hope that some scholars might be encouraged to undertake the task—much as Descartes hoped to encourage the artisans of his time to test and implement his theories and inventions—I suggest that an inquiry into these problems would show that Descartes actually tried to do *two* things concerning the relationship of his metaphysics to the particular sciences. First of all, I believe he tried to prove that the principles of science could be derived either by deduction from the self-evident principles of his theistic metaphysics, which principles are themselves reached through the particular sort of analysis used in the *Meditations,* or else by deriving axioms or generalizations from the experiments performed within the particular sciences, and intended within those sciences to confirm or disconfirm the propositions deduced from the principles *qua* hypotheses. The fact that the *same* principles of the various sciences could be derived by either or both of these methods within the Cartesian framework would seem to serve both as a metaphysical justification for the empirical method, and as an empirical justification for the metaphysical system—or, at least, it would seem reasonable to assume that Descartes would take it as such. Moreover, such an hypothesis has the important virtue of making compatible, and indeed even complementary, the seemingly divergent comments concerning his method which I have quoted here.[42]

Secondly, I believe that an inquiry into the scientific procedures of rationalists and empiricists will show that insofar as the actual *doing* of science is concerned, there is no difference in the two schools of thought. Indeed, a comparison between Descartes' *Optics* and *Meteorology*, and the works of such an eminent scientist as Newton, illustrates such striking similarities of procedure that they can be considered as *prima facie* evidence for this claim.

Finally, if my beliefs about the similarity of scientific practice are confirmed, then it would seem that Descartes ought to be considered as one of the originators of the hypothetico-deductive method, the coping stone of our present-day science.

---

[42] Such as the letters to Mersenne quoted above (p. xiii). Here I believe he is speaking of "applied" physics in the first instance, and "pure" physics, so to speak, in the second.

SELECTED BIBLIOGRAPHY

Descartes' Own Works

Œuvres de Descartes. Edited by CHARLES ADAM and PAUL TAN-NERY. 13 vols. Paris: Cerf, 1897–1913.

Œuvres et Lettres. Edited by A. BRIDOUX. Paris: Éditions de la Nouvelle revue française, 1937.

Discours de la Méthode. Edited, with a commentary, by E. GIL-SON. 2nd edn. Paris: Vrin, 1939.

Discourse on Method and *Meditations*. Edited and translated by L. J. LAFLEUR. "The Library of Liberal Arts," No. 89. New York: The Liberal Arts Press, Inc., 1960.

The Philosophical Works of Descartes. Edited and translated by E. S. HALDANE and G. R. T. ROSS. 2 vols. New York: Dover Publications, Inc., 1955.

Descartes: Philosophical Writings. Edited and translated by E. ANSCOMBE and P. T. GEACH. Introduction by A. KOYRÉ. London: Nelson and Sons Ltd., 1954.

Secondary and Related Readings

ADAM, CHARLES. *Descartes, sa vie, son œuvre*. Paris: Boivin, 1937.

BALZ, A. G. A. *Descartes and the Modern Mind*. New Haven: Yale University Press, 1952.

BECK, L. J. *The Method of Descartes*. Oxford: Clarendon Press, 1952.

BERKELEY, GEORGE. *Works on Vision*. Edited by C. M. TUR-BAYNE. "The Library of Liberal Arts," No. 83. New York: The Liberal Arts Press, Inc., 1963.

KEELING, S. V. *Descartes*. London: Benn, 1934.

SMITH, N. K. *Studies in the Cartesian Philosophy*. New York: Russell and Russell, 1962.

———. *New Studies in the Philosophy of Descartes*. New York: Russell and Russell, 1963.

TURBAYNE, C. M. *The Myth of Metaphor*. New Haven: Yale University Press, 1962.

DISCOURSE ON METHOD

DISCOURSE ON THE METHOD FOR RIGHTLY DIRECTING ONE'S REASON AND SEARCHING FOR TRUTH IN THE SCIENCES

If this discourse seems too long to be read all at once, it may be divided into six parts. In the first, you will find various considerations about the branches of knowledge;

—in the second, the principal rules of the method which the author has sought;

—in the third, some of the moral rules which he has derived from this method;

—in the fourth, the arguments through which he proves the existence of God and the human soul (the fundamentals of his metaphysics);

—in the fifth, the order of the problems of physics that he studied (particularly the explanation of the movement of the heart, and of some other difficulties in medicine, as well as the difference between the souls of men and of beasts);

—and in the last, the things he believes are requisite for going further than he has in the investigation of nature, and the reasons for his writing this work.

First Part

Common sense is the most equitably divided thing in the world, for everyone believes he is so well provided with it that even those who are the hardest to please in everything else usually do not want more of it than they have. It is not likely that everyone is mistaken in this matter; rather, this shows that the power to judge correctly and to distinguish the true from the false—which is, strictly speaking, what we mean by common sense or reason—is naturally equal in all men. Hence the diversity of our opinions arises, not because some of us are more reasonable than others, but only because we direct our thoughts along different paths, and consider different things. For it is not enough to have a good mind; the principal thing is to apply it correctly. The greatest spirits are capable of the greatest vices, as well as the greatest virtues; and those who walk very slowly can go ahead much further, if they always follow the right path, than those who run but stray from it.

As for me, I have never presumed that my mind is in any respect more perfect than that of most men; I have even often wished to have as quick a wit, or as clear and distinct an imagination, or as ample and ready a memory, as some other people. And apart from these, I know of no qualities which serve to perfect the mind; because as to reason, or common sense, inasmuch as it is the only thing that makes us men and distinguishes us from the beasts, I prefer to believe that each of us is equal in the possession of it; and in this I follow the general opinion of the Philosophers, who say that differences of degree exist only among the *accidents,* and not among the *forms* or natures, of *individuals* of the same *species.*

But I do not fear to assert that I think I have had the good luck to have found myself, as early as my youth, upon certain paths which led me to certain considerations and maxims, from which I formed a method through which, it seems to me, I can gradually augment my understanding, and raise it, bit by bit, to the highest point which the mediocrity of my mind and the short duration of my life will allow. For from this I have already gathered such fruits that although in making judgments about myself I always try to think cautiously, rather than be presumptuous; and although, from the viewpoint of a Philosopher, almost all of the various actions and undertakings of men appear vain and useless to me; nevertheless, I have derived such extreme satisfaction from the progress I believe I have already achieved in the search after truth, and from conceiving such hopes for the future, that if, among the occupations of men, as such, there be one which is truly good and important, I believe that it is the one that I have chosen.

Nevertheless it may be that I am wrong, and that what I take for gold and diamonds is but a bit of copper and glass. I know how we are subject to mistakes in what concerns ourselves, and also how the judgments of our friends should be suspected when they are in our favor. But I shall be glad to show in this discourse the paths that I have followed, and to present my life here as in a painting, in order that each may judge of it; and learning what public opinion says of this discourse will be a new means of informing myself, which I shall add to those that I am in the habit of using.

Thus my intention is not to teach here the method which everyone must follow in order to direct his reason correctly, but only to show the manner in which I have tried to direct mine. Those who set themselves up to give precepts to others must esteem themselves more than those to whom they give them; and if they are lacking in the least thing, they are to be blamed for it. But since I am proposing only this work as, so to speak, a history—or if you prefer, a fable—in which, among many examples you might imitate, you will perhaps find as many others which you will have reason not to follow, I hope that it will be useful to some without being harmful to any, and that everyone will find my frankness to his taste.

I have been brought up on books since my childhood, and because I was persuaded that through them we can acquire a clear and certain knowledge of all that is useful in life, I had an extreme desire to learn from them. But as soon as I had completed the entire course of studies, at the end of which one is normally received into the ranks of the learned, I changed my opinion completely. For I found myself so encumbered with doubts and errors that it seemed to me that I had gained nothing by trying to teach myself, except that I had discovered progressively how ignorant I was. And nevertheless I was in one of Europe's most celebrated schools where, I thought, there must be wise men, if there were any on earth. I had learned there all that others learned; and even then, not being satisfied with the knowledge which was taught us, I had perused all the books, treating of the most curious and rarest matters, which I was able to obtain. Moreover, I was aware of how the others judged me; and I saw that they did not esteem me of less value than my fellow students, although there were already among them those who were destined to take the places of our professors. And finally it seemed to me that our age was as flourishing, and as fertile with good minds, as were any of the preceding ones. This caused me to take the liberty of judging others by myself, and of deciding that there was no doctrine in the world such as I had previously hoped for.

Yet I did not cease to value the exercises with which we were occupied in the schools. I realized that the languages we learned there are necessary for understanding the books of the ancients; that the delicacy of myths revives the spirit; that the memorable deeds of history exalt it, and reading them with discretion helps in forming our judgment; that the reading of good books is like a conversation with the greatest gentlemen of past ages, their authors—and even like a studied conversation, in which they make the best of their thoughts known to us; that eloquence has incomparable powers and beauties; that poetry has ravishing delicacy and sweetness; that mathematics has very subtle devices, which can serve to satisfy the curious, as well as to facilitate man's skills and diminish his labor; that the writings which treat of morals contain many teachings and many exhortations to virtue which are very useful; that theology teaches us how to attain heaven; that philosophy gives us the means of speaking plausibly about all things, and of making ourselves admired by the less learned; that jurisprudence, medicine, and other sciences bring honors and riches to those who cultivate them; and finally, that it is good to have examined all of them, even the most superstitious and false, in order to know their true value, and avoid being deceived by them.

But I believed I had already given sufficient time to languages, and even to reading the books of the ancients, both their histories and their myths. For conversing with men of past ages is somewhat like traveling. It is good to know something of the mores of different peoples, in order to judge our own more soundly, and so that we do not think that everything contrary to our way of life is ridiculous and against reason, as those who have seen nothing are accustomed to do. But when one spends too much time traveling, one must eventually become a stranger to one's own country; and when one is too much interested in the practices of times past, one usually stays ignorant of the practices of the present. Besides this, myths portray many events as possible when in fact they are not; and even if the most faithful histories neither change nor augment the value of things to make them more worthy of being read, they almost always omit the basest and least illustrious circumstances. From this it follows that the rest does not appear as it actually is, and that those who govern their behavior by the examples they take from these books are subject to fall into the excesses of the knights of our romances, and to conceive plans that are beyond their capabilities.

I esteemed eloquence highly, and I was enamored of poetry; but I thought that both were gifts of the mind, rather than fruits of study. Those who are the strongest in reasoning, and the best at working over their thoughts to make them clear and intelligible, can always best persuade what they propose, even should they speak nothing but low Breton, and never have learned rhetoric. And those who have the most agreeable thoughts, and who know how to express them with the most embellishment and sweetness, will be the best poets, even though the art of Poetry remains unknown to them.

I was particularly pleased with Mathematics, because of the certitude and clarity of its grounds; but I did not yet note its true use, and thinking that it was useful only in the mechanical arts, I was astonished that, with such firm and solid foundations, we had built nothing more noble above them. Whereas, on the contrary, I compared the ancient pagan writings that treat of morals to very superb and magnificent palaces, built on nothing but sand and mud. They extol the virtues, and make them appear more estimable than anything else in the world; but they do not sufficiently teach us how to recognize them, and often that which they call by such a lovely name is nothing but insensibility or pride, despair or parricide.

I revered our theology, and sought as much as the next man to attain heaven; but having learned, as something very well assured, that the road is no less open to the ignorant as to the learned, and that the revealed truths which lead there are above our intelligence, I did not dare to submit them to the feebleness of my arguments, and I thought that, in order to undertake to examine them and to succeed at it, one would need to have some extraordinary assistance from heaven, and to be more than human.

I shall say nothing of philosophy, except that, seeing that it has been cultivated by the most excellent minds for many centuries, and that nevertheless nothing has yet been discovered in it which is not disputed and thus doubtful, I did not have the presumption to hope to fare better in it than the others. And considering how many diverse opinions about a single subject there are in philosophy, and that these are upheld by learned men, although there can never be more than one among them that is correct, I deemed everything which was merely plausible to be almost false.

Then, as to other learning, inasmuch as it derives its principles from philosophy, I judged that nothing solid could have been constructed on foundations so infirm. And neither the honor nor the gain that they promise were sufficient to make me learn them; for I did not find myself, thanks to God, in a condition which would oblige me to make a career of science to supplement my income. And although I did not profess to scorn glory like a Cynic, I nevertheless thought very little of that which I could not hope to acquire except through false pretenses. And finally, as for shoddy theories, I thought I already knew enough about their worth not to be subject to error, neither through the promises of an alchemist, nor the predictions of an astrologer, nor the impostures of a magician, nor the deceptions and bragging of any of those who profess to know more than they do know.

This is why, as soon as my age permitted me to leave the supervision of my teachers, I gave up entirely the study of letters. And, resolving to search for no knowledge but that which could be found in myself, or in the great book of the world, I used the rest of my youth to travel, to see courts and armies, to frequent people of differing dispositions and conditions, to store up various experiences, to prove myself in the encounters with which fortune confronted me, and everywhere to reflect upon the things that occurred, so that I could derive some profit from them. For it seemed to me that I might discover much more truth in each man's reasoning about affairs that are important to him, in whose aftermath he will suffer if he has judged badly, than in the thoughts of a man of letters in his study, concerning speculations which produce no effect and are of no consequence to him—except perhaps that the further they are removed from common sense, the more vanity he derives from them, because he will have to use that much more intelligence and craft to try to render them plausible. And I always had an extreme desire to learn to distinguish the true from the false, in order to see clearly in my actions, and walk with confidence in this life.

It is true that while I was doing nothing but considering the mores of other men, I found nothing there to satisfy me, and that I noted almost as much diversity there as I had before among the opinions of philosophers. So that the greatest benefit I derived was that, seeing many things which were commonly accepted and approved by other great peoples, although they seemed extravagant and ridiculous to us, I learned to have no very firm belief in anything that had been taught to me only by example and custom; and so I was delivered little by little from many errors, which can obscure our natural light, and render us less capable of listening to reason. But after I had thus spent some years studying the book of the world, and trying to acquire some experience, one day I resolved also to study within myself, and to use all the forces of my mind to choose the roads I should follow. In this I succeeded much better, it seems to me, than if I had never left either my country or my books.

Second Part

I was then in Germany, where the occasion of the wars
which are not yet ended had called me; and as I was returning to the army from the coronation of the Emperor, the
onslaught of winter stopped me in a district where, finding
no conversation to divert me, and furthermore, by good
fortune, having no cares or passions to trouble me, I remained all day alone in a heated room, where I had complete leisure to review my own ideas. One of the first of
these which I undertook to examine was that often there
is not as much perfection in works composed of many pieces,
and made by many masters, as in those on which one man
alone has worked. Thus we see that the buildings designed
and completed by a single architect are usually more beautiful and better planned than those which many have tried
to redesign, making do with old walls which had been built
for other purposes. Thus those ancient towns which were
nothing but hamlets in the beginning, and in the course of
time have become great cities, are ordinarily so badly planned, compared to those regular districts that an engineer
lays out on a plain according to his own imagination, that
although when we consider each of their buildings by itself,
we often find as much or more beauty as in those of the
latter, nevertheless, when we see how they are arranged—
here a large building, there a small—and how their streets
are crooked and uneven, we would say that it was chance,
rather than the wills of some rational men, which so disposed them. And if we consider that in all times there have
been certain officials who had charge of private buildings,
to insure that they contributed to the public adornment, we
will recognize that it is difficult to do good things when

working with nothing but the works of others. And thus, I imagined formerly half-savage peoples, who have only gradually become civilized, and have made their laws only as the harmfulness of crimes and quarrels constrained them to do so, would not be governed as well as those who, from the time they banded together, observed the constitutions of some prudent legislator. Thus it is certain that the condition of the true religion, whose precepts were made by God alone, must be incomparably better ruled than all others. And to speak of human matters, I believe that if Sparta was once very flourishing, it was not because of the goodness of each of its laws in particular (seeing that many of them were very strange, and even contrary to sound morals), but because, having been invented by a single man, they all tended to the same end.

And so I thought that book-learning, at least that whose justification is only probable, and has no certain proof, being composed of and growing little by little from the opinions of many different persons, does not come as close to the truth as the simple reasoning that a man of good sense can naturally make about things which he experiences. And in like manner I thought that, because we were all children before becoming adults, and because it was necessary for us to be governed for a long time by our appetites and our teachers—which were often opposed to one another, and neither of which, perhaps, always gave us the best counsel—it is nearly impossible for our judgments to be as pure and as well-founded as they would have been if we had had the complete use of our reason from the day of our birth, and if we had been guided by it alone.

It is true that we do not see men destroying all the houses of a city for the sole purpose of remaking them in another way, and rendering the streets more beautiful. But we notice that many people tear down their houses to re-build them, and even that sometimes they are forced to do so, when the buildings are in danger of falling all by them-selves, and when the foundations are not firm enough. This example persuaded me that there would truly be no likelihood of an individual planning to reform a state by changing it from the foundations up, and overthrowing it in order to set it straight; or planning to reform the body of the sciences, or the established order of teaching them in the schools. Yet, as for all the opinions I had been accepting since my birth, I could do no better than to undertake, once and for all, to reject them all, in order to replace them afterwards, either with better ones, or else the same ones when I had raised them to the level of reason. And I firmly believed that through this means I would succeed in conducting my life much better than if I merely built upon old foundations, and merely acceded to the principles of which I was persuaded in my childhood, without ever having examined them to see if they were true. For although I noted various difficulties in this, they were nevertheless not without remedy, nor comparable to those which are encountered in reforming lesser things when they concern the public. These great bodies are too difficult to set up once they have been knocked down, or even too difficult to hold up, once they have been shaken, and their fall can only be violent. Then, as to their imperfections, if they have any (as the diversity among them, alone, suffices to assure us that many of them have), familiarity has doubtless tamed them, and has even insensibly avoided or corrected many that prudence could not have attended to so well. And finally, they are almost always more bearable than their changing would be, just as great roads, twisting between mountains, become gradually so even and convenient, through being much traveled, that it is much better to follow them than to go in a straighter path by climbing over rocks and descending to the bottom of precipices.

This is why I cannot approve at all of those unsettled and turbulent spirits who are not summoned either by birth or by fortune to the management of public affairs, and nevertheless are always suggesting ideas for some new reform. And if I thought that there was the slightest thing in this work through which I might be suspected of this folly, I would be very reluctant to permit its publication. Never has my intention extended further than to try and reform my own thoughts, and to build on a foundation all my own. But if my work has rather pleased me, and I provide the model of it for you to see here, it is not because I want to advise anyone to imitate it. Those to whom God has given more of His graces will perhaps have higher aims; but I firmly believe that this one is already too bold for many. Even the resolution to disabuse oneself of all the opinions that one has accepted since birth is not one which everyone ought to follow. The world is largely composed of two kinds of minds which are in no way suited to it: namely, those who, believing themselves more able than they are, cannot keep from making precipitous judgments, and have not enough patience to direct their thoughts in an orderly manner, so that if they once take the liberty of doubting the principles they have accepted, and of leaving the common road, they can never keep to the path they must take to go more directly, and will remain misguided all their lives; then, those who, having sufficient intelligence or modesty to realize that they are less capable of distinguishing the true from the false than certain others by whom they can be taught, should be content to follow the opinions of those others, rather than looking for better ones themselves.

And as for me, I would without doubt have been among the latter had I had but a single teacher, or had I not known the differences that have always existed among the opinions of the most learned. But I had learned, ever since college, that we can imagine nothing so strange and unbelievable that it has not been said by some philosopher; and I had recognized in my travels that those who have feelings very contrary to ours are not, for that alone, either barbarians or savages, but that many of them use reason as much or more than we do; and I had considered how the same man, with the same mind, being raised from childhood among the

French or Germans, becomes different from what he would be if he had always lived among the Chinese or cannibals; and how, regarding the style of our clothes, the same thing which pleased us ten years ago, and perhaps will please us again ten years hence, now seems extravagant and ridiculous to us, so that we are more persuaded by custom and example than by any certain knowledge, even though the majority opinion is a proof that has no worth for any truths that are at all difficult to discover, because it is much more likely that a single man has discovered them than a whole people. Therefore I was unable to choose anyone whose opinions were preferable to those of others, and I found myself forced to undertake to guide myself.

But, as with a man who walks alone and in shadows, I resolved to go so slowly and circumspectly in all things, that if I advanced only a little, I would at least be safe from falling. I even did not want to begin to reject all at once all the opinions which had formerly slipped into my consciousness without having been introduced there by reason, until I had first used sufficient time planning the work I was undertaking, and had looked for the true method for coming to know everything of which my mind was capable.

When younger, I had done a little study of logic among the branches of philosophy, and among those of mathematics, [I had studied] the analysis of the geometers and algebra—three arts or sciences which it seemed should be able to contribute something to my plan. But, in examining them, I noticed that in logic, its syllogisms and most of its other rules serve to explain to others the things that one already knows—or even, as with the art of Lully, to speak without judgment of things that one does not know—rather than to learn them. And although it contains, in effect, many very true and good precepts, there are nevertheless so many others mixed among them which are either harmful or superfluous, that it is nearly as hard to separate them as it is to sculpt a Diana or a Minerva out of a block of marble which is still roughhewn. Then, as for the analysis of the ancients and the algebra of the moderns, aside from the fact that they deal only with very abstract matters, which seem to have no use, the first is always so limited to the consideration of figures that it cannot exercise the understanding without greatly tiring the imagination; and in the second, we are so much subject to certain rules and letters that we have made of it a confused and obscure art, which burdens the mind, rather than a science which cultivates it. This caused me to think that it was essential to search for some other method which included the advantages of these three but was exempt from their faults. And as the multitude of laws often furnishes excuses for vice, so that a state is better ruled when it has but few laws, and they are strictly observed, so, in place of the great number of rules of which logic is composed, I believed that I would have enough with the four following ones, provided that I took a firm and constant vow not to fail, even once, to observe them.

The first was never to accept anything as true that I did not know evidently to be such; that is to say, carefully to avoid haste and bias, and to include nothing more in my judgments than that which presented itself to my mind so clearly and so distinctly that I had no occasion to place it in doubt.

The second was to divide each of the difficulties that I examined into as many parts as possible, and according as such division would be required for the better solution of the problems.

The third was to direct my thinking in an orderly way, by beginning with the objects that were simplest and easiest to understand, in order to climb little by little, gradually, to the knowledge of the most complex; and even for this purpose assuming an order among those objects which do not naturally precede each other.

And the last was at all times to make enumerations so complete, and reviews so general, that I would be sure of omitting nothing.

These long chains of reasoning, so simple and easy, which

the geometers customarily used in order to arrive at their most difficult demonstrations, had given me occasion to imagine that all things that can be understood by men follow from one another in the same way, and that, provided only that we abstain from accepting as true anything which is not, and always follow the order that is necessary to deduce each from the other, there can be none so remote that we cannot eventually come upon it, or so hidden that we cannot discover it. And I did not have very much trouble looking for the ones with which I had to begin, for I already knew that it must be with the simplest and easiest to know. And considering that among all those who had hithertofore searched for truth in the sciences, only the mathematicians had been able to discover some demonstrations—that is, some certain and evident reasons—I did not doubt that it was [this same kind of proposition] that they had examined; although I expected no other advantage from this than to accustom my mind to delight in the truth, and not to be satisfied with false reasons. But this did not mean that I planned to try and learn all the particular sciences commonly called mathematical; and seeing that although their objects are different, they nevertheless all agree in that they treat of nothing else but the diverse relations or ratios found there, I thought that it would be better if I only examined these ratios in general, and only in the subjects which would serve to make it easier for me to know them. Nor did I restrict them to this alone, in order that I could better apply them afterwards to all the others to which they might be suited. Then, having taken note that, in order to understand them, I would sometimes have to consider them each in particular, and sometimes only to keep them in mind, or to understand many of them together, I thought that, in order the better to consider them each in particular, I should conceive of them as [ratios between] lines, because I could find nothing simpler, nor anything which I could more distinctly represent to my imagination and to my senses. But, in order to keep them in mind, or to understand many of them together, it was necessary to explain them by certain numbers, as briefly as possible; and through this method, I would borrow the best of geometrical analysis and algebra, and correct all the errors of the one by the other.

And in effect I daresay that the exact observance of the few rules I had chosen gave me such facility in clarifying all the questions covered by these two sciences that in the two or three months which I took to examine them, having begun with the most simple and the most general, and each truth that I found being a rule which afterwards helped me to find other truths, not only did I finally solve many problems which I had previously judged to be very difficult, but it also seemed to me, toward the end, that I could determine, even in those problems of which I was ignorant, through what means, and just when it was possible to solve them. Perhaps I will not appear too vain about this to you, if you will consider that, there being but one truth for every problem, whoever finds it knows as much as anyone can know about it; and so, for example, a child instructed in arithmetic, having done an addition problem according to its rules, can be assured of having discovered all that the human mind is capable of discovering about the particular sum he has examined. For at bottom the method which shows us how to follow the correct order, and to enumerate exactly all the circumstances of that which we are investigating, contains everything which gives certainty to the rules of arithmetic.

But what pleased me the most about this method was that through it I was assured of using my reason, if not perfectly, then at least as well as was in my power; in addition I felt that in practicing it, my mind was becoming gradually accustomed to conceive its objects more clearly and distinctly, and that, because I had not directed this method to any particular subject matter, it promised to be as usefully applicable to the difficulties of other sciences as I had found it to be in those of algebra. Not that because of this I would dare to undertake to examine all the problems which presented themselves, all at once; for this would have been contrary to the order prescribed by the method. But, having noticed that all the principles of the other sciences were borrowed from philosophy, in which I had not yet found any certain ones, I thought it essential that before anything else, I try to establish some principles of philosophy; and that, this being the most important thing in the world, and the place where haste and bias were most to be feared, I should not undertake to arrive at these principles until I had attained a much more mature age than twenty-three years, which I was then; and until I had beforehand spent much time preparing for it, in ridding my mind of all the false opinions that I accepted before that time and amassing many experiences, which would afterwards be the material of my reasoning, as well as in becoming practiced in the method that I had prescribed for myself, in order to become more and more familiar with it.

Third Part

And finally, it is not sufficient, before beginning to rebuild one's lodging, to pull down the old house, to make provisions for materials and architects, or else train oneself in architecture, and in addition to have carefully drawn the plan for the house; it is also necessary to be provided with some other place where one can stay comfortably during the time that people will be working there. In the same way, so that I would not remain irresolute in my actions, although reason obliged me to be so in my judgments, and in order to live as happily as I could during this time, I formed a provisional code of morals, consisting of only three or four maxims, which I wish to give to you.

The first was to obey the laws and customs of my country, constantly retaining the religion in which God gave me the grace to be instructed since my childhood, and in everything else to govern myself according to the most moderate and least excessive opinions that are commonly accepted in practice by the most intelligent of those with whom I would have to live. For at that time I was beginning to reject my own opinions, since I wanted to subject them all to examination; consequently I could be assured of doing no better than to follow those of the most sensible people. And although there are perhaps as many sensible people among the Persians or the Chinese as among ourselves, it seemed to me that it was more practical to regulate myself according to those with whom I would have to live; and that, in order to learn their true opinions, I should pay attention to what they did rather than what they said, not only because in the corruption of our customs there are few people who are willing to say everything that they believe, but also because many are themselves ignorant of their beliefs. For since the action of thought by means of which we believe something is different from that by means of which we know that we believe it, the one is often found without the other. And among many opinions equally accepted, I chose only the most moderate ones, because these are always the most convenient in practice, and presumably—all excess usually being evil—the best, and also because I should stray less from the true path, in case I failed, than I would if I had chosen one of the extremes, when it was the other that should have been followed. And, in particular, I considered excessive all the promises by which one gives up some of his liberty. Not that I disapproved of laws which, in order to remedy the inconsistancy of feeble minds, permit one, when one has some good plan—or even, for the well-being of business, some merely indifferent one—to make bonds and enter contracts which oblige one to persevere in them. But because I saw nothing in the world that remained forever in the same state, and because, in my particular state, I was promising myself to perfect my judgments more and more, not to make them worse, I would have committed a great sin against common sense if, because I used to approve of something, I obliged myself to accept it later on as praiseworthy, when it had ceased to be so or I had ceased to esteem it as such.

My second maxim was to be as firm and resolute in my action as I could be, and to follow the most doubtful decisions no less constantly, once I had determined to do so, than I would if they had been quite certain. In this I imitated the travelers who, finding themselves lost in some forest, must not make the mistake of wandering sometimes in one direction, sometimes in another, nor stand in one place, but must always walk as straight as they can in a single direction, and not change the direction for weak reasons, even though at the outset it might have been chance alone which determined them to choose it. For through this means, if they do not get right to where they want to be, they will finally at least arrive someplace, where they will probably be better off than in the middle of a forest. And thus, since often the actions of life permit no delay, it is a very certain truth that when it is not in our power to discern the truest opinions, we should follow the most probable ones; and even when we note no probable advantage in some opinions rather than others, we must nevertheless decide upon some of them, and afterwards we must consider them, not as doubtful (insofar as they are related to practice), but as quite true and certain, because the reason which caused us to decide upon them is such. And this [maxim] was capable of thenceforth delivering me from all repentence and remorse, such as usually bothers the consciences of these feeble and unsettled minds, who never cease inconsistently to practice, as worthwhile, things that they later judge to be evil.

My third maxim was always to try to conquer myself rather than fortune, and to modify my desires rather than the order of the world; and generally, to become accustomed to the belief that nothing is entirely within our power except our thoughts, so that after we have done our best concerning matters external to us, anything that is lacking for success is, so far as we are concerned, absolutely impossible. And this [maxim] alone seemed to be sufficient to prevent me from desiring anything in the future which I could not acquire, and so to make me content. For because our will is naturally persuaded to desire only things which our understanding represents to it as being in some way possible, it is certain that, if we consider all goods outside of us as equally removed from our power, we will regret losing those that seem to be our birthright, when we are deprived of them through no fault of our own, no more than we regret not possessing the kingdom of China or of Mexico. And making necessity a virtue, as they say, we will no more desire to be healthy when we are sick, or free when we are in prison, than we now desire to have bodies of a material as incorruptible as diamonds, or wings to fly like the birds. But I admit that it takes long practice, and oft-reiterated meditation, to become accustomed to regard all things in this light;

and I believe that this must have been the secret of these philosophers who in other times were able to withdraw themselves from the dominion of fortune and, despite sorrows and poverty, vie with their gods for happiness. For they were constantly occupied with considering the limits prescribed for them by nature, and were so completely persuaded that nothing but their thoughts was in their power, that that alone was sufficient to prevent them from having any affection for other things. And they ordered their thoughts so absolutely that this gave them some reason to believe themselves richer and more powerful, freer and happier, than any other men, who, not having this philosophy, however they might be favored by nature and fortune, could never thus have at hand all they wanted.

Finally, in concluding this code, I decided to review all the diverse occupations that men have in this life, in order to try and choose the best one; and without wanting to say anything of the occupations of others, I thought that I could do no better than to continue in the very one I was in, that is, to employ my whole life in cultivating my reason, and to advance, as far as I was able, in the knowledge of truth, following the method I had prescribed for myself. Since I had begun using this method, I had experienced such great happiness that I did not believe that any more charming or innocent one could be found in this life; and in discovering through it, every day, some truths which seemed to me sufficiently important, and commonly unknown to other men, my mind was so filled with satisfaction that everything else had no effect on me. Besides this, the three foregoing maxims were based only on the plan I had to continue to instruct myself; for God having given each of us a certain light to distinguish the true from the false, I should not have believed myself to be contented with the opinions of another for a single moment if I had not proposed to use my own judgment to examine them, when it was time; and I could not have been free from scruples in following them, if I had not hoped to lose no occasion to find better opinions, should there be any. And finally, I would not have been able to limit my desires, nor to be content, if I had not followed a path by which I thought I should be assured of acquiring all the knowledge of which I was capable; and by the same means I thought it to be the path to all the true goods which would ever be in my power. In this way, since our will is not attracted to or repelled from anything, except as our understanding represents it as good or evil, judging well is sufficient for doing well, and judging the best that we can also suffices for doing the best that we can—that is, acquiring all the virtues, and with them all the other goods, which we can acquire. And when one is certain that this is so, one's happiness lacks nothing.

After thus having assured myself of these maxims, and having set them apart, with the truths of the Faith—which have always been the first in my belief—I judged that for all the rest of my opinions, I could freely undertake to rid myself of them. And inasmuch as I hoped to be able to achieve my purpose better by conversing with men than by remaining shut up for a long time in the room where I had had these thoughts, I began traveling again before winter was completely over. And during all the following nine years, I wandered here and there in the world, trying to be a spectator rather than an actor in all the dramas that are played there. And giving particular reflection in each matter as to what could render it suspect, and cause us to misapprehend it, I meanwhile tried to uproot from my mind all the errors which had hithertofore slipped into it. Not that I imitated the skeptics, who doubt only for the sake of doubting, and always affect irresolution; for on the contrary, my whole plan was only to assure myself, and to reject shifting earth and sand in order to find rock or clay. In this I succeeded rather well, it seems to me, inasmuch as, trying to discover the falsity or incertitude of the propositions I examined, not by feeble conjectures but by clear and assured reasonings, I encountered among them none so doubtful that I did not always gather from it some sufficiently certain conclusion, even if it was only that it did not contain any-thing certain. And as when we are destroying an old dwell-ing we usually keep the remains in order to use in rebuild-ing, so, in destroying all those of my opinions that I judged to be ill-founded, I made various observations, and acquired many experiences, which have since served me in establish-ing more certain beliefs. Moreover, I continued to become practiced in the method I had prescribed for myself; for besides taking care generally to direct all my thoughts ac-cording to its rules, I reserved a few hours from time to time which I used particularly to practice it in mathematical difficulties, or even also in certain others which I was able to render like those of mathematics, by detaching them from all the principles of the other sciences, which I did not find firm enough, as you will see that I have done in many cases which are explained in this volume. And so I did not ap-pear to live in any other way than those who, having nothing to do but live a pleasant and innocent life, endeavor to distinguish pleasures from vices, and who use all respectable diversions in order to enjoy their leisure without hindrance. Yet I did not cease to pursue my plan, and profited in the knowledge of truth, perhaps more than if I had done nothing but read books, or frequent men of letters.

Nevertheless these nine years elapsed before I had yet taken any position concerning the difficulties commonly dis-puted among the learned, or begun to search for the prin-ciples of any philosophy more certain than the common va-riety. And the example of many excellent minds who had a plan before them, and who seemed to me not to have suc-ceeded, made me imagine so much difficulty that perhaps I still would not have dared to undertake it if I had not seen that some people had started a rumor that I had already arrived at my goal. I did not know on what they based this opinion; if I contributed something to it through my con-versations, it must have been by confessing to what I did not know more ingenuously than is usual for those who have a bit of learning, and also perhaps by making known the reasons for my doubting many things which others took to be certain, rather than by boasting of any doctrine. But being sufficiently good-natured so as not to want to be taken for anything other than I was, I thought it essential to try, by all means, to be worthy of the reputation that was given me; and it was just eight years ago that this desire made me resolve to remove myself from all places where I could have acquaintances, and to retire here, [1] in a country where the long duration of the war has established such regularity that the armies stationed here seem only to insure the more secure enjoyment of the fruits of peace, and where, among the throng of a great and active people, more occupied with their own affairs than curious about those of another, I have been able to have as solitary and retired a life as in the remotest of deserts, without lacking any of the comforts of the most populous cities.

[1] To Holland.

Fourth Part

I do not know whether I should talk to you about the first meditations that I completed here, for they are so metaphyscial and so uncommon that perhaps they will not be to everyone's taste. Nevertheless, so that it may be judged whether the foundations I have chosen are firm enough, I find myself somewhat obliged to speak of them. I had noticed for a long time that so far as customs are concerned, it is sometimes necessary to follow opinions that we know to be highly uncertain, just as if they were indubitable, as was stated above. But because I then desired to occupy myself with nothing but the search for truth, I thought that I should do just the contrary, and reject as absolutely false everything about which I could conceive the least doubt, in order to see if after this there remained anything in my belief which was entirely indubitable. Thus, because our senses sometimes deceive us, I wanted to assume that there was nothing which was such as they cause us to imagine. And because there are men whose reasoning is mistaken, even concerning the simplest matters of geometry, in which they make paralogisms, I judged that I was as subject to failure as any other, and I rejected as false all the reasoning I had hithertofore accepted as demonstrative. And finally, considering that the very same ideas that we have when we are awake may also come to us when we are asleep, without this meaning that any of them are true, I resolved to pretend that all the things that had ever entered into my mind were no more certain than the illusions of my dreams. But, soon afterwards, I noticed that although I wanted thus to think that everything was false, it was necessary that I, who was thinking this, be something. And noting that this truth: *I think, there-*

fore I am, was so firm and well assured that all the most extravagant suppositions of the skeptics were incapable of shaking it, I judged that I could accept it without scruple as the first principle of the philosophy for which I was searching.

Then I examined closely what I was, and saw I could pretend that I had no body, and that there was no world nor any place where I existed; but I could not pretend because of this that I did not exist. On the contrary, from the very fact that I doubted the truth of other things, it followed quite obviously and quite certainly that I existed; whereas, if I had only ceased to think, even though all the rest of what I had imagined remained true, I would have no reason to believe that I existed. From this I knew that I was a substance whose entire essence or nature consists in thinking, and which, to exist, need have no location, nor depend on anything material. So that this *me*—that is, the soul by which I am what I am—is completely distinct from the body; and is even easier to know than is the body; even if the body were not, the soul would not cease to be all that it is.

After this, I considered in general what is required of a proposition in order that it be true and certain; for since I had just discovered one that I knew to be such, I thought that I should also know in what this certitude consisted. And having noted that there is nothing at all in this proposition *I think, therefore I am* which assures me that I speak the truth, except that I see very clearly that in order to think, it is necessary to be, I judged that I could accept as a general rule that the things we conceive very clearly and very distinctly are all true, but that there is some difficulty distinguishing which things we conceive distinctly.

Following this, I reflected that I doubted, and that consequently my being was not perfect, because I saw clearly that it was a greater perfection to know than to doubt; thus I decided to find out how I had learned to think of something more perfect than I was; and I clearly perceived that it must be from some nature which was in effect more

perfect. As to the ideas I had of many other things outside
of me—such as the sky, the earth, light, heat, and thousands
of others—I was not at great pains to know where they
came from; for seeing nothing in these ideas which seemed
to make them superior to me, I could believe that if they
were veridical, they were dependent on my nature, insofar
as it had some perfection; and if they were not veridical,
that I gathered them from nothingness, that is, they were
in me because I had a defect. But this could not be the origin
of the idea of a being more perfect than mine, for to have
gathered this idea from nothingness was something manifestly impossible. And because it is no less repugnant that
the more perfect be an effect and dependent on the less perfect than it is that something proceed from nothing, I
could not have gathered this idea from myself, either. So
that the only thing remaining was that it had been put in
me by another nature that was truly more perfect than I
was, and which even had in itself all the perfections of which
we could have any idea—that is, to explain myself in a word,
by God. To this I added that, since I knew some perfections
which I did not have, I was not the only being which existed
(I shall use freely here, if you will allow me, the terms of
the schoolmen), but that it must, of necessity, be the case
that there was some other more perfect being, on which
I depended, and from which I had acquired all that I was.
For if I had been alone and independent of anything else, so
that I had had by myself all that little which I shared with
the perfect being, I could for the same reason have had all
the rest which I knew I lacked, and so could myself have
been infinite, eternal, immutable, omniscient, omnipotent,
and, in short, could have had every perfection that I could
observe to exist in God. For following the reasoning I just
did, in order to know the nature of God, so far as my own
nature was capable of doing so, I had but to consider all
the properties of which I found any idea in myself, and to
consider whether or not it was a perfection to possess them;
then I would be assured that none of those exhibiting any

imperfection were in Him, but that all the others were. Thus I saw that doubt, inconstancy, sadness, and similar things could not be in the nature of God, seeing that I would myself have been quite content to be exempt from them. Then, besides this, I had ideas of many sensible and corporeal things, for even though I might assume that I was dreaming, and that all I saw or imagined was false, nevertheless I could not deny that the ideas of these things were truly in my thought. But because I had already seen very clearly in myself that the intelligent nature is distinct from the corporeal, I considered that to be composite is evidence of being dependent, and that dependency is manifestly a defect; thus I judged from this that it could not be a perfection in God to be composed of those two natures, and that as a result He was not so composed. But if there were certain bodies in the world, or else certain intelligences or other natures, which were not completely perfect, their being must depend on God's power, so that they could not subsist without Him for a single moment.

After this I wanted to search for other truths, and having proposed to myself the object of the geometers—which I conceived as a continuous body, or a space indefinitely extended in length, breadth, and height or depth, which was divisible into various parts, could have different shapes and sizes, and could be moved or transposed in any way (for the geometers assumed all this of their object)—I undertook some of their simpler demonstrations. And I noticed that that great certainty which everyone attributes to these demonstrations is founded only on the fact that we conceive them evidently, according to the rule I just stated; I also noticed that there was nothing in them which assured me of the existence of their object. For example, I saw clearly that, if we posit a triangle, it is necessary that its three angles be equal to two right angles; but I did not see anything in this which assured me that there was a single triangle in the world. Whereas, returning to examine the idea that I had of a perfect being, I found that it includes existence, just

as, or even more evidently than, the idea of a triangle includes its three angles being equal to two right angles, or
the idea of a sphere, its parts being equally distant from its
center, or even still more evidently. As a result, that this
perfect being, God, is or exists is at least as certain as any
demonstration of geometry could be.

But what causes many people to be persuaded that there
is difficulty in knowing this, and even also in knowing what
their souls are, is that they never raise their minds above
sensible things and are so accustomed to consider nothing
except by forming an image of it, which is a particular mode
of thought for material things, that everything for which
an image cannot be formed seems unintelligible to them.
This is sufficiently obvious from the fact that even the philosophers hold it to be a maxim, in the schools, that nothing
is in the intellect that was not first in the senses—where
nevertheless it is certain that the ideas of God and of the
soul have never been. And it seems to me that those who
wish to comprehend these ideas by means of images are
doing the same thing as using their eyes to hear sounds or
smell odors, except that there is still the difference that the
sense of sight gives us no less assurance of the truth of its
objects than do those of smell and hearing; whereas without
the intervention of our understanding, neither our imagination [1] nor our senses could ever assure us of anything.

Finally, if there are still men who are not sufficiently persuaded of the existence of God and of their souls by the
reasons which I have furnished, I want them to know that
all the other things of which they think they can be more
certain—such as having a body, and there being stars and
an earth, and such things—are less certain. For although
we have a moral assurance of these things which is such that
it seems that unless we are to be extravagant, we cannot
doubt them, yet unless we are to be unreasonable, when it

[1] Throughout this passage Descartes uses *imagination* to denote the
faculty of forming sensory images; no equivalent noun seems to exist in
English.

comes to metaphysical certainty, we cannot deny that these are not matters of which we can be entirely certain. For notice that we can, in the same way, imagine when we are asleep that we have another body, and see other stars and another earth, without any of them existing. Whence do we know that the thoughts which come in dreams, rather than the others, are false, seeing that often they are no less vivid and explicit? Well, the best minds may study this as much as they please; I do not believe that they can give any reason sufficient to remove this doubt, without presupposing the existence of God. Because first, this very rule that I have just accepted, namely that all of the things we conceive very clearly and distinctly are true, is certain only because God is or exists, and because He is a perfect being, and because everything in us comes from Him. From this it follows that our ideas or notions, which are real things, and which come from God insofar as they are clear and distinct, cannot but be true to that extent. Therefore, if we often have ideas which contain falsity, they can only be those that have some confusion and obscurity in them, because in this respect they participate in nothingness—that is, they are thus confused within us because we are not completely perfect. And it is evident that it is no less repugnant for falsity or imperfection to proceed from God as for truth or perfection to proceed from nothingness. But if we did not know that everything real and true within us came from a perfect and infinite being, no matter how clear and distinct our ideas were, we would have no reason to be assured that they had the perfection of being true.

Now after the knowledge of God and of the soul has thus made us certain of this rule, it is easy to understand that the reveries which we imagine while asleep should not in any way cause us to doubt the truth of the thoughts we have while awake. For if it happened that we had some very distinct idea, even while sleeping—as, for example, when a geometer invents some new demonstration—our being asleep would not prevent it from being true. And as to the most ordinary mistake of our dreams, which consists in our representing various objects to ourselves in the same way as our external senses do, it is not important that this gives us occasion to challenge the truth of such ideas; for often they can also deceive us without our being asleep, as when those who have jaundice see everything colored yellow, or as the stars or other very distant bodies appear much smaller to us than they are. For in the end, whether we are awake or asleep, we should never cease to be persuaded only by the evidence of our reason. And note that I say our reason, not our imagination or our senses. Thus, although we see the sun very clearly, we must not judge because of this that it is only as large as we see it; and it is easy for us to imagine distinctly the head of a lion mounted upon the body of a goat, without our having to conclude because of this that there is a chimera in the world. For reason does not dictate that what we see or imagine thus be true. But it does dictate that all our ideas or notions must have some basis in truth; for it would not be possible that God, who is entirely perfect and entirely truthful, would otherwise have placed them in us. And because our reasoning is never as evident or as complete during sleep as when we are awake, although sometimes our imagination is then as vivid and explicit, or more so, reason also dictates to us that since our ideas cannot be entirely true, because we are not entirely perfect, what truth they possess must infallibly be found in the ideas we have when we are awake, rather than in our dreams.

Fifth Part

I would be happy to pursue this, and exhibit here the whole chain of other truths which I deduced from these first ones. But because this would now make it necessary for me to discuss many questions which are a matter of controversy among the learned, with whom I have no desire to become embroiled, I believe that it will be better for me to abstain, and only to say what these questions are in general, and leave wiser men to judge whether it would be useful for the public to be informed of them in greater detail. I have always remained firm in the resolution that I took never to assume any principle other than the one I have just used to demonstrate the existence of God and the soul, and never to accept anything as true which did not seem to me to be clearer and more certain than the demonstrations of the geometers had previously seemed. And yet I venture to say that not only have I found a means for satisfying myself in a short time on all the principal difficulties which we usually treat in philosophy, but I have also noticed certain laws which God has established in nature, and of which he has imprinted notions in our souls, such that after having reflected sufficiently upon them, we could not doubt that they are exactly observed in everything which is or which occurs in the world. Then in considering the effects of these laws, I seem to have discovered several truths more useful and more important than everything I had learned previously, or had even hoped to learn.

But because I have tried to explain the principles of these truths in a treatise which certain considerations prevent me from publishing, I know no better way to make them known than by summarizing its contents here. I had planned, before I wrote it, to include in it all that I thought I knew concern-

ing the nature of material things. But just as painters are
unable to represent all the various surfaces of a solid body
equally well on a flat picture, so that they choose one of the
principal surfaces to place in the light, and shade the others,
so that these other surfaces appear only as we might see them
by looking at the principal one; so, fearing that I could not
put in my discourse all that I had in my thoughts, I undertook to do no more than expose quite amply there what I conceived the nature of light to be. Then I took the occasion to
add something about the sun and the fixed stars, because
almost all light proceeds from them; and about the heavens,
because they transmit light; and about the planets, comets,
and earth, because they reflect it; and in particular about
all the bodies on the earth, because they are either colored
or transparent or luminous; and finally about man, since he
is the observer of light. And—so as to put these things slightly
in the shade, and to be able to judge of them more freely,
without being obliged to follow or refute the opinions
accepted among the learned—I even resolved to leave this whole
world to their disputes, and to speak only of what would
happen in a new world, if God were now to create somewhere,
in imaginary space, enough matter to compose it, and if He agitated the parts of this matter diversely and without order, so
that He made of it a chaos as confused as the poets can imagine, and if afterwards He did nothing else except lend His
ordinary support to nature, and left it to act according to the
laws which He established. So I first described this matter,
and tried to represent it so that nothing in this world, it
seemed to me, was clearer or more intelligible, except that
which has already been said of God and the soul: for I even
assumed, expressly, that it had in it none of these *forms* or
qualities disputed in the schools, nor generally anything the
knowledge of which is not so natural to our minds that we
cannot even pretend not to know it. Moreover, I showed what
the laws of nature were; and without leaning my reasons upon
any other principle but the infinite perfections of God, I
tried to demonstrate all those laws about which we might have

any doubt, and to show that they are such that even if God had created many worlds, there would have been none of them where these laws failed to be observed. After that, I showed how the greatest part of the matter of this chaos must, according to these laws, become disposed and arranged in a certain way, which would make it similar to our heavens; how, meanwhile, some of its parts must compose an earth, some compose planets and comets, and some others a sun and fixed stars. And here, expanding on the subject of light, I explained at great length what sort of light would be found in the sun and the stars, and how from there it would traverse the immense spaces of the heavens in an instant, and how it is reflected from the planets and comets toward the earth. I also added many things concerning the substance, situation, movements, and all the diverse qualities of these heavens and these stars, so that I thought I had said enough about it to make it known that there is nothing to be seen in the phenomena of this world which would not, or at least which could not, appear in the same way in the phenomena of the world I was describing.

From there I went on to speak particularly of the earth: how, although I had expressly assumed that God had not put any weight into the matter of which it was composed, all its parts nevertheless tend exactly toward its center; how, because there are water and air on its surface, the disposition of the heavenly bodies and the stars, especially the moon, should cause an ebb and flow there, similar in all circumstances to what we notice in our seas; and besides this they should also cause a certain current, of water as well as of air, from the east toward the west, such as we also note in the tropics; how the mountains, seas, fountains, and rivers could be formed naturally there, and how metals could come to be in the mines, and plants grow there in the fields, and generally how all the bodies we call mixed or composite are engendered there. And among other things, because aside from the stars I knew nothing in the world but fire which produces light, I studied how to make everything belonging to the nature

of fire very clearly understandable: how it is caused, how
it is fed; how it sometimes has heat without light, and
sometimes light without heat; how it can introduce different colors and diverse other qualities into different bodies;
how it melts some bodies, and hardens others; how it can
consume them almost completely, or convert them into cinders
and smoke; and finally, out of these cinders, solely by the
violence of its action, how it forms glass: for this transmu-
tation of cinders into glass seemed to me as admirable as any
other that occurs in nature, so that I took particular pleasure
in describing it.

Nevertheless I did not wish to infer from all these things
that the world was created in the way I proposed, for it is
much more probable that from the very beginning God made
it such as it ought to be. But it is certain—and this is a commonly accepted opinion among theologians—that the action
by which God now conserves it is the same as that by which
He created it; thus even if He had given it, in the beginning,
no form other than chaos, provided that having established
the laws of nature He gave His consent that the world act as it
normally does, we can believe, without slighting the miracle
of creation, that through this alone all purely material
things would have been able, with time, to become such as
we now see them. And their nature is much easier to conceive, when we picture their birth in this way, little by little,
than when we consider them merely as completed.

From describing inanimate bodies and plants, I went on
to describe animals, and particularly men. But, because
I did not yet have sufficient knowledge of them to speak of
them in the same style as of the rest—that is, by demonstrating the effects through the causes, and showing from
what sources and in what way nature must produce them—
I contented myself with assuming that God formed a man's
body, entirely similar to one of ours, in the exterior shape
of its members as well as in the interior conformation
of its organs, without composing it of any matter other
than that I had described, and without placing in it, at

the beginning, any rational soul, nor any other thing to serve as a vegetative or sensitive soul, except that He excited in its heart one of these fires without light which I had already explained, and which I conceived to be of the same nature as that which heats grain, when we store it before it is dry, or which makes new wines boil, when we leave them to ferment in the pulp. For examining the functions which this body could have after such a fire was excited in it, I discovered precisely all those which can be in us without our thinking about them, and consequently, without our soul—that is, that part distinct from the body whose essence, as has been previously stated, consists only in thinking—contributing to them. And these functions are the same as those in which it can be said that animals lacking reason resemble us. But I could not find among them any of those which, being dependent upon thought, are the only ones that we possess because we are men; and I discovered these qualities afterwards, having assumed that God created a rational soul, and that He joined it to this body in a certain manner which I described.

But in order to show in what way I treated this matter, I wish to explain here the movement of the heart and arteries, which, being the first and the most general ones that we can observe in animals, will enable us to judge easily what we should think of all the others. And so that it will be less difficult to understand what I am going to say, I should like those who are not versed in anatomy to take the trouble, before reading this, to have the heart of some large animal with lungs cut open before them—for it is in every respect quite similar to the heart of a man—and let them be shown the two chambers or concavities [1] which are there. First, there is the one in its right side, to which there are connected two very large tubes, namely, the *vena cava*, which is the principal receptacle of the blood, and serves as the tree trunk, of which all the body's other veins are the branches; and the *vena arteriosa*, which has thus been misnamed, because it is

[1] The ventricles.

actually an artery which originates in the heart and is
divided after leaving it into many branches which come to
be spread throughout the lungs. Then, there is the concavity
in its left side, to which are connected in the same way two
tubes, as large as or larger than, the preceding: namely, the
arteria venosa, which has also been misnamed, because it is
nothing other than a vein coming from the lungs, where it
is divided into many branches which intertwine with those
of the *vena arteriosa* and those of that conduit we call the
windpipe, through which the air enters to be breathed; and
the *great artery*, [2] which, leaving the heart, sends its branches
throughout the body. I would also wish that those unfamil-
iar with anatomy be carefully shown the eleven small membranes which, like so many little doors, open and shut the
four openings in these two concavities. Three of the membranes are at the entrance to the *vena cava*, where they are
so disposed that they cannot prevent the blood which it contains from flowing into the right concavity of the heart, but
nevertheless they quite stop it from flowing back out. Three
are at the entrance of the *vena arteriosa*; these are disposed
in the opposite way, and easily permit the blood in this
concavity to pass into the lungs, but do not allow the blood in
the lungs to return to the heart. So also there are two others
at the entrance to the *arteria venosa*, which let the blood
flow from the lungs to the left concavity of the heart, but
prevent its returning; and three at the entrance to the great
artery, which permit the blood to leave the heart, but prevent it from returning. And there is no need to look for
any reason for the number of these membranes, other than
that the opening of the *arteria venosa*, which is an oval by
virtue of its location, can be easily closed with two of them,
whereas the others, being round, can be better closed with
three. In addition, I would wish that it be pointed out to
them that the great artery and the *vena arteriosa* are of a
much harder and firmer composition than that of the
arteria venosa and the *vena cava*; and that these latter two

2 The aorta.

become larger before entering the heart, and are like two sacs, called the "ears of the heart," which are composed of a flesh similar to that of the heart itself. And there is always more heat in the heart than in any other part of the body; and finally, this heat is capable of causing any drop of blood which enters the concavities of the heart to swell and be dilated immediately, as all liquids generally do when we allow them to fall drop by drop into some vessel which is very hot.

After that, I need not say anything else in order to explain the movement of the heart, except that, when its concavities are not full of blood, blood necessarily runs into it: from the *vena cava* into the right concavity, and from the *arteria venosa* into the left one, inasmuch as these two vessels are always full of blood and their openings, which face toward the heart, cannot then be shut. But as soon as two drops of blood enter thus, one in each of its concavities, these drops (which can only be very large, for the openings through which they enter are very wide, and the vessels from which they come are quite full of blood) become rarefied and dilated, because of the heat they find there. By this means, causing the whole heart to swell, they push and shut the five small valves located at the entrances of the two vessels from which they came, thus preventing any more blood from descending into the heart. And continuing to become more and more rarefied, they push and open the six other small valves, which are located at the entrances of the two other vessels by which they leave, causing all the branches of the *vena arteriosa* and the great artery to inflate by this means, almost at the same instant as the heart. Immediately afterwards, the heart is deflated, as are these arteries as well, because the blood that has entered has cooled there; and their six small valves close, and the five valves of the *vena cava* and the *arteria venosa* reopen, and give passage to two other drops of blood, which again inflate the heart and arteries, the same as before. And because the blood which thus enters the heart passes through those two sacs which we call its ears, it follows from this that their movement is opposed to that of the concavities, and that the former are deflated when the latter are inflated.

As to the rest, in order that those who do not understand the force of mathematical demonstrations and are not accustomed to distinguish true reasons from probable ones do not chance to deny this without examining it, I wish to advise them that this movement I have just explained follows from the mere disposition of the organs of the heart which we can see with the eye, and from the heat which we can feel with the fingers, and from the nature of the blood which we can understand through experiment, just as necessarily as does the motion of a clock from the force, situation and shape of its counterweights and wheels.

But if we ask why the blood of the veins is not exhausted by thus flowing continually into the heart, and why the arteries do not come to be too full of blood, since all the blood that passes through the heart is sent there, I need only respond with what has already been said by an English doctor, [3] to whom must be given the glory of having broken the ice in this matter, and of being the first to have taught that there are many small passages at the extremities of the arteries through which the blood they receive from the heart enters into the small branches of the veins, and from there is sent again toward the heart, so that its course is nothing but a perpetual circulation. This is very well proven by the normal experience of surgeons who, having tied the arm not too tightly, above the spot where they open the vein, cause the blood to flow from it more abundantly than if they had not tied it. And the opposite will happen if they tie the arm below, between the hand and the opening, or even if they tie it very tightly above; for it is obvious that a moderately tight bond can only prevent the blood that is already in the arm from returning toward the heart through the veins. But it cannot, because of that, impede that which is always coming anew from the heart through the arteries; for they are situated below the veins, and their membranes, being harder,

[3] William Harvey.

are less easy to depress. And also, the blood which comes from the heart tends to pass through them toward the hand with more force than it causes when returning from the hand toward the heart through the veins. And since this blood leaves the arm through the opening which is in one of the veins, there must necessarily be some passages below the bond—that is, toward the extremities of the arm—through which it can come from the arteries. What he says about the course of the blood is also soundly proven by certain small membranes, which are disposed in diverse places along the veins in such a manner that they do not permit the blood to pass from the middle of the body toward the extremities, but only to return from the extremities toward the heart; and moreover, by the experiment which shows that all the blood in the body can leave it in a very short time by a single artery, when it is cut, even if it be tightly tied very near to the heart, and cut between the heart and the bond, so that there is no imaginable reason for the blood which leaves the artery to come from any place but the heart.

But there are many other things which witness that the true cause of this movement of the blood is that which I have stated: first, the difference we may note between the blood coming from the veins and that which comes from the arteries, which can proceed only from the fact that because the blood is rarefied and, as it were, distilled by passing through the heart, it is more subtle, more active, and warmer immediately after leaving the heart—that is, when it is in the arteries—than it is just before it enters into the heart—that is, while it is in the veins. And if we look carefully, we will discover that this difference is obvious only near the heart, and not as much in the places which are the farthest away from it. Then the hardness of the membranes of which the *vena arteriosa* and the great artery are composed sufficiently demonstrates that the blood strikes against them with more force than against the veins. And why would the left concavity of the heart and the great artery be ampler and wider than the right concavity and the *vena arteriosa*, if it were not that the blood of the *arteria venosa*, not having been in the lungs since it passed through the heart, is thinner and more easily rarefied than that which comes immediately from the *vena cava*? And what could the doctors find out by testing the pulse, if they did not know that according as the blood changes in nature, it can be rarefied by the heat of the heart more or less strongly, and more or less rapidly than before? And if we examine how this heat is communicated to the other members, is it not necessary to avow that it is by means of the blood, which is reheated in passing through the heart, and is diffused from there throughout the body? From this it follows that, if we remove the blood from some part of the body, we remove the heat by the same means; and even if the heart were as hot as glowing iron, it would not suffice to reheat the hands and feet as much as it does if it did not continually send new blood there. Then also we recognize from this that the true purpose of respiration is to carry enough fresh air into the lungs to cause the blood which comes there from the right concavity of the heart, where it has been rarefied and almost changed into vapors, to be condensed, and again converted into blood, before it returns to the left concavity; without this the blood could not be suitably used to feed the fire in the heart. This is confirmed because we see that animals that have no lungs also have only one concavity in the heart, and that children, who cannot use their lungs while enclosed in their mothers' wombs, have an opening through which blood flows from the *vena cava* into the left concavity of the heart, and a tube through which it comes from the *vena arteriosa* into the great artery, without passing through the lungs. Then, how could digestion occur in the stomach, if the heart did not send heat there through the arteries, together with some of the most liquid parts of the blood, which aid in dissolving the food which we have put there? And the action which converts the juice of these foods into the blood—is it not easy to understand, if we consider that the blood is distilled, by passing and repassing through the heart, perhaps by more than one or two hundred times each day? And is anything else needed to explain nutrition and the production of the various humors of the body, except to say that the force with which the blood is rarefied, passing from the heart to the extremities of the arteries, causes some of its parts to stop among those of the members where they are, and there take the place of certain others which they expel; and that, according to the situation, or the shape, or the smallness of the pores that they encounter, some go to certain places rather than others, in the same way that the various sieves which everyone must have seen, being differently pierced, may be used to separate different grains from one another?

And finally, what is most remarkable in all this is the production of animal spirits, which are like a very subtle wind, or rather like a very pure and lively flame, which, arising continuously and in great abundance from the heart to the brain, goes from there through the nerves into the muscles, and imparts movement to all the members. It is not necessary to imagine any other cause that makes the parts of the blood that are the most agitated and penetrating and therefore the most appropriate to compose these spirits, go toward the brain rather than any other place, than that the arteries which carry them there are the straightest of all; and according to the rules of mathematics, which are the same as those of nature, when many things tend together to move toward the same place, where there is not enough room for all of them, as with the parts of the blood leaving the left concavity of the heart, which tend toward the brain, the weakest and least agitated of them must be turned back by the strongest ones, which by this means reach the brain alone.

I had explained all these things in sufficient detail in the treatise that I had previously intended to publish. And after this I demonstrated how the nerves and muscles of the human body must be made, in order to make the animal spirits inside strong enough to move its members; thus we see that a little while after heads are severed, they still move and bite the earth, even though they are no longer alive. I demonstrated what changes must occur in the brain in order to cause waking, sleep, and dreams; how light, sounds, odors, tastes, heat, and all the other qualities of external objects can there imprint diverse ideas by means of the senses; how hunger, thirst, and the other interior passions can also send their ideas there. I also explained what must be understood as a common sense in the brain, where these ideas are received; and I discussed memory, which retains them, and fantasy, which can change them variously, make new ideas out of them, and by this same means of distributing the animal spirits in the muscles, move the members of this body in reaction to the objects presented to these senses, and the interior passions which are in it, in as many different ways as we can make them move without using will to guide them. This will not seem at all strange to those who know how many various automata, or moving machines, the industry of man can make, using but a few pieces of machinery, in comparison to the great multitude of bones, muscles, nerves, arteries, veins, and all the other parts that are in the body of every animal; and who will consider this body as a machine which, having been made by the hands of God, is incomparably better designed, and has in itself more admirable movements, than any of those which can be invented by men.

And here I particularly stopped to show that if any such machines had the organs and shape of a monkey, or of some other animal that lacked reason, we would have no way of recognizing that they were not of the same nature as these animals; whereas if some of them had a resemblance to our bodies, and imitated our actions as much as would be morally possible, we would always have two very certain means of recognizing that this did not make them men. The first is that they could never use words, or other signs to form words, as we do in order to declare our thoughts to others. For we can easily conceive a machine to be so constructed that it can pronounce words, and even that it can pronounce some that are appropriate to corporeal actions, which cause some change in its organs; as if we touch it in one place, that it ask what we wish to tell it; if in another place, that it cry that we are hurting it, and such things. But we cannot conceive that it arrange words differently so as to answer to the sense of all that is said in its presence, as the dullest men can do. And the second [means of recognizing them] is that although the machines do many things as well as, or perhaps better than any of us, they would inevitably fail in others, by which we would discover that they did not act through understanding, but only through the disposition of their organs. For whereas reason is a universal instrument which can be used in all kinds of encounters, these organs need a certain particular disposition for each particular action; from this it follows that it is morally impossible for a machine to have enough different organs for it to act in all the occurences of life, in the same way that our reason causes us to act.

Now by these two same means, we can also understand the difference between men and beasts. For it is a very remarkable thing that no men are so dull and stupid—not excepting even the insane—that they are not capable of arranging various words together, and making discourse from them through which they make their thoughts understood; and on the contrary, there is no other animal, no matter how perfect and as happily born, which can do the same thing. And this is not so because they lack the organs, for we see that magpies and parrots can pronounce words as well as we, and yet cannot speak as we do, that is, by demonstrating that they think what they say; whereas men born deaf and mute are deprived of the organs which others use to speak as much as is any beast, yet they usually invent certain signs by themselves, which make them understood by those who are used to being with them and have the time to learn their language. And this is evidence not only that beasts have less reason than man, but that they have no reason at all. For we see that only a very little reason is needed to speak; and inasmuch as we notice inequalities among the animals of a single species, as well as among men, and that some are easier to train than others, it is unbelievable that the most perfect monkey or parrot of its species should not equal the stupidest child (or at least an infant who had brain trouble) in this respect, if their soul were not of a completely different nature from ours. And we must not confuse words with natural movements, which testify to the passions and can be imitated by machines as well as by animals. Nor should we think, as did certain of the ancients, that the beasts speak, although we do not understand their language; for if this were true, then since they have many organs related to ours, they could also easily make themselves understood by us as well as by others like themselves. It is also a very remarkable thing that although there are many animals which demonstrate more industry in certain of their actions than we do, we can nevertheless see that these same animals do not demonstrate any at all in many others, so that that which they do better than we does not prove that they have minds; for on this account, they would be more reasonable than any of us, and would be better in everything. Rather it shows that they have no minds at all, and that it is nature which acts in them, according to the disposition of their organs, as we see that a clock, which is composed of nothing but wheels and springs, can count the hours and measure time more accurately than we can with all the care at our command.

After this, I described the rational soul, and showed that it could in no way come from the power of matter, as do the other things of which I have spoken, but that it must be expressly created. And I also explained how it would not suffice that it be placed in the human body, as is a pilot in his ship, unless perhaps to move its members. Instead, it is necessary that the soul be joined and united more closely to the body, in order to have, in addition to this power of movement, feelings and appetites similar to ours, and thus compose a true man. As for the rest, I enlarged a bit here on the subject of the soul, because it is of the greatest importance; for, after the error of those who deny God, which I think I have sufficiently refuted above, there is no other which draws feeble minds away from the straight path of virtue so often than that of imagining that the soul of beasts is of the same nature as ours, and that as a result, we have nothing to fear nor to hope for after this life, any more than do flies and ants; whereas, when we know how much they differ, we have a much better understanding of the reasons which prove that our soul is of a nature entirely independent of the body, and as result, that the soul is not subject to death along with the body. Then, insofar as we do not see any other causes which destroy it, we are naturally led to judge from this that it is immortal.

Sixth Part

It has been three years now, since I reached the end of the treatise containing all these things and began to review it in order to put it in the hands of a publisher, when I learned that people to whom I defer and whose authority over my actions can hardly be less than is that of my own reason over my thoughts, had disapproved of a theory of physics that a certain other person [1] published a little while before. I do not want to say that I agreed with this theory, but before their censure I had noticed nothing in it which I could imagine to be prejudicial to either religion or the state, nor, as a result, anything which should prevent me from writing about it, if reason had persuaded me to do so; and this caused me to fear that in the same way there might be found among my theories some in which I was mistaken, despite the great care I had always taken not to accept into my beliefs any new opinions of which I did not have very certain demonstrations, and not to write of any which might turn out to anyone's disadvantage. This was sufficient to oblige me to change my resolution to publish the treatise. For, although my previous reasons for having made this resolution were very strong, my inclination, which has always made me dislike the profession of writing books, made me immediately find enough other reasons to excuse myself from it. And these reasons on both sides are such that not only do I have some interest in telling them here, but perhaps also the public might have some interest in knowing them.

I have never taken very much account of the things that came out of my mind, and as long as the method I was using gathered me no other fruits than my own satisfaction con-

1 Galileo.

cerning certain difficulties which pertain to the speculative sciences, or else my attempt to regulate my way of life by the principles it taught me, I did not believe myself obliged to write anything about them. For as concerns one's way of life, everyone is so full of opinions that as many reformers could be found as heads, if others, besides those whom God has established as sovereigns over his peoples, or those to whom He has given sufficient grace and zeal to be prophets, were permitted to undertake the changing of anything in this area; and although my speculations pleased me very much, I believed that others, too, had their own, which perhaps pleased them more. But as soon as I had acquired some general notions concerning physics, and when I began to test them in various particular problems and noticed where they could lead and how much they differed from the principles used up to the present, I believed that I could not keep them secret, without sinning gravely against the law which obliges us to procure, to the best of our ability, the general good of all men. For they made me see that it is possible to arrive at knowledge which is very useful in this life, and that instead of that speculative philosophy taught in the schools, we can discover a practical one, through which, knowing the force and action of fire, water, air, the stars, the heavens, and all the other bodies which surround us, as distinctly as we know the different skills of our artisans, we can use them in the same way for all the purposes to which they are suited, and so make ourselves the masters and possessors, as it were, of nature.

This is to be desired not only for the invention of an infinity of artifacts which would allow us the effortless enjoyment of the fruits of the earth and all the commodities that are found there, but especially also for the conservation of health, which is without doubt the primary good, and the basis of all other goods of this life; for even the mind depends so strongly on the temperament and disposition of the organs of the body, that if it is possible to find some means of making men collectively wiser and more skilled than they have been until now, I believe that we must search for it in medicine.

It is true that the medical science which is now in use contains few things that are remarkably useful; but, without any intention of belittling it, I am convinced that there is no one, even among those who make it their profession, who will not admit that everything we know is almost nothing in comparison with what remains to be learned, and that we could rid ourselves of an infinity of illnesses, of the body as well as the mind, and even also perhaps from the debilitation of old age, if we had sufficient knowledge of their causes and of all the remedies with which nature has provided us. Now because I planned to spend my entire life in the pursuit of this very essential knowledge, and because I had found a path which seems to me such that by following it one must infallibly discover this knowledge, were one not prevented from doing so either by the brevity of life or by lack of experiments, I judged that there was no better remedy against those two impediments than to communicate faithfully to the public the little that I had discovered, and to urge good minds to try to go further by contributing, each according to his inclination and ability, to the experiments which would have to be performed, and also by communicating all the things they learned to the public. Thus the later people would begin where the earlier ones had finished; so, joining together the lives and works of many, we would all go much further together than any particular man could by himself.

Concerning the experiments, I even noticed that they become more necessary in proportion as our knowledge advances. For in the beginning using only what presents itself to our senses, which we realize that we cannot ignore provided we reflect upon it just a little, is better than searching for rarer and more ingenious experiences. The reason for this is that these rarer experiences often mislead us, when we do not yet know the causes of the more common ones; and the circumstances upon which they depend are almost always so particular and so minute that it is very difficult to observe them. But the order to which I held in this has been as follows.

First, I tried to discover the general principles, or first causes, of all that is or can be in the world, without for this purpose considering anything but God alone, its Creator, and without deriving these principles from anything but certain seeds of truth which are naturally in our souls. After that, I examined what were the first and most ordinary effects that we could infer from these causes. And it seems to me that I thereby discovered the skies, the stars, an earth, and even, on the earth, water, air, fire, minerals, and certain other such things, which are the commonest and simplest of all, and thus the easiest to understand.

Then, when I wanted to descend to those effects that were more particular, so many diverse ones presented themselves to me that I did not believe it possible for the human mind to distinguish between the forms or species of objects that are on the earth, and an infinity of other ones which could have been, if it had been the will of God to put them there. Nor, as a result, did I believe it possible to direct them to our use, unless it be by arriving at the causes through their effects, and by using many particular experiments. Following this, I reflected upon all the objects that ever presented themselves to my senses, and I venture to say that I never noticed a single thing about them which I could not explain quite conveniently through the principles I had discovered. But I must also confess that the power of nature is so ample and so vast, and these principles so simple and so general, that I almost never notice any particular effect such that I do not see right away that it can be derived from these principles in many different ways; and my greatest difficulty is usually to discover in which of these ways the effect is derived. And to do that I know no other expedient than again to search for certain experiments which are such that their result is not the same when we explain the effect by one hypothesis, as when we explain it by another.

As to the rest, I am now at the point where (it seems to me) I see quite clearly from what angle we must approach the greater part of the experiments which can be used for this purpose; but I also see that they are of such a nature, and so numerous, that neither my hands nor my resources, even if I had a thousand times more of both, would suffice to complete them. Thus, according as I shall have from now on the opportunity to perform more or fewer of these experiments, I shall advance that much more or less in the knowledge of nature. I promised myself to make this known through the treatise that I had written, and to show so clearly how useful it could be to the public that I would oblige all those who desire the general good of men—that is, all those who are indeed virtuous, and not merely by false pretenses nor by mere repute—both to communicate to me the experiments they have already performed, and to help me in seeking out those which remain to be done.

But since that time other considerations have caused me to change my opinion, and to think that I should truly continue to write about everything that I considered to be of some importance, whenever I discovered the truth about these things, and to take the same care in writing as I would if I wanted to have these works published. [I did this] so as to have all the more reason to examine them thoroughly, for there is no doubt that we always look more closely at what we believe will be seen by many than what we do only for ourselves (and often the things which have seemed true to me, when I began to conceive them, have appeared false when I wanted to put them on paper), and also in order to lose no occasion to benefit the public, if I am capable of it, and in order that, if my writings are worth something, those who have them after my death will be able to use them in the most appropriate manner. But I decided that I should not consent to their publication during my life, so that neither the opposition and controversy to which they would perhaps be subject, nor even the reputation they could acquire for me, would give me any occasion to lose the time I plan to use in teaching myself. For although it is true that every man is obliged to procure, so far as he is able, the good of others, and that to be of no use to anyone is actually to be worth nothing, nevertheless it is also true that our interests should extend beyond the present time, and that it is good to omit the things which perhaps might benefit the living, when one does so for the purpose of benefiting our descendents even more. So, in effect, I wish it to be well known that the little I have learned up to now is almost nothing in comparison with that of which I am ignorant. And yet I do not despair of being able to learn, for it is almost the same with those who gradually discover truth in the sciences as with those who, when they begin to be rich, have less trouble acquiring great things than they had before, when poorer, acquiring much lesser ones. Or else we can compare them to leaders of armies, whose forces usually increase in proportion to their victories, and who need more ability to keep their positions after the loss of a battle than they do to take cities and provinces after having won. For trying to conquer all the difficulties and errors that keep us from attaining knowledge of the truth is truly to give battle; and a battle is truly lost when we accept some false opinion concerning a general and important matter. It takes much more skill after such a loss to regain the same state that we had before than to make great progress when we already have principles that are well-founded. As for me, if I have thus far discovered some truths in the sciences (and I hope that the things contained in this volume will cause you to judge that I have found some of them), I can say that they are the results and consequences of but five or six principal problems that I have overcome, and I count these as so many battles where I have had luck on my side. I even do not fear to say that I think I need only win two or three other such battles, in order completely to achieve my goals; and I am not yet so old that, in the normal course of nature, I cannot yet have enough leisure for this purpose. But I feel that much the more obliged to manage the time left to me, the more I hope to be able to use it well; and doubtless I would have many opportunities to waste it, if I published the foundations of my physics. For, although they are almost all so evident that it is necessary only to hear them to believe them, and there is not one whose proof I do not believe I can give, nevertheless, because it is impossible for them to agree with all the diverse opinions of other men, I foresee that I would often be diverted by the opposition that they would awaken.

One could say that this opposition would be useful in making me aware of my mistakes, as well as in enabling others by this means to gain more knowledge, if I have something of value to say; and, because many men can see more than one can see alone, if they began as of now to make use of their insight, they would also help me by their inventiveness. But although I recognize that I am extremely subject to failure, and although I almost never have faith in the first thoughts that come to me, nevertheless my experience of the objections that can be made against me prevents me from hoping for any benefit from them. For I have often been subjected to the judgments both of those whom I have held as friends, and of certain others whom I think are neutral, as well as some I knew whose malignity and envy are sufficient to cause them to try to expose what affection would hide from my friends. But it has rarely happened that anyone has made an objection that I had not completely foreseen, unless it was quite far removed from my subject; so that I have almost never met any censurer of my opinions who did not seem to me either less rigorous or less equitable than I am. And moreover, I have never noticed that through the method of argument which is practiced in the schools anyone has discovered a single truth that was not known before, for when each person tries to win, more effort is put into trying to seem correct than into considering the arguments of both sides; and those who have been good lawyers for a long time are not for that reason better judges afterwards.

As to the usefulness that others might find in knowing of my ideas, this could not be so very great, inasmuch as I have not yet pursued them so far that I do not need to add many things to them before applying them in practice. And I think I can say, without vanity, that if there is anyone who can do this, it ought to be I rather than anyone else—not that there may not be many minds in the world that are incomparably better than mine; but one can never conceive a thing and render it his own so well when one learns it from another, as when one discovers it oneself. This is so true in this case that although I have often explained some of my opinions to persons of very high intelligence, who seemed to understand them very distinctly while I was speaking, nevertheless, when they repeated them, I noticed that they almost always changed them in such a way that I was no longer able to recognize them as my own. I am also happy to have this opportunity to ask posterity never to believe that the things told to them come from me, unless I myself have divulged them. And I am not at all astonished at the extravagances attributed to all these ancient philosophers whose writings we do not have; nor do these extravagances make me judge their ideas to have been very unreasonable—seeing that they were the best minds of their age—but rather, I judge these ideas to have been badly reported. We also see that almost never has it happened that any of their disciples has surpassed them; and I am sure that the most passionate of those who now follow Aristotle would believe themselves fortunate if they had as much knowledge of nature as he had, even if a condition of this knowledge was that they would never know more than he did. They are like the ivy, which cannot tend to climb higher than the trees that support it, and which even often grows downward after it has reached the treetops; for it also seems to me that these followers decline in knowledge, that is, they make themselves in some way less knowledgable than if they abstained from studying, when, not being content with knowing all that is intelligibly explained in their author, they wish besides this to find there the solution to many difficulties of which the author said nothing, and perhaps about which he never thought. Nevertheless, their method of philosophizing is very convenient for those who have only mediocre minds; for the obscurity of the distinctions and principles that they use allows them to speak of all things as confidently as if they knew about them, and to support everything that they say about them against the most subtle and most adroit thinkers, without there being any means to convince them. In this they seem to me to be like a blind man who, in order to fight without disadvantage against someone who can see, would have him come into the depths of a very dark cave. And I might say that those people have an interest in my abstaining from publishing the principles of the philosophy I use, for extremely simple and extremely evident as these principles are, in publishing them I would be doing almost the same thing as if I were to open some windows, and allow the daylight to enter that cave where they have gone down to fight. But even the best minds have no reason to desire to know my principles; for if they want to know how to speak of all things, and to acquire the reputation of being learned, they will more easily achieve this by being content with the semblance of wisdom, which can be found without great difficulty in all sorts of matters, than by searching for the truth; for this truth can be discovered only gradually in some subjects, and when it comes to speaking about others, they would be obliged to confess frankly that they were ignorant of them. But if they prefer the knowledge of a little truth to the vanity of appearing to be ignorant of nothing, as doubtless is very preferable, and if they wish to follow a plan similar to mine, this does not mean that they need me to tell them anything more than what I have already said in this discourse. For if they are capable of passing beyond what I have done, they will also be all the more capable of discovering for themselves all that I think I have discovered. Inasmuch as I have never examined anything except in order of complexity, it is certain that what still remains for me to discover is of itself more difficult and more hidden than what I have encountered thus far, and they would have much less pleasure in learning it from me than in doing so by themselves. In addition, the habit they will acquire of searching first for simple things and passing gradually by degrees to others more difficult will be of more use to them than all my instructions could be. As for me, I am convinced that if in my youth I had been taught all the truths for which I have since sought the demonstrations, and if I had had no difficulty in learning them, I might never have known any others, or at least I would never have acquired the habit and facility that I think I have for always finding new truths in proportion as I apply myself to searching for them. In short, if there is any work in the world that can be completed by no other person so well as by him who has begun it, it is the one at which I am working.

It is true that so far as concerns the experiments that can be used in this work, one man alone would not suffice to do them all. But also, he could not usefully employ other hands than his own, except those of artisans, or such people as he could pay—people whose hope of gain, a very efficacious motive, would insure that they do precisely all the things that he told them. Because, as for the volunteers who, out of curiosity or the desire to learn, might offer to help him—aside from the fact that they usually produce more promises than results, and that they do nothing but make elegant proposals, none of which ever succeed—they would infallibly want to be paid by having certain difficulties explained to them, or at least by compliments and useless discussion, which could only cost him so much of his time that the assistance would not be worth it. And as for the experiments that others have already performed, even if they wanted to communicate them to him (which those who call them secrets never would), these are for the most part composed of so many circumstances or superfluous ingredients, that he would be hard put to unravel the truth from them. Besides this, because those who performed these experiments have forced themselves to make them appear to conform to their principles, he would find almost all of them so badly explained, or even so false, that if there were any useful ones among them, they would again not be worth the time he would have to use in picking them out. Thus if there were someone in the world that we surely knew to be capable of discovering the greatest things, and those that were the most useful to the public, and if for that reason other men exerted themselves by all means to aid him in realizing his designs, I do not see how they could do anything for him except to furnish the cost of the experiments that he would need, and as for the rest, to prevent his leisure being taken from him by anyone's importunity. But aside from the fact that I do not presume so much for myself as to wish to promise anything extraordinary, nor do I entertain thoughts so vain as imagining that the public ought to be very much interested in my plans, I am also not of such a low nature that I would willingly accept any favor which anyone might believe I did not merit.

All these considerations together caused me to decide, three years ago, that I did not wish to divulge the treatise that I had in hand, and even made me resolve never to make known to anyone, during my life, any such general treatise, from which the foundations of my physics could be understood. But since then there have been two other reasons which have obliged me to present certain particular essays here, and to give some account of my actions and plans to the public. The first is that if I did not do this many people who knew of my former intention of publishing certain writings might imagine that the causes for which I abstained from doing so were more to my disadvantage than they are. For although I am not excessively fond of fame, and even, if I dare to say so, dislike it insofar as I judge it to be contrary to the privacy which I esteem above everything else, nevertheless I have also never tried to hide my actions as though they were crimes; nor have I taken very many precautions in order to remain unknown, because I believed this would be doing hurt to myself, as well as because it would have given me a certain sort of uneasiness which would again have been contrary to the perfect repose of mind for which I search. And because I have been unable to keep from acquiring some sort of reputation (for it has always been a matter of indifference to me whether I am known or not known), I thought that I should at least do my best to avoid having a bad one. The other reason which obliged me to write this is that every day I see the greater and greater retardation suffered by my plan to instruct myself, because of an infinity of experiments, which I need and which it is impossible for me to perform without the aid of others. Therefore, although I do not flatter myself with the hope that the public will take a great part in my interests, nevertheless I also do not wish to be so unfaithful to myself as to give those who follow me cause to reproach me some day for not leaving many things much better than I would have if I had not been too negligent to make them understand in what way they could contribute to my plans.

And I thought that it would be easy to choose certain matters which, without being subject to too much controversy, or obliging me to divulge more of my principles than I wish, would nevertheless make what I can or cannot do in the sciences sufficiently clear. I shall not say whether I have succeeded in this, and I do not want to anticipate anyone's judgments by speaking of my writings myself; but I shall be very happy to have you examine them, and in order that you have more opportunity to do so, I beg all those who have some objection to my writings to send them to my publisher, and when I am informed of them, I shall try to append my replies to them at the same time; and by this means the reader, seeing them together, will more easily judge of the truth. For I do not promise ever to make long replies, but only to admit my mistakes very frankly, if I recognize them, or else, if I cannot perceive them, to state simply what I believe is necessary for defending the things I have written, without adding any new material to the explanation, so as not to become endlessly engaged in debate.

And if some of the things of which I have spoken at the beginning of the *Optics* and the *Meteorology* are displeasing at first, because I call them hypotheses and do not seem to worry about proving them, have the patience to read all of it with care, and I hope you will find that you are satisfied with them. For it seems to me that the arguments there follow from each other in such a way that, just as the last ones are proven by the first, which are their causes, so those first [principles or causes] are reciprocally proven by the last, which are their effects. And you must not think that I commit in this the fallacy that the logicians call arguing in a circle; for as experiment makes most of these effects very certain, the causes from which I derive them serve not so much to prove these effects as to explain them; but, on the contrary, the [hypothetical] principles or causes are proven by their effects. And I have called them hypotheses only in order for you to know that I think I can deduce them from these first truths which I have explained above, but that I expressly wished not to do so, because of certain minds who imagine that they can comprehend in a day what has taken another person twenty years to think out, as soon as he has told them only two or three words about it. These people are all the more subject to error, and less capable of truth, when they are penetrating and lively; and I wish to prevent them from taking the opportunity to build some extravagant philosophy on what they will believe to be my principles, and then attributing the blame to me. For as to the opinions which are really mine, I do not apologize for their novelty, inasmuch as, if you consider the arguments for them carefully, I am sure that you will find them so simple and so commensurate with common sense that they will seem less extraordinary and less strange than any others you may have about the same subjects. And I also make no claim that I am the first to invent any of them, but only that I have never accepted them either because they were said by others, or because they were not said by others, but only because reason has persuaded me of them.

And if the artisans cannot immediately execute the invention which is explained in the *Optics*, I do not believe we can say, because of that, that it is worthless; for inasmuch as skill and practice are necessary to make and adjust the machines that I have described, without any detail lacking, I would be no less astonished if they were to accomplish it on the first try than I would be if someone could learn in a day to play the lute excellently, merely because someone had given him some good music. And if I write in French, which is the language of my country, rather than in Latin, which is that of my teachers, it is because I hope that those who use nothing but their unadorned natural reason will judge my opinions better than those who believe only in the ancient writings. And as to those who combine good sense with learning, whom alone I wish for my judges, they will not, I am sure, be so partial to Latin that they will refuse to consider my arguments because I explain them in the common tongue.

For the rest, I do not wish to speak here in any detail of the future progress I hope to make in the sciences, nor to engage myself with the public in any promise which I am not sure of fulfilling; but I will say only that I have resolved to use the time remaining in my life for nothing other than trying to acquire some knowledge of nature, such that we may derive from it more certain rules for medicine than those we have had up to the present. And my inclination is so far removed from any other kind of plan, especially from those which can be of use to some only by harming others, that if I had any opportunity to use them, I do not believe I could succeed in doing so.

Such is the declaration I make here, and I well know that it cannot serve to make me eminent in the world, but I also have no desire to be such; and I shall always hold myself more obliged to those by whose favor I enjoy my leisure without interruption than I would be to those who offered me the most honorable position on earth.

OPTICS

OPTICS

First Discourse

Of Light

All the management of our lives depends on the senses, and since that of sight is the most comprehensive and the noblest of these, there is no doubt that the inventions which serve to augment its power are among the most useful that there can be. And it is difficult to find any of these inventions which augment the power of sight more than that of those marvelous telescopes which, in use for only a short time, have already revealed a greater number of new stars in the sky, and other new objects above the earth, than the sum total of those we have seen there before: so that, carrying our sight much farther than the imagination of our fathers was used to going, they seem to have opened the way for us to attain a knowledge of nature much greater and more perfect than our fathers had. But to the shame of our sciences, this invention, so useful and so admirable, was found in the first place only through experiment and good fortune.

It was about thirty years ago that a man named Jacques Métius, of the city of Alcmar in Holland—a man who had never studied, although he had a father and a brother who made a profession of mathematics, but who particularly enjoyed making mirrors and burning glasses, even making some in winter with ice, as experimentation has shown we can do —having on that occasion many lenses of different shapes, happened by chance to look through two of them, one being slightly thicker in the middle than at the edges, and the other, on the contrary, much thicker at the edges than in the middle. And happily he hit upon the idea of placing them in the two ends of a tube, so that the first of these telescopes of which we are speaking was thereby made. And on this pattern alone, all the others that we have seen since have been made, without anyone yet, to my knowledge, having sufficiently determined the shapes that these lenses must have. For although there have, since then, been many good minds which have greatly cultivated this subject, and in doing so have discovered many things in Optics which are worth more than that which was left to us by the ancients, nevertheless, because inventions that are somewhat difficult do not arrive at their final degree of perfection at the first attempt, there still remain enough difficulties in this one to give me cause to write of it. And, inasmuch as the execution of the things of which I shall speak must depend on the skill of artisans, who ordinarily have not studied, I shall attempt to make myself intelligible to everyone, and to omit nothing, nor to assume anything that might have been learned in the other sciences. This is why I shall begin with the explanation of light and of its rays; then, having given a brief description of the parts of the eye, I shall say specifically how vision is caused; and afterwards, having taken account of all the things capable of improving it, I shall teach how they can be assisted by the inventions which I shall describe.

Thus, not having here any other occasion to speak of light than to explain how its rays enter into the eye, and how they can be deflected by the different bodies that they encounter, I need not undertake to explain its true nature. And I believe that it will suffice that I make use of two or three comparisons which help to conceive it in the manner which to me seems the most convenient to explain all those of its properties that experience acquaints us with, and to deduce afterwards all the others which cannot be so easily observed; imitating in this the Astronomers, who, although their assumptions are almost all false or uncertain, nevertheless, because these assumptions refer to different observations which they have made, never cease to draw many very true and well-assured conclusions from them.

It has sometimes doubtless happened to you, while walking in the night without a light through places which are a little difficult, that it became necessary to use a stick in order to guide yourself; and you may then have been able to notice that you felt, through the medium of this stick, the diverse objects placed around you, and that you were even able to tell whether they were trees, or stones, or sand, or water, or grass, or mud, or any other such thing. True, this sort of sensation is rather confused and obscure in those who do not have much practice with it; but consider it in those who, being born blind, have made use of it all their lives, and you will find it so perfect and so exact that one might almost say that they see with their hands, or that their stick is the organ of some sixth sense given to them in place of sight. And in order to draw a comparison from this, I would have you consider light as nothing else, in bodies that we call luminous, than a certain movement or action, very rapid and very lively, which passes toward our eyes through the medium of the air and other transparent bodies, in the same manner that the movement or resistance of the bodies that this blind man encounters is transmitted to his hand through the medium of his stick. This will prevent you from finding it strange at first that this light can extend its rays in an instant from the sun to us; for you know that the action with which we move one of the ends of a stick must thus be transmitted in an instant to the other end, and that it would have to go from the earth to the heavens in the same manner, although it would have more distance to travel there than it has here. Neither will you find it strange that by means of it we can see all kinds of colors; and you may perhaps even be prepared to believe that these colors are nothing else, in bodies that we call colored, than the diverse ways in which these bodies receive light and reflect it against our eyes: you have only to consider that the differences which a blind man notes among trees, rocks, water, and similar things through the medium of his stick do not seem less to him than those among red, yellow, green, and all the other colors seem to us; and that nevertheless these differences are nothing other, in all these bodies, than the diverse ways of moving, or of resisting the movements of, this stick. In consequence of which, you will have occasion to judge that there is no need to assume that something material passes from the objects to our eyes to make us see colors and light, nor even that there is anything in these objects which is similar to the ideas or the sensations that we have of them: just as nothing comes out of the bodies that a blind man senses, which must be transmitted along the length of his stick into his hand; and as the resistance or the movement of these bodies, which is the sole cause of the sensations he has of them, is nothing like the ideas he forms of them. And by this means your mind will be delivered from all those small images flitting through the air, called *intentional species,* which worry the imagination of Philosophers so much. You will even easily be able to decide the question which is current among them concerning the origin of the action that causes the sensation of sight. For, just as our blind man can sense the bodies which are around him, not only through the action of these bodies when they move against his stick, but also through that of his hand, when they are only resisting it, so we must affirm that the objects of sight can be felt, not only by means of the action which, being in them, tends toward the eyes, but also by means of that which, being in the eyes, tends toward them. Nevertheless, because this action is nothing other than light, we must note that it is only those who can see during the darkness of the night, such as cats, in whose eyes this action is found; and that, as for the ordinary man, he sees only by the action which comes from the objects. For experience shows us that these objects must be luminous or illuminated in order to be seen, and not that our eyes must be luminous or illuminated in order to see them. But because there is a great difference between the stick of this blind man and the air or the other transparent bodies through the medium of which we see, I must here make use of still another comparison.

You see here a vat at vintage time, completely full of half-pressed grapes; in the bottom of this vat we have made a hole or two, such as A and B, through which the smooth wine that it contains can flow. Now consider that, since there is no vacuum in Nature, as almost all the Philosophers affirm, and since there are nevertheless many pores in all the bodies that we perceive around us, as experiment can show quite clearly, it is necessary that these pores be filled with some very sub-

Fig. 1.

tle and very fluid material, extending without interruption from the stars and planets to us. Thus, this subtle material being compared with the wine in that vat, and the less fluid or heavier parts, of the air as well as of other transparent bodies, being compared with the bunches of grapes which are mixed in, you will easily understand the following: Just as the parts of this wine which are for example near C tend to go down in a straight line through the hole A at the very instant that it is open, and at the same time through hole B, and as those which are near D and near E also tend at the same time to go down through these two holes, without any of these actions being impeded by the others, nor by the resistance of the bunches of grapes in this vat (notwithstanding that these bunches, being supported by each other, do not tend in the least to go down through these holes A and B as does the wine, and that they can even meanwhile be moved in many other ways by those who press them) —in the same way, all of the parts of the subtle material, which are touched by the side of the sun that faces us, tend in a straight line toward our eyes at the very instant that we open them, without these parts impeding each other, and even without their being impeded by the heavier particles of transparent bodies which are between the two. This is so whether these bodies are moved in other ways, as is the air, which is almost always agitated by some wind, or whether they are without movement, perhaps like glass or crystal. And note here that it is necessary to distinguish between movement, and the action or inclination to move. For one can very easily conceive that the particles of wine which are for example near *C, tend* toward *B* and also toward *A*, notwithstanding that they cannot *actually* be moved toward these two holes at the same time; and that they *tend* exactly in a straight line toward *B* and toward *A*, notwithstanding that they cannot move *precisely* in a straight line, because of the bunches of grapes which are between the two. And in the same way considering that it is not so much the movement as the action of luminous bodies that must be taken for their light, you must judge that the rays of this light are nothing else but the lines along which this action tends. So that there is an infinity of such rays which come from all points of luminous bodies, toward all points of those that they illuminate, in such a manner that you can imagine an infinity of straight lines, along which the actions coming from all points of the surface of the wine *CDE* tend toward *A*, and another infinity, along which the actions coming from these same points tend also toward *B*, without either impeding the other.

Moreover, these rays should always be imagined to be exactly straight, when they go through only one transparent body which is uniform throughout; but when they meet certain other bodies they are liable to be deflected by them, or weakened, in the same way as the movement of a ball or of a rock thrown in the air is deflected by those bodies it encounters. For it is very easy to believe that the action or the inclination to move which I have said must be taken for light, must follow in this the same laws as does movement. And in order that I may explain this third comparison in full, consider that the bodies which can thus be met by a ball passing through the air are either soft, or hard, or liquid: and that if they are soft, they completely stop the ball and break its movement, as when it is thrown into linen sheets, or sand, or mud; whereas, if they are hard, they deflect it in another direction without stopping it; and they do so in many different ways. For either their surface is completely even and smooth, or it is rough and uneven: and moreover, if even, it is either flat or curved; and, if uneven, either its uneveness consists only in its being composed of many differently curved parts, of which each is in itself sufficiently smooth, or it consists, besides this, in its having many different angles or points, or parts some of which are harder than others, or which move, with variations which can be imagined in a thousand ways. And it is necessary to note that the ball, aside from its simple and ordinary movement, which carries it from one place to another, can have yet a second which makes it revolve around its center, and that the speed of the latter can have many different relations with that of the former. Thus, when many balls coming from the same direction meet a body whose surface is completely smooth and even, they are deflected uniformly, and in the same order, in such a way that if this surface is completely flat, they keep the same distance between them after having met it as they had beforehand; and if it is curved inward or outward, they approach or depart in the same order from each other, more or less, because of this curvature. You can see here that the balls A, B, C, after having met the surfaces of the bodies D, E, F, are deflected toward G, H, I. And if these balls meet an uneven surface, such as L or M, they are deflected in different directions, each according to the position of the part of the surface that it touches. And they change nothing but this in the manner of their movement, when the surface's uneveness consists only in the fact that its parts are differently curved. But it can also consist in many other things and can bring it about, through this means, that if these balls had beforehand only a simple straight movement, they lose part of it, and acquire instead a circular motion, which can have a different relation with that of the straight motion which they retain according as the surface of the bodies they encounter may be differently disposed. Those who play tennis can prove this sufficiently, when their ball encounters uneven ground, or else when they

another direction without stopping it; and they do so in many
different ways. For either their surface is completely even and
smooth, or it is rough and uneven; and moreover each even,
it is either flat or curved; and, if uneven, this unevenness
consists only in its being composed of many differently curved
parts, of which each is in itself sufficiently smooth or consists, besides this, in its having many differently curved points,
or parts; some of which are harder than others, or which move
with variations which can be imagined in a thousand ways.
And it is necessary to note that the ball, aside from its simple
and rectilinear movement, which carries it from one place to
another, can have yet a second which makes it revolve around
its centre; and the velocities of the latter can have many
differences in relation to the former. Thus, when many
balls coming from the same direction meet a body whose
surface is completely smooth, and even they are deflected
uniformly and in the same order, in such a way that if this
surface is completely flat, they keep the same distance between
them after having met it as they had beforehand; and if it
is curved inward or outward, they approach or depart in the
same order they held either more or less, [?] according to this
curvature. You can see here that the balls A, B, C, moving
and the surfaces of the bodies D, E, F, destined to
ward them, which if these balls meet unevenness in them,
[?] then, they are deflected in different directions,
each according to the position it has on the surface
that it touches. And they change nothing, but this in the
manner of their movement, when the surface is uneven, see
you only in the fact that its parts are differently curved; for
it can also consist in many other things; and can being it about,
through, this means, that if these balls had beforehand only
a simple rectilinear movement, they take part of it, and acquire
instead a circular motion, which can in turn, a different relation
with that of the straight motion, which they retain according
as the surface of the body which turned them may be differently
disposed. I here wish to no? unite can prove this sufficiently,
when their ball encounters uneven ground, or else when they

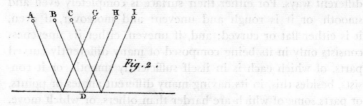

Fig. 2.

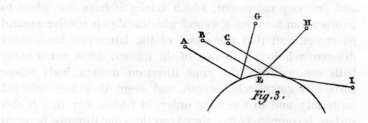

Fig. 3.

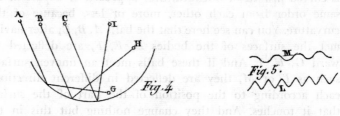

Fig. 5.

Fig. 4.

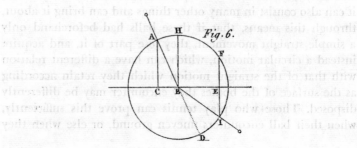

Fig. 6.

hit it obliquely with their racket, which they call, it seems to me, cutting or grazing. Finally, consider that if a moving ball meets obliquely the surface of a liquid body, through which it can pass more easily or less than through that from which it comes, it is diverted and changes its course upon entering it: as, for example, if it is in the air at point *A*, and we impel it toward *B*, it goes exactly in a straight line from *A* to *B* if its weight or some other particular cause does not impede it; but, if it is at point *B*, where I assume that it meets the surface of the water *CBE*, it changes direction and takes its course toward *I*, going anew in a straight line from *B* to *I*, as it is easy to verify through experience. Now it is necessary to consider in the same manner that there are bodies which, being met by rays of light, break them up, and take away all their force, such as those which we call black, which have no more color than shadows; and that there are others which reflect these rays, some in the same order as they receive them, that is to say, those which, having their surface highly polished, can be used as both flat and curved mirrors, and the others reflect them confusedly in many directions. And that again, among the latter, some reflect these rays without causing any other change in their action, such as those which we call white, and the others carry with this reflection a change similar to that which the movement of a ball receives when we graze it, such as those which are red, or yellow, or blue, or any other such color. For I believe I can determine the nature of each of these colors, and demonstrate it through experiment; but this goes beyond the bounds of my subject. And it suffices here for me to inform you that the rays which fall on bodies that are colored and not polished, are ordinarily reflected in all directions, even although they come from but a single direction: as, although those which fall on the surface of the white body *AB* come only from the flame *C*, they are nevertheless reflected in all directions so that in any location that one places the eye, as for example toward *D*, there are always many rays coming from each point of this surface *AB*, which tend toward it. And the same is true if we assume this body to be very thin, such as a paper or a linen sheet, so that the light passes through it;

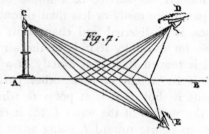

Fig. 7.

for although the eye is on the side away from the flame, as toward *E*, there will nevertheless be reflected toward it some rays from each of the parts of this body. Finally, consider that the rays also are deflected, in the same way that has been mentioned in the case of a ball, when they obliquely encounter the surface of a transparent body, through which they penetrate more easily or less than through that from whence they come, and this method of being deflected is called in them Refraction.

Second Discourse

Of Refraction

Inasmuch as we will later on need to know the exact quantity of this refraction, and as it can rather conveniently be understood through the example which I have just used, I believe it is appropriate that I here try to explain it all at once, and that I speak first of all of reflection, in order to make the knowledge of refraction easier. Let us consider then that a ball, being impelled from *A* toward *B*, meets at point *B* the surface of the ground *CBE* which, preventing it from going further, causes it to turn away; and let us see in what direction. But in order not to involve ourselves in new difficulties, let us assume that the ground is perfectly flat and hard, and that the ball always travels at a constant speed, as much in descending as in reascending, without asking ourselves in any way about the power which continues to move it after it is no longer touched by the racket,

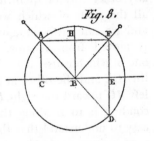

Fig. B.

and without considering any effect of its weight, or of its bulk, or of its shape. For here there is no question of regarding it so closely, and none of these things are relevant in the action of light, to which this inquiry must be related. It is only necessary to note that the power, whatever it be, which causes the movement of this ball to continue is different from that which determines it to move in one direction rather than in another, as is quite easy to know from the fact that it is the force with which the racket has impelled it upon which its movement depends, and that this same force could have been able

to make it move in any other direction as easily as toward *B;*
whereas it is the position of this racket which determines it
to tend toward *B,* and which could have determined it to
tend there in the same way even though another force had
moved it. Which already shows that it is not impossible that
this ball be diverted by the encounter with the ground, and
hence that the determination which it had to tend toward *B*
be changed, without anything being changed by this in the
force of its movement since these are two different things. And
as a result we must not imagine that it is necessary for the
ball to stop for a few moments at point *B* before returning
toward *F,* as many of our philosophers would have it; for,
if its movement was once interrupted by this stop, there could
be found no cause which could make it start up again afterward. Moreover, it must be noted that the determination to
move toward a certain direction, as well as movement and
any other sort of quantity generally, can be divided among
all the parts of which we can imagine that it is composed;
and we can easily imagine that that part of the ball which
is moved from *A* toward *B* is composed of two others,
one of which causes it to descend from the line *AF* toward the
line *CE* and the other at the same time makes it go from the
left *AC* toward the right *FE;* so that the two, joined together,
conduct it to *B* along the straight line *AB.* And then it is
easy to understand that the meeting with the ground can prevent only one of these two determinations, and not in any
way the other. For it must prevent the one which made the
ball go down from *AF* toward *CE,* because it occupies all the
space which is below *CE;* but why would it prevent the other,
which made the ball advance toward the right hand, seeing
that it is not at all opposed to the determination in that
direction? In order to discover, then, precisely in what direction this ball must return, let us describe a circle from the
center *B* which passes through the point *A,* and let us say that
in as much time as the ball will take to move from *A* to *B,*
it must infallibly return from *B* to a certain point on the
circumference of this circle, inasmuch as all the points which

are the same distance away from *B* as *A* is, are to be found
on this circumference, and inasmuch as we assume the movement of this ball to be always of a constant speed. Then in
order to know precisely to which of all the points of this
circumference it must return, let us draw three straight lines
AC, HB, and *FE* perpendicular to *CE,* in such a way that
there is neither more nor less distance between *AC* and *HB*
than between *HB* and *FE;* and let us say that in as much time
as the ball took to advance toward the right side from *A* (one
of the points of the line *AC*) to *B* (one of those of the line
HB), it must also advance from the line *HB* to some point on
the line *FE;* for any point of this line *FE* is as far removed
from *HB* in this direction as is any other, and as far as are
those of the line *AC;* and also the ball is as much determined
to advance toward that side as it had been hithertofore. Thus
it is that it cannot at the same time arrive both at a certain
point of the line *FE* and at a certain point of the circumference of the circle *AFD,* unless it be either at point *D* or
point *F,* inasmuch as there are only these two where the
circumference and the line intersect; so that, since the ground
prevents the ball from passing toward *D,* we must conclude
that it must infallibly go toward *F.* And so you can easily
see how reflection occurs, namely according to an angle which
is always equal to the one we call the angle of incidence; in
the same way that if a ray, coming from point *A,* falls to
point *B* on the surface of the flat mirror *CBE,* it is reflected
toward *F* in such a manner that the angle of reflection *FBE*
is neither greater nor smaller than that of the angle of
incidence *ABC.*

Now we come to refraction. And first let us suppose that a
ball impelled from *A* toward *B* meets, at point *B,* no
longer the surface of the ground but a cloth *CBE,* which is
so weak and loosely woven that this ball has the force to
rupture it and to pass completely through it, while losing only
a part of its speed—namely, for example, a half. Now given
this, to know what path it must follow let us consider once
more that its movement differs entirely from its determination

to move in one direction rather than another, from which it follows that the quantity of these [two factors] must be examined separately. And let us also consider that, of the two parts of which we can imagine this determination to be composed, only the one that was causing the ball to tend from high to low can be changed in any manner through the encounter with the cloth; and that the one that was causing it to tend toward the right hand must always remain the same as it was, because in no way does this cloth oppose its going in this direction. Then, having described from the center B the circle AFD, and drawn at right angles to CBE the three straight lines AC, HB, FE in such a way that there is twice as much distance between FE and HB as between HB and AC, we will see that this ball must tend toward the point I. For, since it loses half of its speed by going through the cloth CBE, it must take twice as much time to pass below, from B to a certain point of the circumference of the circle AFD, as it took above to come from A to B. And since it loses nothing at all of the determination that it had to advance toward the right side, in twice as much time as it took to pass from the line AC to HB, it must make twice as much headway toward this same side, and as a result arrive at a certain point of the straight line FE at the same instant that it arrives at a certain point of the circumference of the circle AFD. This would be impossible were it not going toward I, inasmuch as that is the only point below the cloth CBE where the circle AFD and the straight line FE intersect.

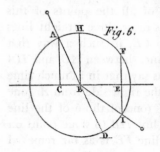

Fig. 6.

Now let us consider that the ball coming from A toward D encounters at point B, no longer a cloth, but water, of which the surface CBE takes from it exactly half of its speed, as did the cloth. And the rest being assumed as before, I say that this ball must pass from B in a straight line, not toward D, but toward I. For, first of all, it is certain that the surface

of the water must deflect it toward there in the same way as
did the cloth, seeing that it takes from the ball the same
amount of its force, and that it is opposed to it in the same
direction. Then, as for the
rest of the body of water that
fills all the space between *B*
and *I*, although it may resist
the ball more or less than did
the air that we assumed to be
there before, this is not to say
that because of this it must
deflect it more or less: for it
can open in order to permit it

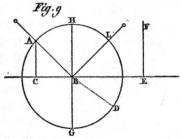

passage, just as easily in one direction as in another, at least
if we always assume, as we do, that neither the heaviness or
lightness of this ball, nor its bulk, nor its shape, nor any other
such foreign cause changes its course. And we can note here
that it is the more deflected by the surface of the water or
the cloth, according as it encounters it more obliquely, in
such a way that, if it encounters it at right angles, as when
it is impelled from *H* toward *B*, it must go on in a straight
line toward *G*, without being deflected at all. But if it is impelled along a line such as *AB*, which is so sharply inclined
to the surface of the water or cloth *CBE* that the line *FE*,
being drawn as before, does not cut the circle *AD* at all, that
ball ought not to penetrate it in any way, but to rebound
from its surface *B* toward the air *L*, in the same way as if it
had encountered some earth. This we have sometimes experienced with regret when, firing artillery pieces toward
the bottom of a river for pleasure, we have wounded those
who were on the other side of the shore.

But let us make yet another assumption here, and consider
that the ball, having been first of all impelled from *A* toward
B, is impelled again, once it is at point *B*, by the racket *CBE*,
which augments the force of its movement by for instance
one-third, so that afterwards it can make as much headway in
two moments as it previously made in three. This will have

the same effect as if the ball were to meet, at point *B*, a body of such a nature that it could pass through the surface *CBE* **one**-third again more easily than through the air. And it

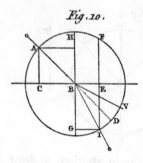

Fig. 10.

follows manifestly from what has already been demonstrated that if we describe the circle *AD* as before, and the lines *AC, HB, FE* in such a manner that there is a third less distance between *FE* and *HB* than between *HB* and *AC*, the point *I*, where the straight line *FE* and the circular *AD* intersect, will designate the place toward which this ball, being at point *B*, must be deflected.

Now we can also take the converse of this conclusion and say that since the ball which comes from *A* in a straight line to *B* changes its direction at the point *B*, and takes its course from there toward *I*, this signifies that the force or facility with which it enters into the body *CBEI* is, to that with which it leaves the body *ACBE*, as the distance between *AC* and *HB* is to that between *HB* and *FI*—that is to say, as the line *CB* is to *BE*.

Finally, inasmuch as the action of light follows in this respect the same laws as the movement of the ball, it is necessary to say that when its rays pass obliquely from one transparent body to another which receives them more or less easily than the first, they are deflected in such a manner that they are always less inclined to the surface of these bodies on the side of the one that receives them most easily than on the side of the other, and this exactly in proportion to the ease with which the one rather than the other receives them. Only it is necessary to take care that this inclination be measured by the quantity of the straight lines, such as *CB* or *AH*, and *EB* or *IG*, and the like, compared with each other; not by that of angles like *ABH* or *GBI*, nor even less by those, like *DBI*, which we call the angles of refraction. For the ratio or proportion between these angles varies with all the different inclinations of the rays; whereas that between the lines *AH* and *IG,* or others such, remains the same in all refractions caused by the same bodies. So, for example, if a ray passing through the air from *A* toward *B* meets the surface of the lens *CBR* at point *B* and is deflected toward *I* in this lens, and if another coming from the air from *K* toward *B* is deflected toward *L,* and another comes from *P* toward *R* and is deflected toward *S,* there must be the same ratio between the lines *KM* and *LN,* or *PQ* and *ST,* as between *AH* and *IG;* but not the same ratio between the angles *KBM* and *LBN,* or *PRQ* and *SRT,* as between *ABH* and *IBG.*

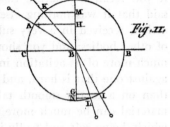

So now you see in what manner refractions must be measured; and although in order to determine their quantity, insofar as it depends on the nature of the particular body where they occur, we must appeal to experience, we nevertheless are able to do so with sufficient certainty and ease, since they are all thereby reduced to a common measure; for it suffices to examine a single ray among them in order to know all those which are caused on an identical surface; and we can avoid all error if in addition we examine some others among them. Thus, if we wish to know the quantity of those which are on the surface *CBR* which separates the air *AKP* from the lens *LIS,* we only have to put it to the test in the refraction of the ray *ABI,* by looking for the ratio between the lines *AH* and *IG.* Then, if we fear we have failed in this experiment, it is then necessary to put it to the test in some other rays, such as *KBL* or *PRS,* and finding the same ratio between *KM* and *LN,* and *PQ* and *ST,* as between *AH* and *IG,* we will have no more occasion to doubt the truth.

But perhaps, in doing these experiments, you will be astonished to find that the rays of light are more sharply inclined in the air than in the water. on the surfaces where their re-

fraction occurs, and still more so in water than in glass—
quite the opposite of a ball which is inclined more sharply
in the water than in the air, and which cannot pass through
glass at all. Because, for example,[1] if it is a ball which, being
impelled in the air from *A* toward *B,* meets at the point *B*
the surface of the water *CBE,* it will be deflected from *B*
toward *V;* and if it is a ray, it will go, quite to the contrary,
from *B* toward *I.* However, you will cease to find this strange
if you recall the nature that I attributed to light, when I
said that it was nothing else but a certain movement or an
action, received in a very subtle material that fills the pores
of other bodies; and you should consider that, as a ball loses
much more of its agitation in falling against a soft body than
against one that is hard, and as it rolls less easily on a carpet
than on a totally smooth table, so the action of this subtle
material can be much more impeded by the particles of air,
which, being soft and badly joined, do not offer it very much
resistance, than by those of water, which offer it much more;
and still more by those of water than by those of glass, or of
crystal. So that, the harder and firmer are the small particles
of a transparent body, the more easily do they allow the light
to pass: for this light does not have to drive any of them out
of their places, as a ball must expel those of water, in order
to find passage among them.

Moreover, knowing thus the cause of the refractions which
occur in water and glass, and commonly in all the other transparent bodies which are around us, we can note that they
must be entirely similar when the rays leave from these bodies
and when they enter them. As, if the ray which comes from
A toward *B* is diverted from *B* toward *I* in passing from the
air into the glass, the one which will return from *I* toward *B*
must also be deflected from *B* toward *A.* Nevertheless, there
can be found other bodies, principally in the sky, where the
refractions, proceeding from other causes, are not reciprocal
in this way. And there can also be found certain cases in
which the rays must be curved, although they pass through
only a single transparent body, in the same way that the
movement of a ball often curves, because it is deflected in

[1] See Fig. 10, p. 80.

one direction by its weight, and in another by the momentum with which we have impelled it, or for diverse other reasons. For finally I dare to say that the three comparisons which I have just used are so correct that all the particularities that it is possible to note about them correspond to certain others which are found to be quite similar in light; but here I have tried to explain only those which have the most bearing upon my subject. And I do not wish you to consider any other thing here, except that the surfaces of transparent bodies which are curved deflect the rays passing through each of their points in the same way as would the flat surfaces that we can imagine touching these bodies at the same points.

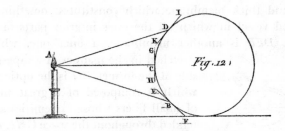

Fig. 12

As, for example, the refraction of the rays *AB, AC, AD*, which, coming from the flame *A*, fall on the curved surface of the crystal ball *BCD*, must be considered in the same way as if *AB* fell on the flat surface *EBF*, and *AC* on *GCH*, and *AD* on *IDK*, and so with the others. From which you can see that these rays can be variously gathered or dispersed, according as they fall on surfaces which are differently curved. And it is time that I start to describe the structure of the eye to you, in order that you will be able to understand how the rays which enter within it are so disposed there as to cause the sensation of sight.

Third Discourse

Of the Eye

If it were possible to cut the eye in half, without the liquids with which it is filled escaping, and without any of its parts changing their places, so that the plane of the section passed right through the middle of the pupil, it would appear such as it is represented in this diagram. *ABCB* is a rather hard and thick membrane which constitutes something like a round vessel in which all the eye's interior parts are contained. *DEF* is another membrane, a finer one, which is

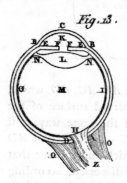

Fig. 13.

stretched in the manner of a tapestry inside of the former. *ZH* is the optic nerve, which is composed of a great number of small fibers whose extremities are extended throughout the space *GHI*, where, minging with an infinity of small veins and arteries, they compose a sort of extremely tender and delicate flesh, which is like a third membrane that covers the entire inside of the second. *K, L, M,* are three kinds of very transparent glairs or humors which will fill the entire space contained within these membranes, and each of them has the shape which you see represented here. And experiment shows that the one in the middle, *L,* which we call the crystalline humor, causes almost the same refraction as glass or crystal, and that the other two, *K* and *M,* cause slightly less, about the same as ordinary water, so that the rays of light pass more readily through that of the middle than through the two others, and yet more easily through these two than through the air. In the first membrane, the part *BCB* is transparent and slightly more bulging than the rest, *BAB*. In the second, the interior surface of the part *EF*, which faces toward the base of the eye, is completely black and obscure; and in the middle it has a small round hole *FF*, which we call the pupil, and which appears quite black in the middle of the eye, when we look at it from the outside. This hole is not always the same size, and the part *EF* of the membrane in which it is found, swimming freely in the humor *K*, which is quite liquid, seems to be like a small muscle which can contract and enlarge as we look at objects which are nearer or farther, or more or less lighted, or else when we wish to see them more or less distinctly.

You will easily see the proof of all this in the eye of a child; for if you have him look fixedly at a nearby object, you will see that the pupil becomes a bit smaller than if you have him look at one that is farther away, but no better lighted. And again, even while he is looking at the same object, the pupil will be much smaller in a well-lighted room than if we make the room quite dark by closing most of the windows. And finally, while he remains in the same light and looks at the same object, if he tries to distinguish the smallest details of it, his pupil will be smaller than if he considered it merely as a whole, without close attention. And notice that this movement must be called voluntary, even though it is ordinarily ignored by those who perform it, because it nevertheless depends on, and follows from, their desire to see well; just as the movements of the lips and tongue, which serve to pronounce words, are called voluntary because they follow from the wish to speak, even though we often ignore the fact that they must be used in the pronunciation of each letter.

EN, EN are many small black fibers which completely enclose the liquid marked *L*, and which also originate from the second membrane at the spot where the third terminates, and seem to be like many small tendons by means of which this liquid *L* becomes now more curved, now flatter, depending upon our intention to look at nearer or farther objects; and thus the entire shape of the body of the eye is slightly changed. And you can recognize this movement through experience; for if, when you are looking fixedly at a tower or a mountain some distance away, someone places a book before your eyes, you will not be able to see any letter distinctly, until the shape of the crystalline humor is slightly changed.

Finally *O, O* are six or seven muscles attached to the eye on the outside, which can move it in all directions, and even also, perhaps, help to change its shape by pressing it or pulling it back. I purposely omit many other details which can be observed about this matter, and with which the anatomists swell their books. For I believe that those I have presented here will suffice in order to explain everything relevant to my subject, and that the others which I could add, while in no wise improving your understanding, would only serve to divert your attention.

Fourth Discourse

Of the Senses in General

But now I must tell you something about the nature of
the senses in general, the more easily to explain that of sight
in particular. We already know sufficiently well that it is the
mind which senses, not the body; for we see that when the
mind is distracted by an ecstasy or deep contemplation, the
entire body remains without sensation, even though it is in
contact with various objects. And we know that it is not
properly because the mind is in the parts serving as organs
to the exterior senses that it experiences sensation, but because
it is in the brain, where it exercises that faculty which is
called common sense: [1] for we observe injuries and illnesses
attacking only the brain, which impede all the senses generally, although the rest of the body does not cease to be ani-
mated because of this. Finally we know that it is through the
medium of the nerves that impressions which objects cause
in the external members are transmitted to the mind in the
brain: for we observe various accidents which, injuring only
some nerve, destroy sensation in all parts of the body where
this nerve sends its branches, without diminishing it anywhere
else. But, in order to understand in greater detail how the
mind, located in the brain, can thus receive impressions of
external objects through the mediation of the nerves, it is
necessary to distinguish three things in these nerves: these
are, first, the membranes which enclose them, and which,
originating in those that enclose the brain, are like little
tubes divided in many branches, which go spreading here and
there throughout the members, in the same way as do the
veins and the arteries; second, their interior substance, which

1 *Sensus communis.*

extends in the form of little threads throughout the length
of these tubes, from the brain whence it originates, all the
way to the extremities of the other members where it is attached, such that we can imagine, in each of these small
tubes, many of these separate little fibers independent of each
other; and finally the animal spirits, which are like a very
subtle wind or air which, coming from the chambers or concavities in the brain, flows away by these same tubes throughout the muscles. Now the anatomists and doctors have adequately demonstrated that these three things are in the nerves;
but it seems to me that no one among them has adequately
distinguished their uses. For, seeing that the nerves not only
serve to give feeling to the members, but also to move them,
and that sometimes there are paralyses which destroy movement without thereby destroying sensation, they have sometimes said that there were two kinds of nerves, some of which
were used only for sensation, and others only for movements;
and at other times, they have said that the faculty of sensation was in the outer coverings or membranes of the nerves,
and that of moving in the interior substance—which are things
very repugnant to experience and reason, for who has ever
been able to observe any nerve that is used for movement,
without its also being used for some sense? And how, if sensation depended upon the membranes, could the diverse impressions of objects be transmitted by these membranes all
the way to the brain? To avoid these difficulties, then, we
must assume that it is the spirits flowing through the nerves
into the muscles, and expanding them more or less—sometimes
these, sometimes those, according to the various ways that
the brain distributes them—which cause the movement of all
the members. We must also assume that it is the small threads
composing the interior substance of the nerves which are
used for sensation. And inasmuch as I have no need here to
speak of movements, I wish you to understand only that these
small fibers, being enclosed, as I have said, in tubes which
are always inflated and held open by the spirits which they
contain, do not crowd or impede each other in any way, and

are extended from the brain to the extremities of all parts
which are capable of any sensation, in such a way that, however slightly we touch and move the spot in these places
where any one of the fibers is attached, we also move at the
same instant the place in the brain from which it comes;
just as pulling one of the ends of a very taut cord makes the
other end move at the same instant. For, knowing that these
fibers are so enclosed in the tubes which the spirits always
keep slightly inflated and open, it is easy to understand that,
even if they were much thinner than those spun by silkworms,
and weaker than those of spiders, they still might be extended
from the head to the most distant parts without any risk
of their breaking, nor would any of the various positions of
the limbs impede their movements. Apart from that, it is
necessary to beware of assuming that in order to sense, the
mind needs to perceive certain images transmitted by the objects to the brain, as our philosophers commonly suppose;
or, at least, the nature of these images must be conceived quite
otherwise than as they do. For, inasmuch as [the philosophers]
do not consider anything about these images except that they
must resemble the objects they represent, it is impossible for
them to show us how they can be formed by these objects,
received by the external sense organs, and transmitted by
the nerves to the brain. And they have had no other reason
for positing them except that, observing that a picture can
easily stimulate our minds to conceive the object painted
there, it seemed to them that in the same way, the mind
should be stimulated by little pictures which form in our
head to conceive of those objects that touch our senses; instead, we should consider that there are many other things
besides pictures which can stimulate our thought, such as,
for example, signs and words, which do not in any way resemble the things which they signify. And if, in order to depart
as little as possible from currently accepted beliefs, we prefer
to avow that the objects which we perceive truly transmit
their images to the inside of our brain, we must at least
observe that there are no images that must resemble in every

respect the objects they represent—for otherwise there would be no distinction between the object and its image—but that it is sufficient for them to resemble the objects in but a few ways, and even that their perfection frequently depends on their not resembling them as much as they might. For example, you can see that engravings, being made of nothing but a little ink placed here and there on the paper, represent to us forests, towns, men, and even battles and storms, even though, among an infinity of diverse qualities which they make us conceive in these objects, only in shape is there actually any resemblance. And even this resemblance is a very imperfect one, seeing that, on a completely flat surface, they represent to us bodies which are of different heights and distances, and even that following the rules of perspective, circles are often better represented by ovals rather than by other circles; and squares by diamonds rather than by other squares; and so for all other shapes. So that often, in order to be more perfect as images and to represent an object better, they must not resemble it. Now we must think in the same way about the images that are formed in our brain, and we must note that it is only a question of knowing how they can enable the mind to perceive all the diverse qualities of the objects to which they refer; not of [knowing] how the images themselves resemble their objects; just as when the blind man of whom we have spoken above touches some object with his cane, it is certain that these objects do not transmit anything to him except that, by making his cane move in different ways according to their different inherent qualities, they likewise and in the same way move the nerves of his hand, and then the places in his brain where these nerves originate. Thus his mind is caused to perceive as many different qualities in these bodies, as there are varieties in the movements that they cause in his brain.

Fifth Discourse

Of the Images That Form on the Back Of the Eye

Thus you can clearly see that in order to perceive, the mind need not contemplate any images resembling the things that it senses. But this makes it no less true that the objects we look at do imprint very perfect images on the back of our eyes. Some people have very ingeniously explained this already, by comparison with the images that appear in a chamber, when having it completely closed except for a single hole, and having put in front of this hole a glass in the form of a lens, we stretch behind, at a specific distance, a white cloth on which the light that comes from the objects outside forms these images. For they say that this chamber represents the eye; this hole, the pupil; this lens, the crystalline humor, or rather, all those parts of the eye which cause some refraction; and this cloth, the interior membrane, which is composed of the extremities of the optic nerve.

But you will be even more certain of this if, taking the eye a newly deceased man, or, for want of that, of an ox or some other large animal, you carefully cut through to the back the three membranes which enclose it, in such a manner that a large part of the humor *M* which is there remains exposed without any of it spilling out because of this. Then, having covered it over with some white body thin enough to let the daylight pass through it, as for example with a piece of paper or with an eggshell, *RST*, place this eye in the hole of a specially made window such as *Z*, in such a manner so that it has its front, *BCD*, turned toward some location where there are various objects, such as *V*, *X*, *Y*, illuminated by the sun; and the back of it, where the white

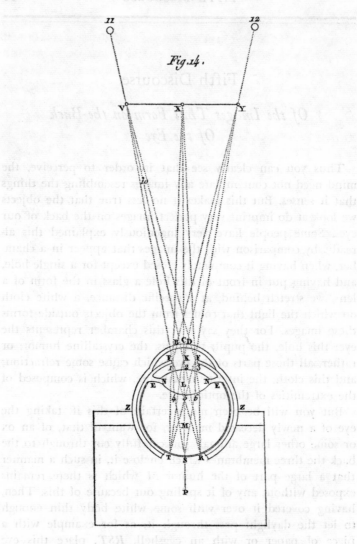

Fig.14.

But you will be more certain of this, if, taking the eye of a newly deceased man, or, for want of that, of an ox or some other large animal, you cut dexterously away about the back three membranes that enclose it, in such a manner that a large part of the humour M, which is there, remains exposed without any of it spreading out because of this, then, having covered it over with some white body thin enough to let the daylight pass through it, as for example with a piece of paper or with an eggshell, RST, place this eye in the hole of a specially made window shut as Z, in such a manner that it has its front, BCD, turned toward some location where there are various objects, such as V, X, Y, Z, illuminated by the sun, and the back of it, where the white body *RST* is located, toward the inside of the chamber *P* (where you will be), into which no other light is allowed to enter except that which will be able to penetrate through this eye, all of whose parts, from *C* to *S*, you know to be transparent. For when this has been done, if you look at that white body *RST*, you will see there, not perhaps without admiration and pleasure, a picture which will represent in natural perspective all the objects which will be outside of it toward *VXY*, at least if you do it in such a way that this eye retains its natural shape, proportionated to the distance of these objects; because, if you squeeze it more or less than is right, no matter how slightly, this picture will become less distinct. And it should be noted that we should squeeze it a bit more, thereby making its shape a bit longer, when the objects are very near than when they are farther away. But I must explain here at greater length how this picture is formed; for, by the same means, I can enable you to understand several things which pertain to vision.

First, then, consider that from each point of the objects *V, X, Y*, there enter into this eye and penetrate to the white body *RST* as many rays as the opening of the pupil *FF* can allow, and that, in consequence of what has been said above about the nature of refraction as well as about that of the three liquids *K, L, M*, all of those rays which come from the same point are curved in passing through the three surfaces *BCD, 123* and *456*, in the way that is required for them to reconverge again at a single point. And it must be noted that in order that the picture which is here in question be as perfect as possible, the shapes of these three surfaces must be such that all the rays coming from one of the points of the objects reconverge exactly at one of the points of the white body *RST*. As you can see here, those from point *X* converge at point *S*; consequently those which come from point *V* assemble also approximately at point *R*; and those from point *Y*, at point *T*. And reciprocally, no ray comes toward *S*, except from point *X*; and almost none toward *R*, except from point *V*; nor toward *T*, except from point *Y*, and so with all the others. Now this being granted, if you remember what has been said above of light and of colors generally, and particularly of white bodies, it will be easy for you to understand that if you are enclosed in the chamber P, and fix your eyes on the white body RST, you ought to see there the likeness of the objects V, X, Y. For first of all, if the light (i.e., the movement or action with which the sun or some other of the bodies which are said to be luminous impels a certain very subtle material which is found in all transparent bodies) is reflected toward R by the object V, which I assume to be, for example, red (i.e., disposed to make the small particles of this subtle material, which are impelled only in straight lines by the luminous bodies, also move around their centers after having met them; and so disposed, too, that their two movements have between them the proportion required to cause the sensation of the color red), it is certain that the action of these two movements, having at point R encountered a white body (i.e., a body disposed to reflect light in all other directions without changing it), must be reflected from there toward our eyes through the pores of this body, which I have assumed for this purpose to be very delicate and, as it were, pierced with light from all sides, and so to cause you to see the color red at point R. Then, if the light is also reflected from the object X, which I assume to be yellow, toward S, and from Y, which I assume to be blue, toward T, whence it is carried toward your eyes, it must cause S to appear to you as yellow, and T as blue. And so the three points RST, appearing to be of the same colors, and keeping between them the same order as the three objects V, X, Y, manifestly do resemble them. And the perfection of this picture depends principally on three things, namely, [1] that, the pupil of the eye having a certain size, many rays enter into it from each point of the object, such as $XB14S$, $XC24S$, $XD36S$ here, and just as many others as we can imagine between these three, all having come there from the single point X; [2] that these rays undergo such refractions in the eye that those coming from various points reconverge in nearly as many other di-

verse points on the white body *RST;* and finally [3] that, since
the small fibers *EN* as well as the inside of the membrane *EF*
are black in color, and since the chamber P is completely
closed and dark, no light but that from the objects *V, X, Y*
comes to interfere with the action of these rays. For, if the
pupil were so small that only a single ray from each point
of the object might pass toward each point of the body *RST,*
[that ray] would not have enough strength to be reflected from
there into the chamber P, toward our eyes. And the pupil
being somewhat large, if there were not any refraction in the
eye, the rays coming from each point of the objects would
spread out here and there all through the space *RST,* in such a
way that, for example, the three points *V, X, Y* would send
three rays toward *R,* which being reflected all together from
there toward our eyes, would make this point *R* appear to you
to be of a color somewhere between red, yellow, and blue,
and similarly with the points *S* and *T,* toward which the
same points *V, X, Y* would also each send one of their
rays. And roughly the same thing would happen if the refraction which is caused in the eye was greater or less than
it ought to be, because of the size of that eye; for if the eye
were too large, the rays which came, for example, from the
point *X* would come together before having reached *S,* perhaps near *M;* and on the other hand, if it were too small,
they would not come together until after S, perhaps near *P;*
so that they would touch the white body *RST* at many points,
toward which other rays would also come from the other parts
of the object. Finally, if the bodies *EN, EF* were not black,
i.e., disposed so as to deaden the light striking against them,
the rays that came toward them from the white body *RST*
would be able to return from them—those from *T* toward *S*
and *R,* those from *R* toward *T* and *S,* and those from *S*
toward *R* and *T*—in the process of which they would interfere
with one another's action; and the rays coming toward *RST*
from the chamber *P* would do the same thing, if there were some
other light in this chamber aside from that sent there by the
objects *V, X, Y.*

But, having spoken to you of the perfections of this picture, it is also necessary that I make you consider its defects, of which the first and principal is that, whatever shapes the parts of the eye may have, it is impossible for them to cause the rays coming from different points to converge in as many other different points; and that the best they can do is to make all those that come from some particular point such as from X assemble at some other point such as S, in the middle of the back of the eye; in which case, only some of those from point V can assemble exactly at point R, or those from point V at point T; and the others have to scatter all around a little, in a manner that I shall later explain. And this is the reason that this picture is never as distinct at its edges as it is in the middle, as has been sufficiently noted by those who have written of Optics; for it is because of this that they have said that vision takes place principally along the straight line which passes through the centers of the crystalline humor and of the pupil, as the line $XKLS$ does here, which they call the axis of vision. And notice that the rays—those coming from point V, for example—are the more spread out around point R in proportion as the opening of the pupil is larger, in such a manner that although its size serves to make the colors of this picture brighter and stronger, on the other hand it prevents its forms from being as distinct; from which it follows that [the pupil] ought to be only moderately large. Let us also note that these rays would be scattered even more than they are around point R if point V, from which they come, were much closer to the eye, such as at *10*, or much further removed, such as at *11*, than is V, to whose distance I am assuming that the shape of the eye is proportioned; so that they would make part R of this picture still less distinct than they do now. And you will easily understand the demonstrations of all this when you have seen, hereinafter, which shapes transparent bodies must have in order to cause the rays coming from a certain point to converge at a certain other point, after having passed through them. As to the other defects of this picture, they consist in the fact that its parts are reversed, i.e., in a position quite the opposite to that of the objects; and in the fact that they are diminished and shortened—some more, some less—owing to the various distances and positions of the things they represent, much in the same manner as in a picture done in perspective. As you can clearly see here, *T*, which is toward the left side, represents *Y*, which is toward the right, and *R*, which is toward the right, represents *V*, which is toward the left. And moreover, the shape of the object *V* must not occupy more of the space toward *R* than that of the object *10*, which is smaller but closer; nor less than that of the object *11*, which is larger but proportionately further removed, except insofar as [the shape of *V*] is slightly more distinct. And finally, the straight line *VXY* is represented by the curve *RST*.

Now, having thus seen this picture in the eye of a dead animal, and having considered its causes, you cannot doubt that an entirely similar one is formed in the eye of a live man, on the interior membrane for which we have substituted the white body *RST;* and even that it is formed much better there, because its humors, being full of spirits, are more transparent and have more exactly the shape which is requisite to this effect. And also, perhaps in the eye of an ox the shape of the pupil, which is not round, prevents this picture from being so perfect there.

Neither can we doubt that the images which we cause to appear on a white cloth in a dark chamber are formed there in the same way and for the same reasons as on the back of the eye; and indeed, because they are ordinarily much larger there, and form there in many more ways, we can more easily note different details there, of which I here desire to inform you so that you can test for them, if you have not already done so. First of all, then, you can see that if we do not place any glass in front of the hole that we have made in this chamber, certain images will certainly appear on the cloth, provided that the hole be quite small, but they will be very confused and imperfect, so much the more so as this hole is less small. And you can also see that they will become proportionately larger as the distance increases between the hole and the cloth, in such a manner that their size must have nearly the same proportion with that distance as the size of the objects which cause these images has with the distance between them and this same hole. Thus it is evident that, if *ACB* is the object, *D* the hole, and *EFG* the image, *EG* is

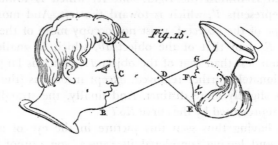

Fig. 15.

to *FD* as *AB* is to *CD*. Then, having placed a glass in the form of a lens in front of this hole, you will note that there is a certain determinate distance at which the images appear quite distinct on the cloth, and that, however slightly we increase or decrease the distance between the cloth and the lens, the images begin to be less distinct. And this distance must be measured by the space between the cloth and the lens, not between the cloth and the hole; so that, if we place the lens a bit beyond the hole on one hand or the other, the cloth or screen must similarly be brought nearer or farther from it. And you will see that the distance depends in part on the shape of this lens, and also in part on the remoteness of the objects: for, leaving the object in the same location, the less the surfaces of the lens are curved, the more the cloth must be distant from it; and using the same lens, if the objects are very near to it, it is necessary to place the cloth a bit further away than if they are more distant from the lens. And the size of the images depends on this distance almost in the same way as when there is no lens in front of the hole. And this hole can be much larger when we put a lens there than when we leave it completely vacant, without the images thereby becoming much less distinct; and the larger it is, the clearer and brighter they appear: so that, if we cover a part of this lens, they will appear much more obscure than before, but they will still occupy as much space as before on the cloth. And the larger and clearer these images are, the more perfectly they are seen: so that, if we could also make an eye whose depth was very great and whose pupil was very large, and if the shapes of those of its surfaces which cause some refraction were proportioned to this magnitude, the images formed there would be to that extent more visible. And if having two or more lens-shaped, but rather flat glasses, we join them one against the other, they will have nearly the same effect as would a single one which was as much curved or convex as those two together; because the number of surfaces where the refractions occur is not important. But if we remove these lenses certain distances away from each other, the second will be able to correct the image that the first will have inverted, and the third will reinvert it again, and so on. All these are things whose causes are very easy to deduce from what I have said, and you will grasp them more completely if you have to use a little reflection in order to conceive them, than if you were to find them better explained here.

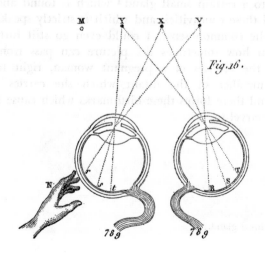

Fig.16.

Further, not only do the images of objects form thus on the back of the eye, but they also pass beyond to the brain, as you will readily understand if you consider that, for example, the rays that come into the eye from the object V touch at point Z the extremity of one of the small fibers of the optic nerve which has its origin in the point 7 of the interior surface of the brain *789;* and those of the object X touch at point S the extremity of another of these fibers, of which the beginning is at point *8;* and those of the object Y touch another of them at point T, which corresponds to the spot of the brain marked *9,* and so with the others. And that, light being nothing but a movement or an action which tends to cause some movement, those of its rays which come from V toward R have the power of moving the entire fiber $R7$, and as a result the point of the brain marked *7;* and those which come from X toward S, of moving the entire nerve $S8$, and even of moving it in a way other than that by which ꞏꞏ is moved, because the objects X and V are of two different colors. And similarly, those which come from Y move point *9,* from which it is manifest that the picture *789,* which is quite similar to the objects $V, X, Y,$ is formed once more on the interior surface of the brain, facing toward its concavities. And from there I could again transport it right to a certain small gland [1] which is found about the center of these concavities, and which is strictly speaking the seat of the common sense. I could even go still further, to show you how sometimes the picture can pass from there through the arteries of a pregnant woman, right to some specific member of the infant which she carries in her womb, and there forms these birthmarks which cause learned men to marvel so.

[1] The pineal gland.

Sixth Discourse

Of Vision

Now although this picture, in being so transmitted into our head, always retains some resemblance to the objects from which it proceeds, nevertheless, as I have already shown, we must not hold that it is by means of this resemblance that the picture causes us to perceive the objects, as if there were yet other eyes in our brain with which we could apprehend it; but rather, that it is the movements of which the picture is composed which, acting immediately on our mind inasmuch as it is united to our body, are so established by nature as to make it have such perceptions; and I would like to explain this to you here in more detail. All the qualities that we apprehend in the objects of sight can be reduced to six principal ones, which are: light, color, location, distance, size, and shape. And first of all, regarding light and color, which alone properly belong to the sense of sight, it is necessary to think that the nature of our mind is such that the force of the movements in the areas of the brain where the small fibers of the optic nerves originate cause it to perceive light; and the character of these movements cause it to have the perception of color: just as the movements of the nerves which respond to the ears cause it to hear sounds, and those of the nerves of the tongue cause it to taste flavors, and, generally, those of the nerves of the entire body cause it to feel some tickling, when they are moderate, and when they are too violent, some pain; yet in all this, there need be no resemblance between the ideas that the mind conceives and the movements which cause these ideas. You will readily believe this if you note that it seems to those who receive some injury in the eye that they see an infinity of fireworks and

lightning flashes before them, even though they shut their
eyes or else are in a very dark place; so that this sensation
can be attributed only to the force of the blow which moves
the small fibers of the optic nerve, as a strong light would do.
And if this same force touched the ears, it could cause some
sound to be heard; and if it touched the body in other parts,
could cause it to feel some pain. And this is also confirmed
by the fact that if you sometimes force your eyes to look at
the sun, or some other very strong light, they retain its impression for a short time afterward, in such a manner that,
even if you keep them shut, you seem to see various colors
which change and pass from one to the other as they grow
weaker. For this can only proceed from the fact that the
little fibers of the optic nerve, having been moved in an extraordinarily strong manner, cannot stop themselves as soon
as is their custom; instead, the agitation which is still in
them after the eyes are closed, not being sufficiently great to
represent this very strong light which caused it, represents
the less vivid colors. And these colors are changed as they
weaken, which shows that their nature consists only in the
diversity of the movement, and that it is nothing other than
what I have already supposed. And finally this is manifested
in the fact that colors often appear in transparent bodies, where
it is certain that nothing can cause them but the different
ways in which the rays of light are received there, as when
the rainbow appears among the clouds; and still more clearly,
when we see their likenesses in a many-faceted glass.

But it is necessary for us here to consider particularly what
determines the quantity of the light which is seen, that is, the
quantity of the force by which each of the small fibers of the
optic nerve is moved. For this is not always equal to the light
which is in the objects, but varies in proportion to their
distance and to the size of the pupil, and also in proportion
to the space that the rays coming from each point of the object can occupy on the back of the eye. For example, it is
manifest that the point X would send more rays into the eye
B than it does, if the pupil FF were open as far as G; and

that it sends just as many of them into this eye *B*, which is close to it and has a very narrow pupil, as it does into the eye *A*, which has a much larger pupil, but is proportionately farther removed. And although no more rays from the different points of the object *VXY*, considered all together, enter into the back of the eye *A* than into that of the eye *B*, nevertheless, in order that these rays extend only in the space *TR*, which is smaller than *HI* where they extend at the back of the eye *B*, they must there act with more force against each of the extremities of the optic nerve that they touch there: which is very easy to calculate. For, if, for example, the space *HI* is four times as large as *TR*, and if it contains the extremities of four thousand of the small fibers of the optic nerve, then *TR* will contain those of only one thousand, and as a result each of these small fibers will be moved in the back of the eye *A* by the thousandth part of the force possessed by all the rays, joined together, which enter there, and, at the back of the eye, *B*, by only a quarter of

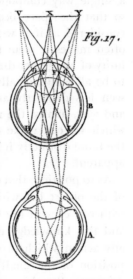

Fig. 17.

the thousandth part. It is necessary also to notice that we can distinguish the parts of the bodies at which we are looking only insofar as they differ in some manner in their coloring; and that the distinct vision of these colors does not depend only on the fact that all the rays coming from each point of the object come back together in approximately as many other different points on the back of the eye, nor only on the fact that no others come from eleswhere toward these same points, as has just now been amply explained; but also on the multitude of small fibers of the optic nerve, which are in the space that the image occupies at the back of the eye. For if, for example, the object *VXY* is composed of ten thousand parts, capable of sending rays toward the back of the eye *RST* in ten thousand different ways, and consequently of making ten thousand colors visible at once, nonetheless they will enable the mind to distinguish no more than a thousand, at the most, if we suppose that there are but a thousand fibers of the optic nerve in the space *RST*. Thus ten parts of the object, acting together upon each of these fibers, can move it in only a single way composed of all those ways in which they act, so that the space occupied by each of these fibers must be considered as if it were only one point. And it is this which often makes it seem that a meadow which is painted an infinity of altogether different colors will appear from a distance to be all white, or all blue; and why, generally, all bodies are seen less distinctly at a distance than when they are near; and why, finally, the more of the space at the back of the eye which we can make the image of one single object occupy, the more distinctly it can be seen. This will later become very apparent.

As to position, that is to say the direction in which each part of the object lies with respect to our body, we perceive this with our eyes in the same way as we would with our hands; and this knowledge does not depend on any image, nor on any action which proceeds from the object, but only on the position of the small points of the brain whence the nerves originate. For this position, changing ever so little each time that of the members where the nerves are inserted changes, is established by nature not only in order that the mind may know how each part of the body which it animates is placed with respect to all the others, but also so that it may transfer its attention from there to any of the locations contained in the straight lines that we can imagine to be drawn from the extremity of each of these parts, and prolonged to infinity. In the same way, when the blind man of whom we have already spoken above moves his hand *A* toward *E,* or similarly *C* toward *E,* the nerves inserted in that hand cause a certain change in his brain, which gives his mind the means to know, not only the location *A* or *C,* but also all the others which are in the straight line *AE* or *CE,* so that [the mind] can turn its attention to the objects *B* and *D,* and determine their locations; yet for this he does not need to know, or to consider at all, the locations of his two hands. And similarly, when our eye or our head turns in some particular direction, our mind is informed of this by the change which the nerves inserted in the muscles used for these movements cause in our brain. In the eye *RST,* for

Fig. 18.

example,[1] it is necessary to assume that the position of the small fiber of the optic nerve, which is at point *R,* or *S,* or *T,* corresponds to a certain other position of the part of the brain 7, or 8, or 9, which enables the mind to know all the locations along the line *RV,* or *SX,* or *TY.* So that you must not be surprised that the objects can be seen in their true position, even though the picture they imprint upon the eye is inverted: for this is just like our blind man's being able to sense the object *B,* which is to his right, by means of his left hand, and the object *D,* which is to his left, by means of his right hand at one and the same time. And just as this blind man does not judge that a body is double, although he touches it with his two hands, so likewise when both our eyes are disposed in the manner which is required in order to carry our attention toward one and the same location, they need only cause us to see a single object there, even though a picture of it is formed in each of our eyes.

The seeing of distance depends no more than does the seeing of location upon any images emitted from objects; but in the first place upon the shape of the body of the eye. For as we have said, for us to see that which is close to our eyes, and to see what is farther away, this shape has to be slightly different. And as we change it in order to adjust the eye to the distance of objects, we also change a certain part of our brain, in a way that is established by nature to allow our mind to per-

1 See Fig. 16, p. 99.

ceive that distance. And this we ordinarily do without reflecting upon it, just as when we squeeze some body with our
hand, we adjust our hand to the size and shape of the body,
and thus feel it by means of the hand without having to think
of these movements.

In the second place, we know distance by the relation of the
eyes to one another. For just as our blind man, holding the
two sticks *AE, CE,* of whose length I am assuming that he is
ignorant, and knowing only the interval which is between his
two hands *A* and *C,* and the size of the angles *ACE, CAE,* can
from that, as if by a natural geometry, know the location of
the point *E;* so also when our two eyes, *RST* and *rst,* are
turned toward *X,* the length of the line *Ss* and the size of the
two angles *XSs* and *XsS* enable us to know the location of
the point *X.* We can also do the same thing with the aid of one
eye alone, by changing its position: as, if keeping it turned
toward *X,* we place it first of all at the point *S* and immediately
afterwards at point *s,* this will suffice to cause the magnitude
of the line *Ss* and of the two angles *XSs* and *XsS* to combine
together in our imagination, making us perceive the distance
of the point *X:* and this happens by an action of thought
which, although it is only a simple act of imagination, nevertheless implicitly contains a reasoning quite similar to that
used by surveyors, when, by means of two different stations,
they measure inaccessible places.

We have yet another way of perceiving distance, which is
through the distinctness or indistinctness of the shape seen,
together with the strength or weakness of the light. Thus
when we gaze fixedly toward *X,*[2] the rays coming from the objects *10* and *12* do not converge as exactly at *R* and *T,* at the
back of our eye, as they would if these objects were at points
V and *Y;* from which we see that they are either farther away
from us, or else nearer, than is the point *X.* Then from the
fact that the light coming from the object *10* toward our eye
is stronger than it would be if that object were toward *V,* we
judge it to be nearer; and from the fact that the light coming

[2] See Fig. 14, p. 92.

from the object *12* is weaker than it would be if it were toward *Y*, we judge it to be farther away. Finally, when moreover we already imagine the size of an object, or its position, or the distinctness of its shape and of its colors, or merely the strength of the light which comes from it, this enables us, not actually to see, but to imagine its distance. Thus, looking from afar at some body which we are used to seeing close at hand, we judge its distance much better than we would if its size were not so well known to us. And, looking at a mountain exposed to the sun beyond a forest covered with shade, it is only the position of this forest which makes us judge it the nearer; and looking at two ships on the sea, one of which is smaller than the other but proportionately closer, so that they appear equal in size, we will be able to judge which is farther away by the difference in their shapes and colors and in the light which they send toward us.

As to the manner in which we see the size and shape of objects, I need not say anything in particular, inasmuch as it is all included in the manner in which we see the distance and the position of their parts. Thus, their size is estimated according to the knowledge, or the opinion, that we have of their distance, compared with the size of the images that they imprint on the back of the eye; and not absolutely by the size of these images, as is obvious enough from this: while the images may be, for example, one hundred times larger when the objects are quite close to us than when they are ten times farther away, they do not make us see the objects as one hundred times larger because of this, but as almost equal in size, at least if their distance does not deceive us. And it is also obvious that shape is judged by the knowledge, or opinion, that we have of the position of various parts of the objects, and not by the resemblance of the pictures in the eye; for these pictures usually contain only ovals and diamond shapes, yet they cause us to see circles and squares.

But in order that you may have no doubts whatever that vision works as I have explained it, here again I would have you consider the reasons why it occasionally deceives us.

First of all, it is the mind which sees, not the eye; and it can see immediately only through the intervention of the brain. This is why madmen and those who are asleep often see, or think that they see, various objects which, in spite of this, are not actually before their eyes: that is, when certain vapors, disturbing the brain, dispose those of its parts which are usually used for sight in the same way as would these objects if they were present. Also, because the impressions which come from without pass to the common sense by way of the nerves, if the position of these nerves is constrained by some extraordinary cause, it can make us see objects in places other than where they are. Thus, if the eye *rst*,[3] being by itself disposed to look toward *X*, is forced by the finger *N* to turn toward *M*, the parts of the brain where its nerves originate are not disposed in quite the same way as if its muscles were turning it toward *M*, nor again are they disposed in the same way as if it were truly looking toward *X*, but in a manner somewhere between the two, that is, as if it were looking toward *Y*. And so through this eye the object *M* will appear where *Y* is, and *Y* will appear where *X* is, and *X* where *V* is; and since at the same time, through the other eye *RST*, these objects also appear in their true locations, they will seem to be double. In the same way, if we touch the little ball *G* with the two crossed fingers *A* and *D*, we think we are touching two balls; for while these fingers remain so crossed, the muscles of each tend to separate them, *A* toward

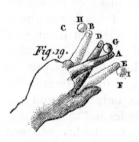

Fig. 19.

C and *D* toward *F;* by this means the parts of the brain where the nerves inserted in these muscles originate are themselves disposed in such a manner as to make it seem that *A* is toward *B*, and *D* toward *E*, and as a result they seem to touch two different balls, *H* and *I*. Moreover, because we are accustomed to judge that the impressions which move our sight

[3] See Fig. 16, p. 99.

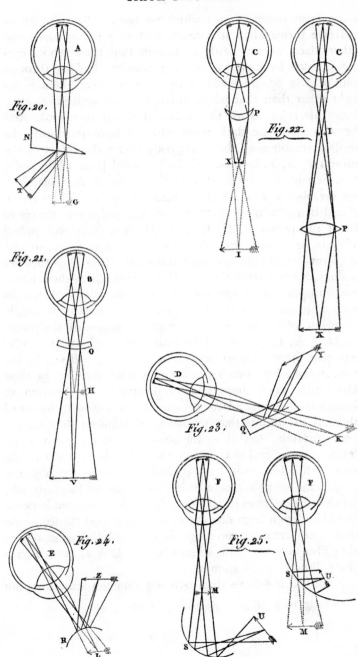

Fig. 20.

Fig. 21.

Fig. 22.

Fig. 23.

Fig. 24.

Fig. 25.

come from places toward which we must look in order to perceive them, when it happens that they come from some other place, we can easily be fooled; thus those whose eyes are infected by jaundice, or those who are looking through yellow glass or are enclosed in a room where there is no light other than that which enters through such glass, attribute this color to all the bodies at which they look. And he who is in the dark room which I have previously described attributes to the white body *RST*[4] the colors of the objects *V*, *X*, *Y*, because it is only toward [that white body] that he addresses his sight. And if the eyes *A*, *B*, *C*, *D*, *E*, *F* see the objects *T*, *V*, *X*, *Y*, *Z*, etc., through the lenses *N*, *O*, *P* and in the mirrors *Q*, *R*, *S*, they will judge the objects to be at the points *G*, *H*, *I*, *K*, *L*, *M*. And [they will judge] *V*, *Z* to be smaller, and *X*, *U* greater than they are, or else *X*, *U* smaller and also reversed; at least, this is so when they are a short distance from the eyes *C*, *F*, inasmuch as these lenses and mirrors deflect the rays coming from these objects in such a manner that these eyes can only see them distinctly by adjusting themselves as they must to look toward the points *G*, *H*, *I*, *K*, *L*, *M*, as will be easily perceived by those who will take the trouble to examine it. And they will see, by the same means, how much the ancients were deceived in their Catoptrics, when they tried to determine the location of images in concave and convex mirrors. It is also to be noted that all the means that we have for knowing distance are very uncertain; for, as to the shape of the eye, there is no longer any noticeable variation when the object is more than four or five feet away from it, and even when the object is nearer, this shape varies so little that we cannot have any very precise cognizance of it; and as to the angles contained between the lines drawn from one eye to the other, and thence to the object, or from two positions of one and the same object, they also vary but little when what we look at is at even a short distance away from us.

From this it follows that even our common sense does not

4 See Fig. 14, p. 92.

seem to be capable of accepting by itself the idea of a distance greater than approximately one or two hundred feet, as can be verified from the fact that the moon and the sun, which number among the most distant bodies that we can see, and whose diameters are approximately one per cent of their distances, normally appear to us as one or two feet in diameter at the most, notwithstanding that we know well, through reason, that they are extremely large and extremely far away. This is not because we are unable to conceive them as any greater than we do, since we easily conceive towers and mountains which are far larger; rather, it is due to the fact that, not being able to imagine them as farther away than one or two hundred feet, it follows from this that their diameters cannot appear to us as more than one or two feet. In this matter their position also helps to deceive us; for ordinarily when these heavenly bodies are very high in the sky toward midday, they seem smaller than when, as they rise or set, various objects are between them and our eyes, which causes us to take better notice of their distance. And, by measuring them with their instruments, the astronomers definitely prove that the fact that they appear greater at one time than at another does not come from their being seen under a larger angle, but from our judging them to be farther away; from which it follows that the axiom of the ancient Optics,[5] which says that the apparent size of objects is proportional to the size of the angle of vision, is not always true. We are also deceived because white or luminous bodies, and generally all those possessing much power to affect the sense of sight, always appear to be a little closer and larger than they would if they had less such power. Thus the reason for their appearing closer is that the movement with which the pupil contracts in order to avoid the force of their light is so joined with the power that disposes the entire eye to see close objects distinctly (by which we judge their distance) that the one can hardly occur but that the other does not also occur to some extent, just as we cannot completely close the first two

[5] That of the Babylonians.

fingers of the hand, without the third finger also bending a certain amount as if to close with them. And the reason why these white or luminous bodies appear larger consists not only in the fact that the estimate we make of their size depends on that of their distance, but also on the fact that they impress bigger images on the back of the eye. For it is necessary to notice that the ends of the fibers of the optic nerve which line the eye, although they are very small, nevertheless have a certain bulk, so that each of them can be affected in one of its parts by one object, and in other parts by others; and that nonetheless, since each one is capable of being moved in only a single way at any given time, when the smallest of its parts is touched by some very brilliant object, and the others by other objects which are less brilliant, the whole of it follows the movement of that which is the brightest, and represents the image of it without representing that of the others. Thus, if the ends of these small fibers are *1, 2, 3,* and the rays which come, for example, to trace the image of a star on the back of the eye are extended on that

Fig.26.

which is marked *1,* as well as slightly extended beyond, over the extremities of the six others marked *2,* to which I assume there come no other rays except very feeble ones from the sections of the sky neighboring this star, the image of this star will be extended throughout the space occupied by the six nerve endings marked *2,* and it may even extend throughout all that occupied by the twelve nerve endings marked *3,* if the force of the movement is so great that it is communicated to them too. And thus you see that the stars, even though they appear quite small, nevertheless appear very much larger than their extreme distance should cause them to appear. And even if they were not entirely round they would still appear to be so, in the same way that a square tower seen from afar looks round, and all bodies which trace only very small images in the eye cannot trace there the shapes of their angles.

To sum up, in judging of distance by size, or shape, or

color, or light, pictures in perspective sufficiently demonstrate to us how easy it is to be mistaken. For often because the things which are pictured there are smaller than we imagine that they should be, and because their outlines are less distinct, and their colors darker or more feeble, they appear to us to be farther away than they are in actuality.

Seventh Discourse

Of the Means of Perfecting Vision

Now that we have sufficiently examined how vision oper-
ates, let us summarize in a few words, re-examining all the
conditions which are required for its perfection, so that, considering in what manner it has already been provided to each
by nature, we can make an exact enumeration of all that
still remains for art to add to it. We can reduce all the things
that must concern us here to three principles, namely the objects, the internal organs which receive the impulses of these
objects, and the external organs which dispose these impulses
to be received as they ought. And concerning the objects, it
suffices to know that some are close or accessible, and others
distant and inaccessible, and, moreover, that some are more
illuminated, and others less, in order that we be informed
that, as far as the accessible ones are concerned, we can bring
them closer or put them at a distance, and increase or diminish the light which illuminates them, according as it will
be most convenient for us; but that, as far as the others are
concerned, we cannot change anything.

Then, concerning the interior organs, which are the nerves
and the brain, it is also certain that we could not add anything to their fabric through art; for we could not make a
new body, and if the doctors can help here in some way, this
does not belong to our subject. Thus only the external organs
—among which I include all the transparent parts of the eye,
as well as all the other bodies that we can place between the
eye and the object—remain for us to consider. And I find that
all the provisions that must be made for these exterior organs
can be reduced to four points. The first is that all the rays
traveling toward each of the extremities of the optic nerve

must come, as much as is possible, from but a single part of the object, and that they must suffer no change in the space between them: for were this not so, the images they form could be neither very similar to their original, nor very distinct. The second provision is that these images be very large; not in the extent of space they occupy—for they could occupy only the small space at the back of the eye—but in the extent of their lineaments or of their lines, for it is certain that the larger they are, the easier they will be to discern. The third provision is that the rays forming them be sufficiently strong to move the small fibers of the optic nerve, and by this means be felt, but that they not be so strong as to injure vision. And the fourth, that there be as many objects as possible whose images form in the eye at the same time, in order that we can see as much as possible of them at a single glance.

Now Nature has used many means to provide for the first of these things. First, by filling the eye with very transparent liquids which are not tinted with any color, she has enabled the impulses coming from outside to pass to the back of the eye without being changed. And by the refractions caused by the surfaces of these liquids, she has made it possible that among these rays along which these impulses are conducted, those coming from a single point converge at a single point against the nerve; and then that those coming from other points also converge in as many other diverse points, as precisely as is possible (for we must suppose that Nature has done all that is possible in this, inasmuch as experience does not cause us to perceive anything to the contrary). And we even see that, in order to render the error which in this cannot be totally avoided as small as possible, she has enabled us to contract the pupil almost as much as the force of the light permits. And by the black color with which she has tinted all the nontransparent parts of the eye placed opposite to the nerve, she has prevented any other rays from going toward these same points. And finally, by changing the shape of the body of the eye, she has brought it about that although the objects can be more or less distant from it at one time than at another, the rays coming from each of their points nevertheless always converge as exactly as they can in as many other points at the back of the eye. Nevertheless, she has not so completely provided for this last part that something cannot still be found to add to it: for granted that she has not given each of us the same means of so curving the surface of our eyes that we may see very close objects distinctly, e.g., at a distance of an inch or half an inch, yet she has failed more seriously with some, to whom she has given eyes of such a shape that they can use them only to look at things that are far away, which happens principally to the aged; and also with certain others whose eyes, on the other hand, she has made such that they can use them only to look at things that are near, which is more common in young people. So that it seems that the eyes are formed, in the beginning, a bit longer and narrower than they ought to be, and that afterwards, as we grow old, they become flatter and wider. Thus, in order for us to be able to remedy these deficiencies through art, it will first be necessary that we seek what shapes the surfaces of a piece of glass or of some other transparent body must have, in order to curve the rays falling on them in such a manner that all those rays coming from a certain point of the object are disposed, in passing through these surfaces, as if they had come from another point, which was nearer or farther away, that is, a point that is nearer to aid those who are nearsighted, and one that is farther away for the aged as well as, generally, for all those who wish to see objects nearer than the shape of their eyes

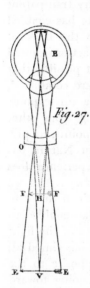

Fig. 27.

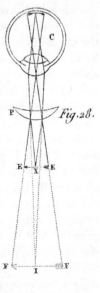

Fig. 28.

will permit. Because, for example, if the eye B or C is disposed so that all the rays coming from point H or I are gathered together in the middle of its back, and if it is not able to make those from point V or X assemble there, it is evident that, if we put in front of it the lens O or P, which cause all the rays from point V or X to enter inside in the same way as if they came from point H or I, by this means we will make up its deficiency. And because there can be lenses of many different shapes which in this case have exactly the same effect, it will be necessary, in order to choose those most suited to our purpose, that we still bear in mind two primary conditions: first, that these shapes be the simplest and the easiest possible to describe and to fashion; and second, that through their means the rays which come from other points of the object, such as E, E, enter into the eye in approximately the same manner as if they came from as many other points, such as F, F. And note that I say here only "approximately," not "as much as is possible." For, aside from the fact that it would perhaps be difficult enough to determine through Geometry, among an infinity of shapes which can be used for this same purpose, those which are exactly the most suitable, this would be utterly useless; for, since the eye itself does not cause all the rays coming from diverse points to converge in exactly as many other diverse points, because of this the lenses would doubtless not be the best suited to render vision quite distinct, and it is impossible in this matter to choose otherwise than approximately, because the precise shape of the eye cannot be known to us. Moreover, we will always have to take care, when we thus place some body before our eyes, that we imitate Nature as much as possible, in all the things that we see she has observed in constructing them; and that we lose none of the advantages that she has given us, unless it be to gain another more important one.

As to the size of the images, it is to be noted that this depends solely on three things, namely, on the distance between the object and the place where the rays that it sends from its different points toward the back of the eye intersect; next, on the distance between this same place and the base of the eye; and finally, on the refraction of these rays. Thus it is evident that the image *RST* would be greater than it is, if the object *VXY* were nearer to the place *K*, where the rays *VKR* and *YKT* intersect, or rather to the surface *BCD*, which is properly speaking the place where they begin to intersect, as you will see below; or, if we were able to arrange it so that the body of the eye were longer, in such a way that there were more distance than there is from its surface *BCD*, which causes these rays to intersect, to the back of the eye *RST;* or finally, if the refraction did not curve them so much inward toward the middle point *S*, but rather, if it were possible, outward. And whatever we conceive besides these three things, there is nothing which can make this image larger. Even the last of these is scarcely to be considered at all, because by means of it we can augment the image no more than a little bit, and this with so much difficulty that we can always augment it more easily by one of the others, as you shall now discover. So let us see how Nature has neglected it; for causing rays such as *VKR* and *YKT* to curve inward toward *S* on the surfaces *BCD* and *123,* she has made the image *RST* a bit smaller than if she had caused them to curve outward, as they do toward *5* on the surface *456,* or if she had let them all be straight. We also need not consider the first of these three things, when the objects are not at all accessible: but, when they are, it is obvious that, the closer we look at them, the larger are the images that form on the back of our eyes; so that, inasmuch as Nature has not given us the means of looking at them closer than about half a foot or a foot away, in order to add to this all that we can through art, we need only interpose a lens such as that which is marked *P,* mentioned above, which causes all the rays coming from the closest possible point to enter into the eye as if they came from another point that is more distant. Now by this means, the most that we can bring about is that there be only a twelfth or a fifteenth as much space between the eye and the object as would be there otherwise; so that the rays that will come from the different points of this object, intersecting twelve or fifteen times closer to it—or even a little more, for they will no longer begin to cross on the surface of the eye, but rather on that of the lens, to which the object will be a bit closer— will form an image whose diameter will be twelve or fifteen times greater than it would be if we were not making use of this lens; and as a result its surface will be approximately two hundred times greater, which will make the object appear approximately two hundred times more distinctly; by this means it will also appear much larger, not exactly two hundred times as large, but more so or less in proportion to how far away we judge it to be. For example, if in looking at the object X through the lens P, we dispose our eye C in the same way that it should be disposed in order to see another object twenty or thirty paces away from it, and if, having besides no knowledge of the location of this object X, we judge it to be truly at thirty paces, it will seem more than a million times greater than it is; thus it will be possible to turn a flea into an elephant, for it is certain that the image formed by a flea on the back of the eye, when the flea is so close to it, is no less great than that which is formed there by an elephant, when it is thirty paces away. And on this alone is founded the entire invention of these small flea glasses [1] made of a single lens, whose use is now quite common everywhere, although we have not yet discovered the true shape that they should have; and because we usually know that the object is quite near when we use them to look at it, it cannot appear as large as it would if we were to imagine it farther away.

There remains but one other means for augmenting the size of images, namely, by causing the rays that come from the diverse points of the object to intersect as far away as possible from the back of the eye; but this is incomparably the most important and the most significant of all. For it is the only means which can be used for inaccessible objects, as well as for accessible ones, and its effect has no limitations; thus we can,

___

[1] *Lunetes à puces.*

by making use of it, increase the size of the images indefinitely. For example, inasmuch as the first of the three liquids that fill the eye causes nearly the same refraction as common water, if we place right against it a tube full of water, such as *EF*,

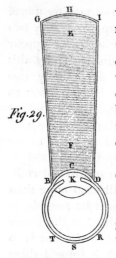

Fig. 29.

at the end of which there is a lens *GHI* whose shape is quite similar to that of the membrane *BCD* which covers the liquid [of the eye], and has the same relation to the distance from the back of the eye, there will be no more refraction at the entrance of that eye; but that which occurred there before (and which was the reason that all the rays coming from the same point of the object began to curve at that place, in order to go to converge in a similar point on the extremities of the optic nerve, and then that all those coming from diverse points intersected there, in order to come back together on the diverse points of this nerve) will occur as early as the entrance to the tube *GI*. Thus the rays, intersecting from there, will form the image *RST* much larger than if they did not intersect until the surface *BCD;* and the longer that tube, the larger the image they will form. And so, since the water *EF* performs the function of the liquid *K*, the lens *GHI* that of the membrane *BCD*, and the entrance to the tube *GI* that of the pupil, sight will take place in the same way as if Nature had made the eye longer than it is by the entire length of this tube. There is nothing else to note, except that the true pupil will be at that time not only useless, but even a nuisance; for because of its smallness, it will exclude the rays which would be able to go toward the sides of the back of the eye, and so will prevent the images from extending there in as much space as they would, if it were not so narrow. Also, I must not neglect to inform you that the particular refractions, which occur slightly differently in the lens *GHI* than in the water *EF*, are not important here;

for since this lens is of equal thickness throughout, if the
first of these surfaces makes the rays curve a bit more than
would that of the water, at the same time the second straightens them out just as much. And it is for that same reason
that, in the foregoing, I have not spoken of refractions which
can occur in the membranes that enclose the liquids of the eye
but only of those of its liquids themselves.

Now, inasmuch as it would be very
inconvenient to join water against the
eye in the manner that I have just explained, and even though since we cannot know precisely what is the shape of
the membrane *BCD* which covers it, we
would not know how to determine exactly that of the lens *GHI*, to substitute
it instead; still, it will be better to make
use of another invention, and by means
of one or of many lenses or other transparent bodies—also enclosed in a tube
but not joined to the eye so exactly that
a little air does not remain between the
two—to bring it about that from the entrance of this tube the rays coming from
a single point of the object bend, or
curve, in the way that is required in
order to make them reconverge in another point, near the place where the
middle of the back of the eye will be
when this tube is placed in front of it.
Then, again, these same rays, in coming

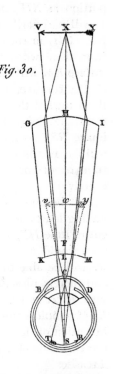

Fig. 3o.

out of this tube, bend and straighten themselves in such a manner that they can enter into the eye the same as if they had
not been bent at all, as if they merely came from some nearer
place. And then, those which will come from various points,
having intersected at the entrance of this tube, do not come
apart at the exit, but go toward the eye in the same way as
if they came from a larger or closer object. Thus, if the tube

HF is filled with a completely solid lens, whose surface *GHI* is of such a shape that it causes all the rays coming from point *X*, once in the lens, to tend toward *S;* and if it causes its other surface *KM* to bend them again in such a way that they tend from there towards the eye in the same way as if they came from the point *x*, which I assume to be so located that the lines *xC* and *CS* have between them the same proportion as *XH* and *HS;* then those which come from point *V* will necessarily intersect the rays from point *x* on the surface *GHI,* in such a way that, since they are already distant from them when they are at the other end of the tube, the surface *KM* will not be able to bring them together, especially if it is concave, as I suppose it to be; instead it will reflect them toward the eye, in nearly the same way as if they came from the point *Y*. By means of this, they will make the image *RST* as much larger as the tube is longer, and there will be no need, in order to determine the shapes of the transparent bodies we will wish to use for this effect, to know exactly the shape of the surface *BCD*.

But, because there would again be some inconvenience in finding lenses or other such bodies sufficiently thick to fill the entire tube *HF*, and sufficiently clear and transparent so that they would not impede the passage of light because of this, we will be able to leave the whole inside of this tube empty, and merely place, at its two ends, two lenses which have the same effect as I have just said that the two surfaces *GHI* and *KLM* should cause. And on this alone is founded the entire invention of these telescopes composed of two lenses placed in the two ends of a tube, which gave me occasion to write this Treatise.

As to the third condition required on the part of the exterior organs for the improvement of sight, that is, that the actions which move each fiber of the optic nerve be neither too strong nor too feeble, Nature has very well provided for this in giving us the power to contract and to dilate the pupils of our eyes. But she has still left something for art to add to it. For, first of all, when the actions of the object are so strong that we cannot contract our pupils enough to bear them, as when we want to look at the sun, it is easy to remedy this by placing against the eye some black body, in which there is only a very narrow hole performing the function of the pupil; or else by looking through a veil, or some other such slightly obscure body, which allows into the eye only as many rays from each part of the object as are needed to move the optic nerve without hurting it. And when, on the contrary, its actions are too feeble to be felt, we can render them stronger, at least when the objects are accessible, by exposing them to the rays of the sun, so gathered with the aid of a mirror or burning glass that they have the greatest possible power to illuminate these bodies without corrupting them.

And besides this, when we use these telescopes of which we have just spoken, inasmuch as they render the pupil useless, and inasmuch as the opening through which they receive the light from outside performs the function of the pupil, it is also this opening which we must dilate or contract, according as we wish to render sight stronger or weaker. And it is to be noted that, if we did not make this opening larger than the pupil, the rays would act less strongly against each part of the back of the eye than if we did not use the telescopes at all; and this would happen in proportion to the size of the images that they formed there, not to mention that which the surfaces of the interposed lenses take away of their power. But we can render the image much larger, the more so as the lens that straightens the rays is situated nearer the point toward which they were made to tend by the lens that bent them. Thus, if the lens *GgHi* makes all the rays coming from the point we wish to look at tend toward *S*, and if they are straightened by the lens *KLM* in such a way that from there they tend in a parallel manner toward the eye, to find the greatest breadth that the opening to the tube can have, it is necessary to make the distance between points *K* and *M* equal to the diameter of the pupil; then, drawing from point *S* two straight lines which pass through *K* and *M*—that is, *SK*, which must be extended to *g*, and *SM*, to *i*—we will have *gi* as the diameter for which we were looking. For it is obvious that, if we were to make it larger, no more rays would enter into the eye from the point toward which we are addressing our sight because of this, and that those which came there in addition from the other places, since they could not assist sight, would only render it more confused. But if, in place of the lens *KLM*, we use the lens *klm* which, because of its shape, must be placed closer to point *S*, we will once more take the distance between points *k* and *m* equal to the diameter of the pupil; then drawing the lines *SkG* and *SmI*, we will have *GI* for the diameter of the opening that we are looking for, which, as you can see, is larger than *gi*, in the same ratio as the line *SL* surpasses *Sl*. And if this line *Sl* is no greater than the diameter of the eye, the vision will be as strong and nearly as clear as if we were not using glasses and the objects were, in compensation, nearer than they are, insofar as they appear larger. Thus, if the length of the tube causes the image of an object at, for example, thirty leagues' distance to be formed as large in the eye, as if it were at a distance of only thirty paces, the width of its entrance, being such as I have just determined it, will make it so that this object is seen as clearly as if, being really only thirty paces away, we were looking at it without glasses. And if we can make this distance between the points *S* and *l* still less, the vision will be still clearer.

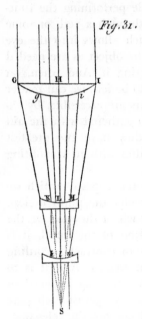

Fig. 31.

But this is used principally only for inaccessible objects, because for those that are accessible, the opening of the tube can be as much the narrower as we bring the objects closer to it, without vision being any less clear because of this. Thus you can see that there enter no fewer rays from point X into the small lens *gi*, than into the large one *GI*. And finally, the opening cannot be larger than the lenses that we apply to it, and because of their shapes these must not exceed a certain magnitude, which I shall determine here-inafter. But if sometimes the light coming from the objects is too strong, it will be easy to weaken it by covering all around the edges of the lens at the entrance to the tube, which is better than placing certain other more cloudy or colored lenses in front of it, as many are accustomed to do to look at the sun; for, the narrower this entrance is, the more distinct vision will be, as has been said above of the pupil. And it is even necessary to ob-

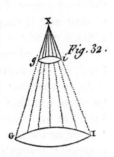

Fig. 32.

serve that it will be better to cover the lens from the outside than from the inside, in order that the reflections which might be caused on the edges of its surface not send any rays toward the eye: for these rays, contributing nothing to vision, could hinder it.

There is only one other condition which is desirable on the part of the exterior organs, which is that they cause us to perceive as many objects as possible at the same time. And it is to be noted that this condition is not in any way requisite for the improvement of seeing *better,* but only for the con-venience of seeing *more;* and it should even be noted that it is impossible to see more than one object distinctly at the same time, so that this convenience, of seeing many others confusedly, at the same time, is principally useful only in order to ascertain toward what direction we must subsequently turn our eyes in order to look at the one among them which we will wish to consider better. And for this, Nature has so provided that it is impossible for art to add anything to it. Indeed, on the contrary: so much as, by means of certain glasses, we increase the magnitude of the lineaments of the image imprinted on the back of the eye, so much do we make the eye represent fewer objects; for the space that the image occupies cannot be increased in any way, unless perhaps by a very small amount through reversing it, which I judge is to be rejected for other reasons. But it is easy, if the objects are accessible, to place the one we wish to look at in the spot where it can be seen most distinctly through the glasses; and if they are inaccessible, to place the telescope on a machine which can be used to turn it easily toward whatever specific place we wish. And so we will lack nothing in fulfilling this fourth condition to be considered.

As to the rest: that I may omit nothing here, I have still to warn you that the faults of the eye, which consist in our inability to change sufficiently the shape of the crystalline humor or the size of the pupil, can bit by bit diminish or be corrected through practice: for since this crystalline humor and the membrane which contains this pupil are true muscles, their functions become easier and greater as we exercise them, just like those of the other muscles of our body. And it is in this way that hunters and sailors train themselves to look at very distant objects, and engravers or other artisans who do very subtle work, to look at very close ones; thus they ordinarily acquire the power of seeing them more distinctly than other men. And it is also in this way that those Indians who are said to be able to gaze fixedly at the sun, without their sight being obscured, must have doubtless beforehand, by often looking at very brilliant objects, trained their pupils little by little to contract more than ours. But these things belong rather to medicine, whose purpose is to remedy the deficiencies of sight through the correction of natural organs, than to Optics, whose purpose is only to minister to the same deficiencies through the application of other organs that are artificial.

Eighth Discourse

Of the Shapes That Transparent Bodies Must Have in Order to Divert Rays Through Refraction in Every Way That Is Useful to Sight

Now, so that later on I can tell you more exactly in what way we must make these artificial organs in order to render them as perfect as they can be, I must explain beforehand what shapes the surfaces of the transparent bodies must have in order to bend and divert rays of light in all the ways that can serve my purpose. If I cannot make myself sufficiently clear and intelligible to everyone on this subject—for it is a slightly difficult matter of Geometry—I will at least try to be clear enough for those who have learned the first elements of that science. And at the outset, in order not to keep them in suspense, I shall say that all the figures of which I shall speak to them here will be composed only of ellipses or of hyperbolas, and of circles or straight lines.

The Ellipse, or the Oval, is a curved line which the mathematicians are in the habit of showing us by cutting through a cone or cylinder, and which I have also seen used sometimes by gardeners in partitioning off their flower beds, where they describe it in a manner which, although it is really very clumsy and inexact, seems to me to render its nature more comprehensible than the section of a cylinder or of a cone. They plant two pickets in the earth—for

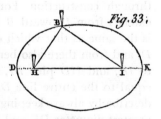

example, the one at point *H*, the other at point *I*—and having tied the two ends of a string together, they put it around them in the way that you see here (*BHI*). Then, placing the end of their finger in this string, they conduct it all around these two pickets, by always pulling it to them with equal tension in order to hold it extended evenly, and so they describe on the ground the curved line *DBK*, which is an ellipse. And if, without changing the length of this cord *BHI*, they merely plant their pickets *H* and *I* slightly closer to one another, they will again describe an ellipse, but of another sort than the preceding one; and if they plant them still closer together, they will describe still another; and finally, if they join them completely together, what they describe will be a circle. Whereas, if they shorten the length of the cord in the same proportion as they shorten the distance between these pickets, they will describe many ellipses which will be of different sizes, but all of the same kind.

And so you can see that there can be an infinity of completely different kinds of them, so that they differ no less from one another than the last differs from the circle; and that, within each kind, there can be all sizes of them; and that if from a point, say *B*, taken at random in some one of these ellipses, we draw two straight lines toward the two points *H* and *I*, where the two pickets must be planted in order to describe it, these two lines *BH* and *BI*, joined together, will be equal to its greatest diameter *DK*, as can easily be proven through construction. For the portion of the string which extends from *I* toward *B* and from there is bent back to *H*, is the same as that which extends from *I* toward *K* or toward *D*, and from there also bends back to *H*: so that *DH* is equal to *IK*, and *HD* plus *DI*, which is equal to *HB* plus *BI*, is equal to the entire line *DK*. And finally, the ellipses that we describe by always keeping the same proportion between their greatest diameter *DK* and the distance from the points *H* and *I*, are all of the same sort. And because of a certain property of these points *H* and *I*, which you will hear of afterwards, we will name them the burning points, the one in-

terior, the other exterior: that is to say, if we relate them
to the half of the ellipse which is toward *D*, *I* will be the
exterior; and if we relate them to the other half which is
toward *K*, it will be the interior; and when we speak without
distinction of the burning point, we will always be understood
to speak of the exterior one. Then besides this, you need to
know that if through point *B* we draw the two straight lines
LBG and *CBE*, which cut each other at right angles, and of
which the one, *LG*, divides
the angle *HBI* in two equal
parts, then the other, *CE*,
will touch that ellipse at
this point *B* without cutting it. I do not furnish a
demonstration of this, because the geometers know
it well enough, and others

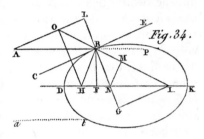

would only be bored to hear it. But what I intend to explain
here particularly is that if we draw again from this point *B*,
away from the ellipse, the straight line *BA* parallel to the greatest diameter *DK*, and if, having made it equal to *BI*, from the
points *A* and *I* we draw on *LG* the two perpendiculars *AL*
and *IG*, these two latter, *AL* and *IG*, will have between them
the same ratio as *DK* and *HI* have. So that, if the line *AB* is
a ray of light, and if this ellipse *DBK* is on the surface of a
completely solid transparent body through which, following
upon what has been said above, the rays pass more easily than
through the air, in the same proportion that the line *DK* is
larger than *HI*, this ray *AB* will be diverted at point *B* by the
surface of the transparent body, so that it will go from there
toward *I*. And because this point *B* is taken at random on the
ellipse, all that is said here of the ray *AB* should be generally
understood of all the rays parallel to the axis *DK*, which fall
on some point of this ellipse; that is, they will all be diverted
in such a way that they will go from there toward point *I*.

Now this is demonstrated as follows: First, if we draw from
point *B* the line *BF* perpendicular to *KD*, and if from point

N, where LG and KD intersect, we also draw the line NM perpendicular to IB, we will find that AL is to IG as BF is to NM. For, on the one hand, the triangles BFN and BLA are similar, because they are both right angled and because, since NF and BA are parallel, the angles FNB and ABL are equal; and on the other hand, the triangles NBM and IBG are also similar, because they are right angled, and because the angle toward B is common to both of them. And besides this, the two triangles BFN and BMN have the same relation between them as do the two ALB and BGI, because as the bases of these, BA and BI, are equal, so BN, which is the base of the triangle BFN, is equal to itself insofar as it is also the base of the triangle BMN. From which it obviously follows that, as BF is to NM, so AL, the side of the triangle ALB which is analogous to BF in the triangle BFN (i.e., which is the base of the same angle), is to IG, the side of the triangle BGI which is analogous to the side NM of the triangle BNM. Then BF is to NM as BI is to NI, because the two triangles BIF and NIM, being right angled and having the same angle at I, are alike. Moreover, because so long as the lines AB and NI, as well as AL and GI, are parallel, the triangles ALB and IGN are similar; therefore it follows that AL is to IG as AB is to NI; or else, because AB and BI are equal, as BI is to NI. Then, if we draw HO parallel to NB and if we lengthen IB to O, we will see that BI is to NI as OI is to HI, because the triangles BNI and OHI are similar. Finally, since the two angles HBG and GBI are equal by construction, HOB, which is equal to GBI, is also equal to OHB, because the latter is equal to HBG; and as a result the triangle HBO is isosceles, and since the line OB is equal to HB, the whole line OI is equal to DK, inasmuch as the two lines HB and IB together are equal to it. And so to review from first to last, AL is to IG as BI is to NI, and BI to NI as OI to HI, and OI is equal to DK; thus AL is to IG as DK is to HI.

Therefore if, in order to trace the ellipse DBK, we give to the lines DK and HI the proportion that we will have discovered through experiment to be that which serves to mea-

sure the refraction of all the rays which pass obliquely from
the air into some glass, or whatever other transparent material we wish to employ, and if we fashion out of this glass a
body with the shape which would be described by this ellipse
if it were moved circularly around the axis *DK*, the rays
which in the air will be parallel to this axis, such as *AB* and
ab, will be diverted upon entering it, in such a way that they
will all go to converge at the burning point *I*, which of the
two burning points *H* and *I* is the farthest removed from the
place from which they come. For you can see that the ray *AB*
must be deflected at point *B* by the curved surface of the
glass, which is represented by the ellipse *DBK*, in the same
way as it would be deflected by the flat surface of the same
glass represented by the straight line *CBE*, in which it must
go from *B* toward *I*, because *AL* and *IG* are to each other as
are *DK* and *HI*, that is, as they must be in order to measure
the refraction. And the point *B* having been taken at random
on the ellipse, all that we have demonstrated of this ray *AB*
must be understood to hold in the same manner for all the
others parallel to *DK*, which fall on the other points of this
ellipse; so that they must all go toward *I*.

Moreover, because all the rays which tend toward the
center of a circle or of a globe, falling perpendicularly on
its surface, should not undergo any refraction there, if from
the center *I* we make a circle to whatever distance we wish,
provided that it passes between *D* and *I*, such as *BQB*, the
lines *DB* and *QB*, revolving around the axis *DQ*, will describe
the shape of a lens which will bring together in the air at
point *I* all the rays which on the other side, also in the air,
were parallel to this axis: and reciprocally this lens will make
it so that all those which came from point *I* will be rendered
parallel on the other side.

And if from the same center *I* we describe the circle *RO*, at
any distance we wish on the other side of the point *D*; and if
having taken the point *B* at random on the ellipse—provided
always that it is not further removed from *D* than from *K*—we
draw the straight line *BO* so that it tends toward *I*; the lines

RO, OB, and *BD,* moved circularly around the axis *DR,* will describe the shape of a lens which will cause the rays that, on the side of the ellipse, were parallel to this axis, to spread

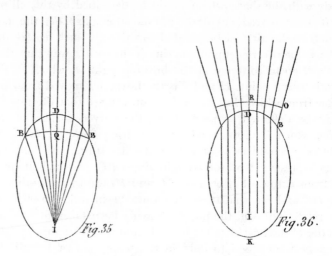

Fig.35   *Fig.36.*

out here and there on the other side, as if they all came from point *I.* For it is manifest that, for example, the ray *PB* [1] must be as much deflected by the hollow surface of the lens *DBA,* as *AB* must be by the convex surface of the lens *DBK,* and as a result that *BO* must be in the same straight line as *BI,* since *PB* is in the same straight line as *BA;* and so with the others.

And if again, in the ellipse *DBK,* we describe another ellipse, smaller but of the same kind, such as *bdk,* whose burning point marked *I* is in the same place as that of the preceding, also marked *I,* and whose other burning point, marked *h,* is in the same straight line and toward the same side as *DH;* and if having taken *B* at random, as aforementioned, we draw the straight line *Bb* tending toward *I,* the lines *DB, Bb, bd,* moved around the axis *Dd,* will describe the shape of a lens which will cause all the rays which before meeting it were parallel, once more to be parallel after coming out

[1] See Fig. 34, p. 129.

of it; and along with this, they will be closer together, and occupy less space on the side of the smaller ellipse *db,* than on that of the larger. And if, in order to avoid the thickness of this lens *DBbd,* we describe from the center *I* the circles *QB* and *ro,* the surfaces *DBQ* and *robd* will represent the shapes and the position of two thinner lenses, which in this matter will have an identical effect.

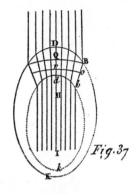

Fig.37

And if we dispose the two lenses *DBQ* and *dbq,* similar but unequal in size, in such a way that their axes are in the same straight line and their two exterior burning points, marked *I,* in the same place; and such, too, that their circular surfaces *BQ, bq* are facing one another, they will also have the same effect in this matter.

And if we join these two lenses *DBQ* and *dbq,* similar but unequal in size, or if we place them at any distance we wish from one another—provided only that their axes be in the same straight line and that their elliptical surfaces face one another—they will cause all the rays coming from the burning point of one, marked *I,* to converge in the other, marked *i.*

And if we join the two different lenses *dbq* and *DBOR,* and join them so that their surfaces *db* and *BD* face each other, they will cause the rays coming from point *i*—which the ellipse of the lens *dbq* has for its burning point—to scatter as if they came from point *I,* which is the burning point of the lens *BDOR;* or reciprocally, they will cause those tending toward this point *I* to converge at the other, marked *i.*

And finally, if we join the two, *dbor* and *DBOR,* still so that their surfaces *db, BD* face each other, we will cause the rays which by passing through one of these lenses, tend beyond toward *I,* to diverge again in coming out of the other, as if they came from the other point *i.* And we can lengthen or shorten the distance from each of these points marked *I, i*

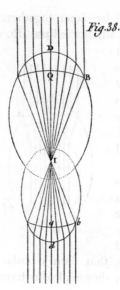

Fig.38.

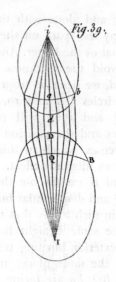

Fig.39.

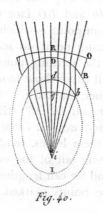

Fig.40.

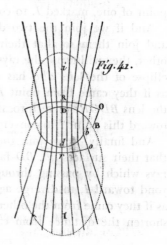

Fig.41.

by as much as we wish, by changing the size of the ellipse on which it depends. So that, with only the ellipse and the circular lines, we can describe lenses which cause the rays that come from one point, or tend toward one point, or are parallel, to change from one to another of these three kinds of dispositions, in every imaginable fashion.

The hyperbola is also a curved line which the mathematicians explain by the section of a cone, as with the ellipse. But

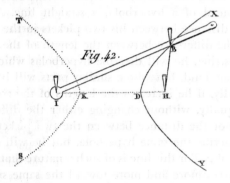

Fig. 42.

in order for you to understand it better, I shall again introduce a gardener who makes use of it to plot the symmetrical embellishment of a certain garden. Once more he plants his two pickets at the points *H* and *I*; and having attached to the end of a long ruler the end of a string which is slightly shorter, he makes a round hole in the other end of this ruler, in which he places the picket *I*, and at the other end of the string, he makes a loop, which he passes around the picket *H*. Then, placing his finger at point *X*, where the two are attached to each other, he runs it from there all the way down to *D*; meanwhile he always keeps the string quite taut, and completely joined to the ruler as if by glue, from point *X* to the place where he is touching it. By this means, forcing this ruler to turn around the picket *I* while he lowers his finger, he describes the curved line *XBD*, which is part of a hyperbola, on the ground. And after this, he describes another part of this hyperbola, *YD*, in the same manner, by turning his ruler in the other direction toward *Y*. And more-over, if he passes the loop of his string around the picket *I,* and the end of his ruler around the picket *H*, he will describe another hyperbola, *SKT*, completely similar to the preceding one, in reverse. But if, without changing his pickets or his ruler, he merely lengthens the string a little, he will describe a hyperbola of another kind; and if he lengthens it yet a little more, he will describe still another kind of hyperbola, until, if he makes it completely equal to the ruler, he will describe, instead of a hyperbola, a straight line. And if he changes the distance between his two pickets in the same pro-portion as the difference between the length of the ruler and that of the string, he will describe hyperbolas which will all be of the same kind, but whose similar parts will be different in size. Finally, if he increases the lengths of the cord and of the ruler equally, without changing either the difference be-tween them or the distance between the two pickets, he will still only describe the same hyperbola, but he will describe a greater part of it. For this line is of such a nature that, although it always curves more and more toward the same side, it can nevertheless extend to infinity without its extremities ever meeting. And so you can see that in several ways this line has the same relation to a straight line, as an ellipse to a

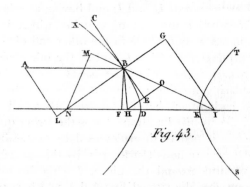

Fig. 43.

circular one; and you can also see that it has an infinity of different kinds, and that in each kind there are an infinity of those whose similar parts are different in size. And in addition, [you can see] that if from a point such as *B*, taken at random in one of them, we draw two straight lines toward the two points, such as *H* and *I*, at which the two pickets must be planted in order to describe it, and which we shall call again the burning points, the difference of these two lines, *HB* and *IB*, will always be equal to the line *DK*, which marks the distance between the opposing hyperbolas. This happens because *BI* is longer than *BH*, to the same extent that the ruler has been measured to be longer than the string, and also because *DI* is that much longer than *DH*. For, if we were to shorten this one, *DI*, by [the length of] *KI*, which is equal to *DH*, we would have *DK* as their difference. And finally, you can see that the hyperbolas that we describe by always keeping the same proportion between *KD* and *HI* are all of the same sort. Then, besides this, you must know that if through point *B*, taken at random in a hyperbola, we draw the straight line *CE*, which divides the angle *HBI* in two equal parts, this same CE will touch this hyperbole in this point *B*, without intersecting it; the geometers know the demonstration of this sufficiently well.

But hereinafter I wish to show you that if from this same point *B* we draw the straight line *BA* toward the inside of the hyperbola and parallel to *DK*, and if we also draw through the same point *B* the line *LG* which cuts *CE* at right angles, then, having taken *BA* as equal to *BI*, if there are drawn on *LG*, from the points *A* and *I*, the two perpendiculars *AL* and *IG*, the two latter, *AL* and *IG*, will have between them the same proportion as the two lines *DK* and *HI*. And then, if we give the shape of this hyperbola to a body of glass in which the refractions are measured by the ratio between the lines *DK* and *HI*, this hyperbola will cause all the rays parallel to its axis in this lens to converge outside at the point *I*, at least if this lens is convex; and if it is concave, it will cause them to diverge here and there, as if they came from that point *I*.

This can be demonstrated as follows: First of all, if we draw from the point B the line BF perpendicular to KD (extended as much as is necessary), and from the point N, where LG and KD intersect, the line NM perpendicular to IB (also prolonged), we will find that AL is to IG as BF is to NM. For on the one hand, the triangles BFN and BLA are similar because they are both right angled and because, since NF and BA are parallel, the angles FNB and LBA are equal. And, on the other hand, the triangles IGB and NMB are also similar, because they are right angled, and because the angles IBG and NBM are equal. And also, besides this, since the same BN serves as the base of the two triangles BFN and NMB, then BA, the base of the triangle ALB, is equal to BI, the base of the triangle IGB; from which it follows that the sides of the triangle BFN are to those of the triangle NMB as those of the triangle ALB are to those of the triangle IBG. And BF is to NM as BI is to NI, because the two triangles BIF and NIM, being right angled and having the same angle at I, are similar. Then, if we draw HO parallel to LG, we will see that BI is to NI as OI is to HI, because the triangles BNI and OHI are similar. Finally, since the two angles EBH and EBI are equal by construction, and since HO, which is parallel to LG, cuts the line CE at right angles, the two triangles BEH and BEO are entirely equal. And so, since BH, the base of the one, is equal to BO, the base of the other, there remains OI as the difference between BH and BI, and we have said that this difference is equal to DK. So that AL is to IG as DK is to HI. From whence it follows that, always keeping between the lines DK and HI the proportion which can be used to measure the refractions from the glass or other matter that we wish to employ—as we did in order to trace the ellipses, except that here DK can only be the shortest, whereas hitherto-fore it could only be the longest—if we trace a portion of the hyperbola as large as we wish, such as DB, and if from B we extend downward, at right angles to KD, the straight line BQ, then the two lines DB and QB, revolving around the axis DQ, will describe the shape of a lens which will cause all the rays passing through it, and will be parallel to this axis in the air on the side of the flat surface *BD* (in which, as you know, they will not undergo any refraction), to assemble on the other side at point *I*.

And if, having traced the hyperbola *db* similar to the preceding one, we draw the straight line *ro* in any place we wish—provided that, without cutting this hyperbola, it falls perpendicular to its axis *dk*—and if we join the two points *b* and *o* by another straight line parallel to *dk*, the three lines *ro*, *ob*, and *bd*, moved around the axis *dk*, will describe the shape of a lens which will cause all the rays parallel to its axis on the side of its flat surface to diverge here and there on the other side, as if they came from the point *I*.

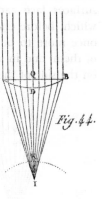

Fig. 44.

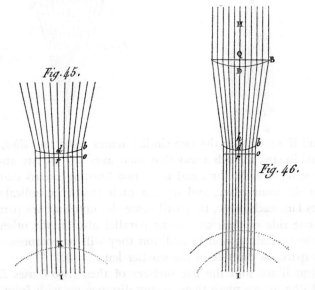

And if, having made the line *hI* shorter for tracing the hyperbola of the lens *robd* than for that of the lens *DBQ*, we dispose these two lenses in such a manner that their axes DQ, rd are in the same straight line, and their two burning points marked I in the same place, and so that their two hyperbolical surfaces face each other, then they will cause all the rays which, before encountering them, were parallel to their axes, once more to be parallel after having gone through the two of them; and in addition, they will be compressed in less space on the side of the lens $robd$ than on the other side.

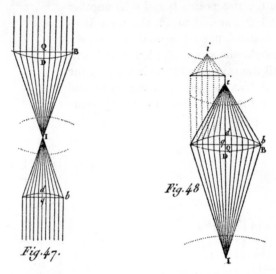

Fig.47.

Fig.48

And if we dispose the two similar lenses DBQ and dbq, un-equal in size, in such a way that their axes DQ, dq are also in the same straight line, and their two burning points marked I in the same place, and so that their two hyperbolical sur-faces face each other, they will cause the rays that are parallel on one side of their axis to be parallel also on the other, as in the preceding; and in addition they will be compressed in less space on the side of the smaller lens.

And if we join the flat surfaces of these two lenses DBQ and dbq, or we place them at any distance we wish from one another, provided only that their flat surfaces face each other (without its being necessary, in addition, for their axes to be in the same straight line)—or better, if we make another lens which has the shape of these two so conjoined—we will thereby cause the rays coming from one of the points marked *I* to converge at the other, on the other side.

And if we compose one lens having the shape of the two *DBQ* and *robd*, joined so that their flat surfaces touch one another, we will cause the rays which came from one of the points marked *I* to spread out as if they had come from the other.

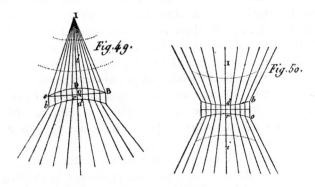

And finally, if we compose one lens having the shape of two lenses like *robd*, again so joined that their flat surfaces touch each other, we will cause the rays which, when going to meet this lens, are separated as if to converge at point *I* on the other side, to be again separated after passing through it, as if they had come from the other point *i*.

And all this is, it seems to me, so clear that one need only open one's eyes and consider the diagrams, to understand it.

Moreover, the same changes in these rays, which I have just explained first by two elliptical lenses and then by two hyperbolical ones, can also be caused by two lenses, one of which is elliptical and the other hyperbolical. And furthermore, we can still imagine an infinity of other lenses which, like the above-mentioned, cause all the rays which come from a certain point, or tend toward a point, or are parallel, to be exactly changed from one of these three dispositions to another. But

I do not think I need to speak of them here, because I shall be able to explain them afterwards more conveniently in the *Geometry,* and because those that I have described are the most appropriate of all for my purpose, as I shall now try to prove, and by the same means to make you see which among them are the most appropriate by having you consider all the principal ways in which they differ.

The first is that the shapes of some are much easier to trace than those of others; and it is certain that after the straight line, the circular line, and the parabola—which alone cannot suffice for tracing any of these lenses, as everyone can easily see if they examine it—there are none simpler than the ellipse and the hyperbola. So that, since the straight line is easier to trace than the circular, and the hyperbola no less easy than the ellipse, those lenses whose shapes are composed of hyperbolas and straight lines are the easiest possible to cut, and next those whose shapes are composed of ellipses and circles; so that all the others, which I have not explained, are less easy.

The second [way in which they differ] is that among many lenses which all cause the same sort of change in the disposition of the rays that relate to a certain point, or come from a single side as parallel, those whose surfaces are the least curved, or else the least unevenly curved, so that they cause the least uneven refractions, always change the disposition of the rays that relate to other points, or come from other directions, a bit more exactly. But, in order to understand this perfectly, it is necessary to consider that it is only the uneven curvature of the lines composing the shapes of the lenses which prevents them from changing the disposition of the rays which have reference to many different points, or come parallel from many different directions, as exactly as they change that of those which relate to a single point, or come parallel from a single direction. If, for example, in order to make all the rays coming from point *A* converge at point *B*, it were necessary for the lens *GHIK*, which we would place between them, to have its surfaces completely flat—such that

the straight line *GH*, representing one surface, would have the
property of causing all those rays coming from point *A* to become parallel in the lens, and by the
same means, such that the other straight
line *KI* causes them to go from there to
converge at point *B*—these same lines *GH*
and *KI* would also cause all the rays
coming from point *C* to converge at point
D; and generally, all those rays coming
from any one point on the straight line
AC, which I assume to be parallel to
GH, would converge at some one point

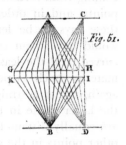

Fig. 51.

of *BD*, which I also assume to be parallel to *KI*, and as far
away from it as *AC* is from *GH;* for, since these lines *GH* and
KI are not curved at all, every point of the other lines *AC* and
BD relates to these lines in the same way as every other point.

Nevertheless, if it were the lens *LMNO*, whose surfaces
LMN and *LON* I assume to be two equal portions of a
sphere, which had the property of causing
all the rays coming from point *A* to converge at point *B*, it would also have that
of causing those coming from point *C* to
converge at point *D*, and generally, [of
bringing it about] that all those from some
one of the points of the surface *CA*, which
I asume to be a portion of a sphere having
the same center as *LMN*, would converge
at some one of the points of *BD*, which I

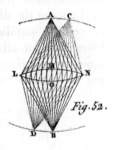

Fig. 52.

assume also to be a portion of a sphere having the same center
as *LON* and as far removed from it as *AC* is from *LMN;* for all
the parts of these surfaces *LMN* and *LON* are equally curved
with respect to all the points on the surfaces *CA* and *BD*. But,
because there are no other lines in nature except the
straight and the circular, of which all the parts relate in
the same way to many diverse points, and because neither the
one nor the other alone can suffice for composing the shape
of a lens that would cause all rays coming from one point

to assemble exactly at another point, it is evident that no one of those lines which are required for it will cause all the rays coming from certain other points to converge exactly in other points; and in order to choose those lines which can cause these rays to be least scattered from the places where we would have them converge, it is necessary to take the least curved, and the least unevenly curved, so that they approximate as much as possible a straight or a circular line; and again, rather a straight than a circular line, for the parts of the latter relate in the same way only to all the points that are equally distant from its center, and do not relate to any other points in the same way as they do to this center. From which it is easy to conclude that in this matter the hyperbola surpasses the ellipse, and that it is impossible to imagine lenses of any other shape which reconverge all the rays coming from diverse points in as many other points equidistant from them, as exactly as that whose shape is composed of hyperbolas. And without my stopping to give you a more exact demonstration, you can even easily apply this to the other ways of changing the disposition of rays relating to different points or coming parallel from different directions, and you can know that for all of them, either the hyperbolical lenses are more appropriate than any others, or, at least, they are not so notably less appropriate, that this cannot be counter-

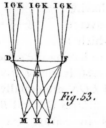

Fig. 53.

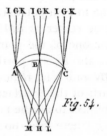

Fig. 54.

balanced with the facility of being cut, in which they surpass all the others.

The third difference of these lenses is that some cause the

rays which cross while going through them to be slightly more scattered on one side than on the other, and others do just the opposite. Thus if the rays G, G are those which come from the center of the sun, and if I, I are those which come from the left side of its circumference, and K, K those which come from the right, some of these rays diverge a little more from one another after they have gone through the hyperbolical lens DEF than they did before, and on the other hand, they diverge less after having gone through the elliptical lens ABC; so that this ellipse brings points L, H, M nearer to each other than does the hyperbola, and it brings them even closer in proportion as it is thicker. But nevertheless, however thick we make it, it cannot bring them more than around a quarter or a third nearer together than does the hyperbolical lens. This is measured by the quantity of the refractions which the lens causes, so that rock crystal, in which the refractions are slightly larger, must render this inequality slightly greater. But there is no lens of any other shape that we can imagine which causes the points L, H, M to be notably more distant than does the hyperbolical lens, nor less distant than does the elliptical.

Now you have the opportunity to note here in what sense you must understand what I have said above: that the rays coming from different points, or coming parallel from different directions, all cross one another as early as the first surface which has the power to cause them to reconverge, more or less, in as many other different points, as when I said that those of the object VXY,[2] which form the image RST on the base of the eye, cross as early as the first of its surfaces BCD. This depends on the fact that, for example, the three rays VCR, XCS, and YCT actually cross on this surface BCD at point C, from which it follows that although VDR crosses with YBT much higher up, and BVR with YDT much lower down, nevertheless, because they tend toward the same points as VCR and YCT, we can nevertheless consider all of them as if they also crossed in the same place. And because it is

2 See Fig. 14, p. 92.

this surface *BCD* which causes them thus to tend toward the same points, we must think that they all cross where *BCD* is, rather than either higher or lower. And even the other surfaces capable of changing their direction, such as *123* and

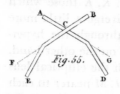

Fig. 55.

456, do not keep them from crossing there; any more than the bent sticks *ACD* and *BCE* are prevented from crossing at point *C,* even though they are considerably separated from the points *F* and *G* toward which they would have gone if, being crossed as they are at point *C,* they were also straight. But they could well be so bent as to make them cross again in another place. And, in the same way, the rays which go through the two convex lenses *DBQ* and *dbq* [3] cross on the surface of the first, then recross on that of the other; at least those which come from different directions do so, for, as to those which come from a single direction, it is manifest that it is only at the burning point marked *I* that they cross.

Also, from time to time, you may note that the rays of the sun gathered by the elliptical lens *ABC* [4] must burn with more force than [when they are] gathered by the hyperbolical lens *DEF.*[5] For it is not only necessary to be careful of the rays which come from the center of the sun, such as *G, G,* but also of all those others which, coming from other points of its surface, are not noticeably less in force than those from the center: so that the violence of the heat that they can cause must be gauged according to the size of the body that converges them, compared with the size of the space where they are converged. Thus, if the diameter of the lens *ABC* [6] is four times as great as the distance between the points *M* and *L,* the rays gathered by this lens must have sixteen times more force than if they had merely passed through a flat lens which did not change their direction in any way. And because the

[3] See Fig. 47, p. 140.
[4] See Fig. 54, p. 144.
[5] See Fig. 53, p. 144.
[6] See Fig. 54.

distance between these points M and L is greater or lesser in proportion to the distance between them and the lens ABC, or some other such body which makes the rays converge there —without the diameter of this body, nor its particular shape, being able to augment it by more than approximately a quarter or a third at the most—it is certain that that line burning to infinity, as some have imagined, is nothing but a delusion. And if we have two lenses or magnifying glasses, one of which is much larger than the other (in whatever way they can be, provided that their shapes are entirely the same), the greater must gather the rays of the sun in a greater space and farther away from itself than does the smaller; but these rays cannot have more force in each part of this space than in that where the smaller gathers them. So that we can make extremely small lenses or glasses which will burn with as much violence as the largest ones. And if the diameter of a magnifying glass is no greater than about a hundredth part of the distance between it and the place where it must reassemble the rays of the sun—that is, [the diameter] has the same proportion to this distance as the diameter of the sun has to that which is beween it and us—be it polished by an angel, it cannot make the rays that it converges burn more in the spot where they are converged than those which come directly from the sun; which also must be understood in relation to burning glasses. From this you can see that those who are only half informed in Optics allow themselves to be persuaded of many things which are impossible, and that those mirrors with which, it is said, Archimedes burned far-off ships must have been extremely large—or rather, they are fabulous.

The fourth difference which must be noted among the lenses here in question pertains particularly to those which change the disposition of the rays coming from some point rather close to them, and consists in this: that some of them, that is, those of which the surface facing toward this point is the more concave, by reason of their size, can receive a greater quantity of these rays than the others, although their diameter is no greater. And in this the elliptical lens NOP, which I assume to be so large that its extremities N and P are the points where the smallest diameter of the ellipse terminates, surpasses the hyperbolical lens QRS, however large we may wish to assume it to be; and it cannot be surpassed by lenses of any other shape. Finally, these lenses again differ in this: that in order to produce the same effects with regard to the rays relating to a single point or a single direction, some must be more in number than others, or must make the rays which relate to different points or to different directions cross more often. Thus you have seen that, in order to make the rays coming from one point converge in another point, by means of elliptical lenses, or make them diverge as if they came from another point, or to cause those which tend toward one point to diverge once more as if they came from another point, it is always necessary to employ two [elliptical] lenses there, whereas, if we use hyperbolical lenses, it is only necessary to employ one; and we can cause parallel rays, remaining parallel, to occupy less space than beforehand, by means of two hyperbolical convex lenses which cause the rays coming from different directions to cross twice, as well as by means of one convex and one concave lens, which cause them to cross only once. But obviously we should never use many lenses for what can be accomplished as well with the aid of a single one, nor make the rays cross many times when once will suffice.

And generally, we must conclude from all this that the hyperbolical and elliptical lenses are preferable to all the others which can be imagined, and even that the hyperbolical are in almost everything preferable to the elliptical. Following which, I shall now say in what way it seems to me we must compose each sort of telescope, in order to make them as perfect as is possible.

Ninth Discourse

The Description of Telescopes

First it is necessary to choose a transparent material, which, being tolerably easy to cut, is nonetheless hard enough to retain the form that we shall give it; in addition, it must have the least color and cause the least reflection possible. And we have not yet found anything which has these qualities to greater perfection than glass, when it is very clear and very pure, and made from very fine ashes. For, although rock crystal seems cleaner and more transparent, nevertheless, because its surfaces cause the reflection of more rays than those of glass, as experiment seems to teach us, it will not perhaps be so appropriate for our purpose. Thus, in order for you to know the cause of this reflection, and why it occurs on the surfaces of both glass and of crystal rather than in the density of their bodies, and why it is greater in crystal than in glass, you must recall the method by which I made you conceive the nature of light above, when I said that it was nothing else, in transparent bodies, than the action or inclination to move of a certain very subtle matter which fills their pores. You should also consider that the pores of each of these transparent bodies are so uniform and so straight that the subtle matter which can enter there flows easily all along them, without finding anything to stop it there; but that those of two transparent bodies of different nature, such as those of air and those of glass or crystal, are never so exactly related to each other that there are not always many of the parts of the subtle matter—coming, for example, from the air toward the glass—which are reflected there because they encounter the solid parts of its surface; and in the same way, coming from the glass toward the air, they are reflected and return to the inside of this glass, because they encounter the solid parts of the surface of this air (for there are also many parts in the air which can be called solid by comparison with this subtle matter). Then, by considering that the solid parts of the crystal are larger yet than those of glass, and its pores narrower, as it is easy to judge from the fact that it is harder and heavier, we can easily see that it must cause still stronger reflections, and as a result give passage to fewer rays than either air or glass; although at the same time it gives passage more freely to those to which it does give passage, in consequence of what has been said above.

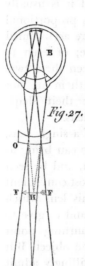

Fig. 27.

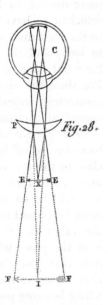

Fig. 28.

Having accordingly thus chosen the glass which is the purest and the least colored, and which causes the least possible reflection, if we wish by means of it to correct the defect of those who cannot see objects at some distance as well as close ones, or the close as well as the distant, the most appropriate shapes for this effect are those which are traced by hyperbolas. For example, if the eye *B* or *C* is disposed to cause all the rays coming from point *H* or *I* to converge exactly in the center of its base, and not those from point *V* or *X*, in order to make it see the object near *V* or *X* distinctly, it is necessary to place the lens *O* or *P* between the two, whose surfaces, the one convex and the other concave, have the shapes traced by two hyperbolas which are such that *H* or *I* is the burning point of the concave surface, which must be turned toward the eye, and *V* or *X* that of the convex.

And if we assume the point *I* or *V* to be sufficiently re-

moved, as only fifteen or twenty feet distant, instead of the
hyperbola of which it ought to be the burning point, it will
suffice to use a straight line, and so to make one of the surfaces of the lens completely flat; i.e., the interior surface
facing toward the eye, if it is *I* which is somewhat removed,
or the exterior, if it is *V*. For then one part of the object, the
size of the pupil, will be able to occupy the space of a single
point, because its image will occupy hardly more space on
the base of the eye than the extremity of one of the small
fibers of the optic nerve. And it is not even necessary to use
different lenses each time we wish to look at objects slightly
more distant, or less, than one another; instead it is usually
sufficient to have two of them, one of which is proportional
to the least distance of the things at which we are accustomed
to look, and the other to the greatest distance; or even to
have only one of them, which is a mean between these two.
For since the eyes to which we wish to adapt them are not
completely inflexible, they can easily change their shape
enough to accommodate it to that of one such lens.

So that if we wish, also through the means of a single lens,
to make accessible objects—that is, those that we can bring as
close to the eye as we want—appear much larger, and be seen
much more distinctly than without glasses, the most convenient
way will be to make that of the surfaces of this lens which
must be turned toward the eye completely flat, and to give to
the other the shape of a hyperbola, whose burning point
is at the place where we shall wish to place the object. But
note that I say "the most convenient"; for I willingly admit
that, giving to the surface of this lens the shape of an ellipse
whose burning point is also in the place where we wish to put
the object, and to the other the shape of a part of a sphere,
whose center is at the same place as the burning point, their
effect will be slightly greater; but on the other hand such a lens
cannot be so easily cut.

Thus this burning point, either of the hyperbola or of the
ellipse, must be so close that when the object, which we must
suppose to be very small, is placed there, there is nothing be-

tween it and the lens except exactly as much space as is necessary to give passage to the light which must illuminate it.
And it is necessary to encase this lens in such a way that
none of it remains uncovered except the middle, which is
about the same size as the pupil, or even a bit smaller; and
the material in which it will be encased must be completely
black on the side which has to be turned toward the eye,
where it would even be useful that it be trimmed all around
with a border of black plush or velvet, in order that we can
easily apply it against the eye, and thus stop any light from
going toward the eye, except through the opening of the
lens. But on the outside it will be good for it to be very white,
or rather very highly polished, and for it to have the shape of
a hollow mirror, so that it reflects upon the object all
the rays of light coming toward it. And in order to sustain
this object in the place where it must be in order to be seen,
I do not disapprove of these little cylinders of glass or of
very transparent crystal, whose use is already
fairly common in France; but, to render the
thing more exact, it would be still better if it
were held firm by one or two small springs in
the form of arms, which protrude from the
case of the telescope. Finally, in order not to
lose any light, it will be necessary while looking at this object to turn it straight toward
the sun. Thus if *A* is the lens, *C* the interior
part of the material in which it is encased, *D*
the exterior, *E* the object, *G* the little arm
which holds it, *H* the eye, and *I* the sun,

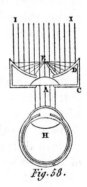

Fig. 58.

whose rays do not go directly into the eye (because the telescope, as well as the object, are interposed), but falling against
the white body or mirror *D*, they are reflected toward the
eye.

So that, if we wish to make the most perfect possible telescope for observing the planets or other very distant and inaccessible objects, we must compose it of two hyperbolical
lenses, the one convex and the other concave, placed in the

two ends of a tube in the way that you see represented here.
And first of all, *abc,* the surface of the concave lens *abcdef,*
must have the shape of a hyperbola whose burning point is

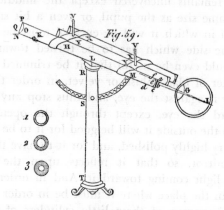

Fig. 69.

at whatever distance at which the eye for which we are preparing this telescope can see its objects most distinctly. Here,
then, since the eye *G* is disposed to see objects near *H* more
distinctly than any others, *H* must be the burning point of
the hyperbola *abc;* and for the aged, who see distant objects
better than close ones, this surface *abc* must be completely
flat; whereas for those who have short sight, it must be somewhat concave. Then the other surface, *def,* must have the
shape of another hyperbola, whose burning point *I* is about
an inch distant from it, so that it is located toward the base
of the eye when this lens is applied immediately against its
surface. Note, nevertheless, that these proportions are not so
absolutely necessary that they cannot be greatly changed;
thus, without cutting the surface *abc* otherwise for those who
have short or long sight than for the others, we can adequately
enough use the same telescope for all kinds of eyes, merely by
elongating or shortening the tube. And as to the surface
def, perhaps—because of the difficulty that we will have in
hollowing it as I said—it will be easier to give it the shape of
a hyperbola whose burning point is a bit further removed:

experiment will teach this better than my explanations. And then I can only say in general that, other things being equal, to the extent that this point *I* is nearer, the objects will appear larger, because it will be necessary to dispose the eye as if they were nearer to it; and vision will be able to be stronger and clearer, because the other lens will be larger, but it will not be so distinct, if we make [the burning point] too near, because there will be many rays which will fall too obliquely on its surface at the price of the others. As to the size of this lens, the portion of it that remains uncovered when it is encased in the tube *KLM* need not exceed by more than a small amount the greatest opening of the pupil. And as to its thickness, it should be as thin as possible; for although by increasing the thickness we can make the image of the objects slightly larger (since the rays coming from diverse points are slightly more spread out on the side of the eye), on the other hand we also make them appear in less quantity, and less clearly; and the advantage of enlarging their images can be better gained by other means. As for the convex lens *NOPQ*, its surface *NQP*, which is turned toward the objects, must be completely flat; and the other, *NOP*, must have the shape of a hyperbola whose burning point *I* falls exactly in the same place as that of the other lens' hyperbola *def*; and, the more perfect we wish the telescope to be, the further [the burning point] will be from point *O*. Consequently the size of its diameter *NP* is determined by the two straight lines *IdN* and *IfP*, drawn from the burning point *I* through *d* and *f*, the edges of the diameter of the hyperbolical lens *def*, which I assume equal to [the diameter] of the pupil. Here, however, it is necessary to remark that even if the diameter of this lens *NOPQ* is smaller, the objects will only appear more distinct thereby, and none of them will appear smaller because of this, nor in less quantity, but only less illuminated. This is why when they are too much illuminated, we must have various circles of black pasteboard or some other such material, such as *1, 2, 3*, in order to cover the edges [of the lens] and to render it by this means as small as the force of the light coming from the objects can permit. As to the thickness of this lens, it can neither benefit nor harm anything, except that the lens can never be so pure or so clean that it does not prevent the passage of a few more rays than does the air. As to the tube *KLM*, it must be of some material that is firm and solid enough that the two lenses encased in its two ends always retain their exact positions there. And it must be completely black on the inside, and even have a border of black plush or velvet near *M*, so that by applying it right against the eye, we can stop any light from entering there except what comes through the lens *NOPQ*. And as to its length and width, they are sufficiently determined by the distance and size of the two lenses.

Moreover, it is necessary that this tube be mounted on some machine, such as *RST*, by means of which it can be conveniently turned in all directions, and stopped facing the object at which we want to look. And to this end, there must also be a sight or two pinnules, such as *V, V*, on this machine; and—since, as these telescopes make objects appear larger, they let us see less of them at one glance—it is even necessary, besides this, to join the most perfect telescopes to some others of less strength, through the aid of which we can, as if by degrees, come to know the location of the object that these more perfect ones can make us perceive; such are *XX* and *YY* here, which I assume to be so united with the most perfect, *QLM*, that if we turn the machine in such a way that, for example, the planet Jupiter appears through the two pinnules *V, V*, it will also appear through the telescope *XX*, through which, besides Jupiter, we will also be able to distinguish those other lesser planets which accompany it. And if we cause some one of these lesser planets to appear exactly in the middle of this telescope *XX*, it will also be seen through the other, *YY*, where, since it appears alone and much larger than through the former, we will be able to distinguish different regions.

And again, among these different regions, the middle one will be seen through the telescope *KLM*, and we will be able to distinguish many particular things there by means of it; but we could not know that these things were in one certain location of one certain planet accompanying Jupiter, without the aid of the two others, nor also could we dispose it to show that which is in any other determined place toward which we wish to look.

We can still add one or several more perfect telescopes to these three, at least if the artifice of men can go this far. And there is no difference between the method of [making] the more perfect ones, and those that are less perfect, except that the convex lens of the former ones must be larger, and their burning point farther removed. So that, if the hand of the workers does not fail us, we will be able through this invention to see objects as particular and as small among the stars, as those that we commonly see on the earth.

Finally, if we wish to have a telescope which allows us to see close and accessible objects as distinctly as possible (much

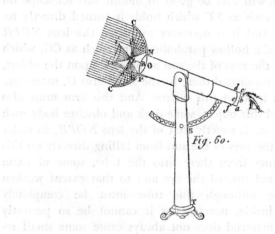

Fig. 60.

more so than the one that I have presently described for the same purpose), we must also compose it of two hyperbolical lenses, one concave and the other convex, enclosed in the two ends of a tube; the concave, *abcdef,* should be exactly similar to that of the preceding, as also should *NOP,* the in-

terior surface of the convex one. But, as to the exterior surface NRP, instead of being completely flat, it must here be
quite convex and have the shape of a hyperbola whose exterior burning point Z is so close that, when the object is
placed there, there is only as much space between it and the
lens as is necessary to give passage to the light which must
illuminate it. And the diameter of this lens does not need to
be as great as for the preceding telescope, nor again must it
be as small as that of the lens A of the other of which I spoke
earlier; [1] but it must be more or less such that the straight
line NP can pass through the interior burning point of the
hyperbola NRP. For if less, it would receive fewer of the rays
from the object Z, and if greater, it would only receive a very
few more of them; so that, since its thickness would have to
be proportionately much more increased than before, it would
take away from them as much of their force as its magnitude
would give them, and besides this, the object could not be as
well lighted. It will also be good to mount this telescope on
some machine such as ST which holds it turned directly toward the sun. And it is necessary to encase the lens NOPR
in the middle of a hollow parabolic mirror such as CC, which
reconverges all the rays of the sun at point Z upon the object,
which must be supported there by the small arm G, extending
from a certain spot on this mirror. And this arm must also
support, around this object, some dark and obscure body such
as HH, whose size is exactly that of the lens NOPR, in order
to stop any of the rays of the sun from falling directly on this
lens; for entering from there into the tube, some of them
could be reflected toward the eye and to that extent weaken
vision, because although this tube must be completely
black on the inside, nevertheless it cannot be so perfectly
black that its material does not always cause some small reflection when the light is very strong, as is that of the sun.
Besides this, this black body HH must have a hole in the
middle, marked Z, which is of the size of the object, in order
that, if this object is in some way transparent, it can also be

[1] See Fig. 58, p. 153.

lighted by the rays which come directly from the sun; or even yet, if necessary, by the rays focused at point Z by a burning glass such as II, of the size of the lens NOPR, so that there comes from all directions as much light on the object as it can stand without thereby being consumed. And it will be easy to cover a part of this mirror CC, or this lens II, in order to stop too much light from coming there. You can well see why I have taken so much trouble here to see that the object is well lighted, and that many of its rays come toward the eye; for since the lens NOPR—which in this telescope plays the part of the pupil, and in which these rays coming from diverse points intersect—is much closer to the object than to the eye, it causes them to extend on the extremities of the optic nerve, in a space that is much larger than the surface of the object from which they come. And you know that the more they are extended, the weaker they must be; as we see that, on the contrary, when they are reassembled in a smaller space by a mirror or burning glass, they have more force. And it is on this that the length of this telescope depends, that is, the distance which must be between the hyperbola NOP and its burning point. Because, the longer it is, the more extended is the object's image on the base of the eye, which causes all of its small parts to be more distinct there. But this itself also weakens their action so much that finally it could not be perceived, if this telescope were excessively long. So that its greatest length can only be determined through experiment, and it even varies according as the objects can receive more or less light without its consuming them. I am well aware that we could still add certain other means for making this light stronger; but aside from the fact that they would be more difficult to put in practice, we could hardly find objects which could stand more light. We might also well be able, in place of the hyperbolical lens NOPR, to find others which would receive some slightly greater quantity of rays; but either they would not cause these rays, coming from different points of the object, to converge as exactly toward the eye in as many other different points; or it would be necessary to use two lenses in the place of one, so that the strength of these rays would be no less diminished by these lenses' multitude of surfaces, as it would be increased by their shapes; and finally the execution of them would be much more difficult. I only wish to warn you again that, since these lenses are to be applied to only a single eye, it will be better to bandage the other, or to cover it with some very dark mask so that its pupil remains as open as possible, than to leave it exposed to the light, or to close it by the help of the muscles which move its lids. For there is ordinarily such a connection between the two eyes that the one can hardly be moved in any way, without the other being disposed to imitate it. Moreover it will not be useless, not only to apply this telescope right against the eye so that no light can come toward it except through there, but also to have previously sensitized its sight by staying in a dark place, and to have disposed the imagination so as to look at things which are far removed and very obscure; in this way the pupil may be opened so much the more, and thus we can see an object as so much the larger. For you know that this action of the pupil does not follow immediately from our willing to open it, but rather from the idea or the feeling that we have of the obscurity and distance of the things at which we are looking.

Moreover, if you reflect a little on everything that has been said above, and particularly on what we have required on the part of the exterior organs in order to make vision as perfect as it can be, it will not be difficult for you to understand that, through these diverse kinds of telescopes, we are adding to vision all that art can add, without it being necessary for me to stop and deduce the proof for you at greater length. Nor will it be difficult for you to recognize that all those [telescopes] which we have had up until now could not have been in the least perfect, seeing that there is a very great difference between the circular line and the hyperbola, and that in making them people have only attempted to use the former, for effects which, as I have demonstrated, require the latter. So that they have never been able to hit upon perfection, except when they failed so happily that, intending to make the surfaces of the lenses they cut spherical, they made them hyperbolical or some other equivalent shape. And this is principally what has stopped us from being able to make telescopes which can be used to see inaccessible objects well; for their convex lens must be larger than that of the others, and aside from the fact that it is hard to find much difference between the hyperbolical and the spherical shape, this difference is much more apparent toward the extremities of the lens than toward its center. But, because the artisans will perhaps judge that there is a great deal of difficulty in cutting lenses exactly according to this hyperbolical shape, I shall again try to give them an invention here, by means of which I am persuaded that they will be able to master this difficulty conveniently.

Tenth Discourse

Of the Method of Cutting Lenses

After having chosen the glass or crystal with which we intend to work, it is first necessary to look for the proportion
which, in accordance with what was said above, is used to
measure its refractions. And we will be able to find it conveniently through the aid of an instrument such as this: *EFI*

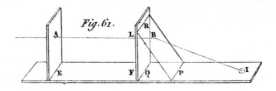

Fig. 61.

is a completely flat and completely straight plank or ruler,
and is made of whatever material we may wish, provided that
it is neither too shiny nor transparent, in order that the light
falling on it can easily be distinguished from the shadow
there. *EA* and *FL* are two sights, that is, two small plates—
also of whatever material we may wish, provided it is not
transparent—raised at right angles on *EFI,* and in which there
are two small round holes, *A* and *L,* placed exactly opposite
each other, so that the ray *AL,* passing through them, is parallel to the line *EF.* Then *RPQ* is a piece of glass that you wish
to test, cut in the form of a triangle of which *RQP* is a right
angle, and *PRQ* is more acute than *RPQ.* The three sides,
RQ, QP, and *RP,* are three completely flat and polished
faces, so that if the face *QP* is applied against the plank *EFI,*
and the other face *QR* against the sight *FL,* the ray of sunlight passing through the two holes *A* and *L* penetrates right
to *B* through the glass *PQR* without undergoing any refrac-

tion there, because it meets the surface *RQ* perpendicularly. But, having arrived at point *B*, where it encounters the other surface *RP* obliquely, the ray cannot leave it without being bent toward some point on the plank *EF*, as for example toward *I*. And the entire use of this instrument consists only in thus making the ray of sunlight pass through these holes *A* and *L*, in order to know, by this means, the relation which the point *I* (that is, the center of the small oval of light that this ray describes on the plank *EFI*), has with the two other points *B* and *P*, which are: *B*, where the straight line passing through the centers of these two holes *A* and *L* terminates on the surface *RP;* and *P*, where this surface *RP* and that of the plank *EFI* are cut by the plane that we can imagine to pass through the points *B* and *I*, and at the same time through the centers of the two holes *A* and *L*.

Thus, knowing so exactly these three points *B, P, I,* and as a result also the triangle that they determine, we must trans-

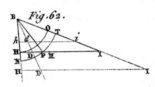

Fig. 62.

fer this triangle with a compass onto a paper or some other very even plane, and then from the center *B* describe through point *P* the circle *NPT* and, taking the arc *NP* equal to *PT*, draw the straight line *BN* which cuts *IP* extended to point *H;* then again, from the center *B* describe through *H* the circle *HO*, which intersects *BI* at point *O;* and we will have the ratio between the lines *HI* and *OI* as the common measure of all refractions that can be caused by the difference between the air and the glass that we are examining. If you are not yet certain of this, you can cut from the same glass other small right-angled triangles, different from this one; and using them in the same way to look for this proportion, you will always find it similar, and thus you will have no occasion to doubt that this is truly the one for which you were looking. And if, after that, on the straight line *HI*, we take *MI* equal to *OI*, and *HD* equal to *DM*, we will have *D* for the apex and *H* and *I* for the burning

points of the hyperbola whose shape this glass must have, in
order to be used in the telescopes I have described.

And we can make these three points *H, D, I* more or less
distant than they are, by as much as we wish, merely by
drawing one other straight line parallel to *HI,* farther from or
nearer to point *B* than it is, and drawing from this point *B*
three straight lines *BH, BD, BI,* which intersect it. As you can
see here, there is the same relation among the points *H, D, I*
and *h, d, i* as among the three *H, D, I.*

Then, having these three points, it is easy to trace the
hyperbola in the way that was explained above; that is, by
planting two pickets at points *H* and *I*,[1] so that the string
placed around the picket *H* be so attached to the ruler that
it cannot twist, toward *I,* further than down to *D.*

But if you would rather trace it with an ordinary compass,
looking for several points through which it passes, place one
of the legs of this compass at point *H;*
and opening it enough for its other
leg to pass slightly beyond point *D* (as
far as *1,* for example), from the center
H describe the circle *133;* then, having made *M2* equal to *H1,* from the
center *I* through point *2* describe the
circle *233,* which intersects the former

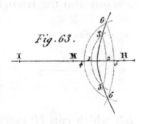

Fig. 63.

at the points *3, 3,* through which this hyperbola must pass, as
well as through point *D,* which is its apex. Afterwards put one
of the legs of the compass back in the same way at point *H,*
and opening it so that its other leg passes slightly beyond the
point *1* (for example, as far as *4*), from the center *H* describe
the circle *466.* Then, having taken *M5* equal to *H4* from the
center *I* through *5* describe the circle *566,* which intersects the
former one at the points *6, 6,* which are in the hyperbola; and
so, continuing to place the point of the compass at point *H,*
and the rest as before, you can find as many of the points of
this hyperbola as you please.

Perhaps this will not be bad for making some rough model

[1] See Fig. 42, p. 135.

which approximately represents the shape of the lenses we
wish to cut. But in order to give them this exact shape, we
must have some other invention by means of which we can
describe hyperbolas at a stroke, as, with
a compass, we describe circles; and I
know of none better than the following.
First, from the center T, which is the
middle of the line HI, we must describe
the circle HVI, then from point D, con-

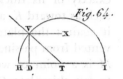

Fig. 64.

struct a perpendicular to HI, cutting this circle at point V;
and if we draw a straight line from T through this point V,
we will have the angle HTV, which is such that if we imagine
it to revolve on the axis HT, the line TV will describe the
surface of a cone, in which the section made by the plane
VX—which is parallel to this axis HT, and on which DV
falls at right angles—will be a hyperbola completely similar
and equal to the preceding one. And all the other planes
parallel to this one will also cut quite similar but unequal
hyperbolas in this cone; [and these hyperbolas] will have their
burning points more or less distant from this axis, according as these planes are distant from it.

In consequence, we can make the following machine: AB
is a lathe or roller of wood or metal, which, turning on the
poles $1, 2$, represents the axis HI of the other diagram. CG, EF
are two plates or planks, completely flat and
even, particularly on the side where they
touch each other; so that the surface that we
can imagine to be between the two of them—
since it is parallel to the roller AB, and intersected at right angles by the plane that we
can imagine passing through the points $1, 2$,
and C, O, G—represents the plane VX which
cuts the cone. And NP, the width of the
upper plate CG, is equal to the diameter of

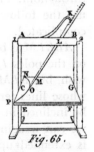

Fig. 65.

the lens that we wish to cut, or is not much larger. Finally
KLM is a ruler which, turning with the roller AB on the poles
$1, 2$, so that the angle ALM always remains equal to HTV,

represents the line *TV* that describes the cone. And this ruler must be thought to pass through this roller in such a way that it can be raised and lowered by sliding in the hole *L*, which is exactly of its thickness; and even that there is somewhere, such as toward *K*, a weight or spring, which constantly presses it against the plate *CG*, by which it is supported and prevented from passing further; and, moreover, that its extremity *M* is a point of well-tempered steel, which has the strength to cut this plate *CG*, but not the other plate *EF*, which is underneath. From this it is manifest that, if we make this ruler *KLM* move on the poles *1, 2*, so that the steel point *M* passes from *N* through *O* toward *P*, and back from *P* through *O* toward *N*, it will divide this plate *CG* into two others, *CNOP* and *GNOP*, whose side *NOP* will be terminated by a sharp line—convex on *CNOP*, and concave on *GNOP*—which will have exactly the shape of a hyperbola. And since these two plates, *CNOP* and *GNOP*, are of steel or some other very hard material, they may be used not only as models, but perhaps also as tools or instruments for cutting certain wheels, with which I shall presently say that the shapes of the lenses should be cut. Nevertheless there is still something missing here: for since, when the steel point *M* is toward *O*, it is placed slightly otherwise than when it is toward *N* or toward *P*, the cutting edge that it gives to these tools cannot be equal throughout. This makes me believe that it would be better to use the following machine, even though it is a little more complicated.

ABKLM is but a single piece, which is moved in its entirety on the poles *1, 2*; its part *ABK* can have any shape that we wish, but *KLM* must have that of a ruler or other such body, whose lines terminating its surfaces are parallel; and it must be inclined in such a way that if the straight line *43* (which we can imagine to pass through the center of its thickness) is extended up to [the line] which we can imagine to pass through the poles *1, 2*, it makes there an angle *234*, equal to that which was presently marked with the letters *HTV*.[2] *CG*,

2 See Fig. 64, p. 165.

EF are two planks parallel to the axis *12;* their surfaces facing each other are very flat and smooth, and are cut at right angles by the plane *12GOC.* But, instead of touching each other as be-

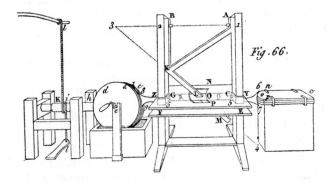

Fig.66.

fore, here they are removed from each other only as far as is necessary to give passage between them to a cylinder or roller *QR,* which is exactly round, and of equal size throughout. And, moreover, they each have a slit *NOP,* which is so long and so wide that the ruler *KLM,* passing within it, can be moved here and there on the poles *1, 2,* as much as is necessary in order to trace between these two planks a part of a hyperbola, of the size of the diameter of the lenses we wish to cut. And this ruler is also passed through the roller *QR,* in such a way that the roller is made to move with it on the poles *1, 2,* yet always remains enclosed between the two planks *CG, EF* and parallel to the axis *12.* Finally, *Y67* and *Z89* are the tools which must be used to cut whatever bodies we may wish into a hyperbola, and their handles *Y, Z* are of such a thickness that their surfaces, which are completely flat, touch exactly on all sides those of the two planks *CG, EF,* without ceasing because of that to slide between the two, because they are highly polished. And they each have a round hole, *5, 5,* in which one of the ends of the roller *QR* is enclosed, in such a way that this roller can easily be turned around the straight line *55* which is, as it were, its axis, without making them turn with it (for their flat surfaces, being engaged between the planks, stop them from so doing); but in whatever other way the roller moves, it compels them also to move with it. And from all this it is manifest that, while the ruler *KLM* is pushed from *N* toward *O* and from *O* toward *P,* or from *P* toward *O* and from *O* toward N, causing the roller *QR* to move with it, it causes these tools *Y67* and *Z89* to move by the same means, in such a way that the particular movement of each of their parts describes exactly the same hyperbola as is made by the intersection of the two lines *34* and *55,* of which the one, i.e., *34,* describes by its movement the cone, and the other, *55,* describes the plane which cuts it.

As to the points or cutting edges of these tools, we can make them in diverse ways, according to the different uses to which we wish to put them. And in order to give the convex lenses their shape, it seems to me that it will be good first of all to use the tool *Y67,* and with it to cut many plates of steel nearly similar to *CNOP* which has presently been described; [3] then, by means of these plates as well as of the tool *Z89,* we will cut a wheel such as *d,* conforming all around to its thickness *abc,* so that all the sections that we can imagine to be made there by any planes where *ee,* the axis of this wheel, is located, have the shape of the hyperbola traced by this machine; and finally, we will attach the lens that we wish to cut on a lathe such as *hik,* and apply it against this wheel *d,* in such a way that making this lathe move on its axis *hk* by pulling the cord *ll,* and also making this wheel move on its axis by turning it, the lens placed between them takes exactly the shape that we must give to it.

Now concerning the method of using the tool *Y67:* it is to be noted that we must cut only half of the plates *cnop* at one time; for example, that half which is between the points *n* and *o.* And to this end, it is necessary to put a bar in the machine toward *P,* which, when the ruler *KLM* is moved from *N* toward *O,* prevents it from being able to advance toward *P,* except as much as is necessary to make the line *34* (which marks the middle of its thickness) reach the plane *12GOC,* which we imagine to cut the planks at right angles. And the blade of this tool *Y67* must be of such a shape that

3 See Fig. 65, p. 165.

all the parts of its cutting edge be in this same plane when the line *34* is found to be there; and that there be no others besides, projecting from there toward the side marked *P*, but rather that the entire slope of its thickness goes toward *N*. Moreover, we can make it as dull or as sharp, and as much or as little inclined, and of such a length as we wish, according as we judge it to be more appropriate. Then, having forged the plates *cnop*, and having given them, with a file, a shape which is as close as we can get to that which they should have, it is necessary to apply them to this tool *Y67* and press them against it; and, making the ruler *KLM* move from *N* toward *O*, and back again from *O* toward *N*, we will cut one of their halves. Then, in order to be able to make the other identical, there must be a bar there, or some other such thing, which will make it impossible for the plates to advance toward this tool beyond the place where they are when their half *NO* is finished being cut; and then, having pulled them back from it a little, it is necessary to change the blade of this tool *Y67*, and put in its place another blade whose cutting edge is exactly in the same plane and of the same form, and as far advanced as the preceding, but which has the entire slope of its thickness going toward *P*, so that, if we were to put these two irons flat against one another, their two cutting edges would seem to be but one. Then, having transferred toward *N* the bar that we had previously placed toward *P*, in order to prevent the movement of this ruler *KLM*, we must make this ruler move from *O* toward *P* and from *P* toward *O*, until the plates *cnop* are as much advanced toward the tool *Y67* as hithertofore, and, this being so, they will have finished being cut.

As to the wheel *d*, which must be made of some very hard material: after we have given it with the file the shape that as closely as possible approximates the one it must have, it will be very easy to finish it; first, with the plates *cnop*, provided that at the beginning they were so well forged that the tempering has not since changed their shape, and that we apply them on this wheel in such a way that their cutting edge *nop* and its axis *ee* are in the same plane, and finally, that there be a spring or counterweight which presses the plates against the wheel while we make it turn on its axis. Then [we will also finish the wheel] with this tool *Z89,* whose iron must be evenly sloped on two sides; but aside from this it can have almost any shape we wish, provided that all the parts of its cutting edge *89* are in a plane that intersects the surfaces of the planks *CG, EF* at right angles. And in order to use it, we must make the ruler *KLM* move on the poles *1, 2* so that it passes immediately from *P* to *N,* then back again from *N* to *P,* while we cause the wheel to turn on its axis. By this means, the cutting edge of this tool will remove all the unevennesses that are on either side of this wheel, and its point will remove all those that are above or below—for the tool must have a cutting edge and a point.

When this wheel has thus acquired all the perfection it can have, the lens can easily be cut by the two different movements—of the wheel, and of the lathe upon which it must be attached—provided only that there be some spring, or other invention, which, without preventing the movement that the lathe gives to it, presses the lens constantly against the wheel; and provided that the bottom of this wheel be constantly immersed in a vessel containing grease, or emery, or tripoli, or emery dust, or other such material which must be used to cut and polish the lens.

And with this as an example, you can well understand in what way we must shape concave lenses, that is to say by making, first, plates such as *cnop* with the tool *Z89;* then by cutting a wheel, with these plates as well as with the tool *Y67;* and all the rest, in the manner which has just been explained. It is only necessary to observe that the wheel we use for the convex lenses can be as large as we wish to make it, but the one we use for the concave lenses must be so small that when its center is facing the line *55* of the machine that we use to cut it, its circumference does not pass above the line *12* of the same machine. And to polish these concave lenses, we must make this wheel move much faster than the lathe; whereas it is better, for convex lenses, to make the lathe move more quickly, for the reason that the movement of the lathe wears down the edges of the lens much faster than the middle, and that on the contrary that of the wheel wears them down less. As to the usefulness of these diverse movements, it is quite manifest: for, polishing the lenses by hand in a form—in the only way that has been in use up to the present—it would be impossible to do anything well except through chance, although the forms be quite perfect; and polishing them with the single movement of a lathe on a model, all the small faults of this model would mark entire circles on the lens.

I do not add here the demonstrations of many things which belong to Geometry: for those who are somewhat versed in this science will be able to understand them adequately themselves, and I am persuaded that the others will be happier to believe me about them, than to have the trouble of reading them. Moreover, in order that everything be done in order, I would want first of all for us to train ourselves to polish some lenses, flat on the one side and convex on the other, which have the shape of a hyperbola whose burning points are two or three feet from each other: for this length is sufficient for a telescope used to see inaccessible objects perfectly enough. Then I would have us make concave lenses of diverse shapes, by hollowing them ever more and more, until we have found by experience the exact shape of the one which would make this telescope as perfect as possible, and with the best adjustment to the eye which would have to use it. For you know that these lenses must be a bit more concave for those who are short-sighted than for other people. Now having thus discovered this concave lens, inasmuch as the same one can be used by the same eye for all other kinds of telescopes, we have only to practice making, for telescopes which are used to see inaccessible objects, other convex lenses which must be placed farther away from the concave one than the first; and also making some by degrees which must be placed further and further away, up the the greatest possible distance, and which are also proportionately larger. But note that, to the extent that these convex lenses must be placed farther away from the concave ones, and also as a result from the eye, to this extent must they be cut more exactly, because the same faults there deflect the rays that much further away from the place where

they must go. Thus, if the lens *F* deflects the ray *CF* as much
as the lens *E* deflects *AE*, so that the angles *AEG* and *CFH*
are equal, it is obvious that *CF*, going toward *H*, is much
more distant from point *D*, where it would otherwise go, than
AE is distant from point *B*, going toward *G*. Finally, the last
and principal thing that I would have us practice is to polish
the convex lenses on both sides for telescopes that are used to

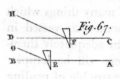

Fig. 67.

see accessible objects, and that having
first of all practiced making those lenses
which make these telescopes very short—
for these will be the easiest—we try by
degrees afterwards to make those which
make them longer, until we have arrived

at the longest that we can use. And, so that the difficulty which
you may find in constructing these last telescopes does not
discourage you, I wish to advise you that although at first their
use is not as attractive as that of those others (which seem
to promise to lift us into the heavens and to show us, there on
the planets, bodies that are as unique and perhaps as diverse
as those we see on the earth), I nevertheless judge them much
more useful, because by means of them we will be able to see
the diverse mixtures and arrangements of the small particles
which compose the animals and plants, and perhaps also
the other bodies which surround us, and thereby derive great
advantage in order to arrive at the knowledge of their nature.
For already, according to the opinion of many philosophers,
all these bodies are made from nothing but the parts of the
elements, differently mingled together; and according to my
view, their total nature and essence—at least of those that
are inanimate—consists in nothing but the weight, shape,
arrangement and movements of their parts.

As to the difficulty we encounter when we arch or hollow
these lenses on both sides, so that the apexes of the two hyperbolas are directly opposite one another, we will be able to
remedy it by rounding off their circumference on the lathe,
and rendering it exactly equal to that of the handles to which

they must be attached in order to polish them; then, when we attach them there, and while the plaster or the pitch and cement with which we join them there is still fresh and flexible, [we must make] them pass with these handles through a ring into which they enter only with difficulty. I do not speak to you of many other particularities which we must observe in cutting them, nor also of many other things which earlier I said to be required in the construction of telescopes; for there is not one of them that I judge so difficult that it can hold back inquiring minds. And I am not guided by the ordinary intelligence of artisans; instead I dare to hope that the inventions I have presented in this Treatise will be esteemed beautiful and important enough so as to oblige some of the more curious and skillful persons of our age to undertake their execution.

GEOMETRY

GEOMETRY

GEOMETRY

First Book

Of Problems That Can Be Constructed Using Only Circles and Straight Lines

All the problems of geometry can easily be reduced to such terms that thereafter we need to know only the length of certain straight lines in order to construct them.

And just as all of arithmetic is composed of but four or five operations—namely, addition, subtraction, multiplication, division, and the extraction of roots, which may be considered a species of division—so in geometry, in order to find the lines for which we are looking, we need only add to them, or subtract from them, other lines; or else, by taking one line which I shall call unity, in order to relate it as closely as possible to numbers, and which usually can be chosen arbitrarily, and then by taking two others, [we may] find a fourth line which is to one of these two lines as the other is to the unity—which is the same as multiplication; or else [we may] find a fourth line which is to one of the two as the unity is to the other—which is the same as division; or finally, [we may] find one, or two, or several mean proportionals between the unity and some other line—which is the same as extracting the square root, or cube root, etc. And I shall not hesitate to introduce these arithmetical terms into geometry, in order to make myself more intelligible.

For example, let *AB* be unity, and let it be necessary to multiply *BD* by *BC*; I have only to join the points *A* and *C*, then to draw *DE* parallel to *CA*, and *BE* is the product of this multiplication.

Or else, if it is necessary to divide *BE* by *BD*, having joined

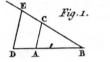

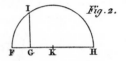

the points *E* and *D*, I draw *AC* parallel to *DE*, and *BC* is the product of this division.

Or, if it is necessary to extract the square root of *GH*, I add to it, along the same straight line, *FG*, which is the unity; and, dividing *FH* into two equal parts at point *K*, from the center *K* I draw the circle *FIH*; then, if I construct from point *G* to point *I* a straight line at right angles to *FH*, *GI* is the required root. I do not speak here of the cube root or of other roots, for I shall speak of them more conveniently afterwards.

But often one has no need so to trace these lines on paper, and it suffices to designate them by certain letters, one for each. Thus, in order to add the line *BD* to *GH*, I name the one *a* and the other *b*, and write $a + b$; and $a - b$, in order to subtract *b* from *a*; and *ab*, in order to multiply the one by the other; and a/b, in order to divide *a* by *b*; and *aa* or a^2, in order to multiply *a* by itself; and a^3, in order to multiply this again by *a*, and so on to infinity. And in order to extract the square root of $a^2 + b^2$, I write $\sqrt{a^2 + b^2}$; and in order to extract the cube root of $a^3 - b^3 + ab^2$, I write $\sqrt[3]{a^3 - b^3 + ab^2}$, and so on for the others.

Here it is to be noted that by a^2 or b^3 or the like, I ordinarily mean only simple lines, although, in order to make use of the names used in algebra, I call them squares, cubes, etc.

It is also to be noted that each of the parts of a single line should ordinarily be expressed by as many dimensions as each other part, when the unity is not determined in the problem: thus, here, a^3 contains as many dimensions as *abb* or b^3, which compose the line which I have called $\sqrt[3]{a^3 - b^3 + ab^2}$; but it is not the same thing when the unity is determined, because unity can be understood throughout, [even] where there are too many or too few dimensions; thus, if it is necessary to extract the cube root of $a^2b^2 - b$, we must consider that the quantity a^2b^2 is divided once by the unity, and that the other quantity b is multiplied twice by the same.

Finally, so as not to forget the names of these lines, it is always essential to make a separate list as often as one assigns or changes them, writing, for example:

$AB = 1$, that is, AB equals 1
$GH = a$
$BD = b$, etc.

Thus, if we wish to solve some problem, we should first of all consider it solved, and give names to all the lines—the unknown ones as well as the others—which seem necessary in order to construct it. Then, without considering any difference between the known and the unknown lines, we should go through the problem in the order which most naturally shows the mutual dependency between these lines, until we have found a means of expressing a single quantity in two ways. This will be called an equation, for the terms of one of the two ways [of expressing the quantity] are equal to those of the other. And we must find as many such equations as we assume there to be unknown lines. Or else, if we cannot find many of them, and if nonetheless we have omitted nothing that is to be desired in the question, this indicates that it is not entirely determined; and in this case, we can take at random lines of known length, for all the unknown lines to which no equation corresponds. After this, if there still remain many [unknown lines], we must use, in order, each of the equations that also remain, either using it alone or comparing it with the others, in order to explain each of these unknown lines; and thus, by untangling them, [we will ascertain] that there remains but a single unknown line, equal to some other which is known, or whose square, cube, or fourth power, fifth power, sixth power, etc., is equal to the sum or difference of two or more quantities, one of which is known, while the others are composed of mean proportionals between the unity and this square, or cube, or fourth power, etc., multiplied by other known lines. I express this as follows:

$$z = b,$$

or $$z^2 = -az + b^2,$$

or $$z^3 = +az^2 + b^2z - c^3,$$

or $$z^4 = az^3 - c^3z + d^4,$$ etc.

That is, z, which I take to be the unknown quantity, is equal to b; or, the square of z is equal to the square of b, minus a multiplied by z; or, the cube of z is equal to a multiplied by the square of z, plus the square of b multiplied by z, minus the cube of c; and so on with the others.

And we can always thus reduce all the unknown quantities to a single one, so long as the problem can be constructed by circles and straight lines, or by conic sections, or even by some other line which is only one or two degrees greater. But I shall not pause here to explain this in greater detail, because I should be depriving you of the pleasure of learning it for yourself, as well as the advantage of cultivating your mind by training yourself in it, which is, in my opinion, the principal advantage we can derive from this science. Moreover, I do not observe here anything so difficult that it cannot be discovered by those who are slightly versed in common geometry and in algebra, and who pay close attention to everything in this treatise.

This is why I shall content myself here with advising you that in solving these equations, provided that we do not fail to use division whenever possible, we will infallibly reach the simplest terms to which the problem can be reduced.

And if the problem can be solved by ordinary geometry—that is, by the use of straight and circular lines traced on a plane surface—when the last equation has been completely solved there will remain, at the most, the square of an unknown quantity, equal to that which will be produced through multiplying its root by a certain known quantity, and adding or subtracting some other quantity which is also known.

And then this root, or unknown line, can easily be found. For if I have, for example, $z^2 = az + b^2$, I make the right triangle NLM, whose side LM is equal to b, the square root of the known quantity b^2, and the other LN is $\frac{1}{2}a$, the half of the other known quantity, which was multiplied by z which I assume to be the unknown line. Then, extending MN, the base [1] of this triangle, to O, so that NO is equal to NL, the whole line OM is z, the required line. And it is this way:

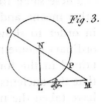

Fig. 3.

$$z = \tfrac{1}{2}a + \sqrt{\tfrac{1}{4}a^2 + b^2}.$$

But if I have $y^2 = -ay + b^2$, and if y is the quantity that must be found, I make the same right triangle NLM, and from its base MN I take NP equal to NL; and the remainder, PM, is y, the desired root. So that I have

$$y = -\tfrac{1}{2}a + \sqrt{\tfrac{1}{4}a^2 + b^2}.$$

And in the same way, if I had $x^4 = -ax^2 + b^2$, then PM would be x^2, and I would have

$$x = \sqrt{-\tfrac{1}{2}a + \sqrt{\tfrac{1}{4}a^2 + b^2}},$$

Fig. 4.

and so for the others. If I have $z^2 = az - b^2$, finally, I make NL equal to $\frac{1}{2}a$, and LM equal to b, as before; then, instead of joining the points M, N, I draw MQR parallel to LN, and having described, from the center N through L, a circle which cuts MQR at points Q and R, the desired line z is MQ, or else MR; for in this case it can be expressed in two ways, namely

$$z = \tfrac{1}{2}a + \sqrt{\tfrac{1}{4}a^2 - b^2}$$

and

$$z = \tfrac{1}{2}a - \sqrt{\tfrac{1}{4}a^2 - b^2}.$$

And if the circle which, having its center at point N, passes through point L, neither cuts nor touches the straight line

---

[1] Actually the hypotenuse, which was commonly called the base at that time.

MQR, then there is no root for the equation, so that we may say that the construction of the problem is impossible.

These same roots can be discovered through an infinity of other means, and I have only given these very simple ones here in order to show that we can construct all the problems of ordinary geometry by doing no more than the little that is contained in the four figures I have explained. I do not believe that the ancients observed this; for otherwise, they would not have taken the trouble to write so many big books, where the order of their propositions alone makes us aware that they had no true method for discovering all of them, but that they had only gathered together those propositions they had stumbled upon.

And we can also see this very clearly from what Pappus put at the beginning of his seventh book, where, having stopped several times to enumerate everything that has been written in geometry by his predecessors, he finally refers to a problem which he says neither Euclid, nor Apollonius, nor any other, had been able to solve entirely; and here are his words (I cite the Latin version rather than the Greek text, so that everyone may understand it more easily):

> Moreover, he [Apollonius] says that the problem of the locus related to three or four lines was not solved by Euclid perfectly, nor has he or anyone else been able to solve it completely, nor were they able to add anything to what Euclid had written, by means of the conic [sections] only which had been demonstrated before Euclid, etc.

And, a bit later, he explains the question as follows:

> The problem of the locus related to three or four lines, of which Apollonius boasts so proudly, giving no credit to the writer who came before him, is of this nature: if three straight lines are given in position, and if straight lines be drawn from one and the same point, making given angles with the three given lines, and if there be given the ratio of the rectangle contained by two of the lines so drawn to the square of the other, the point lies on a solid locus given in position, namely, one of the three conic sections.

And, if lines be drawn making given angles with four straight lines given in position, and if the rectangle of two of them bears a given ratio to the rectangle of the other two; then, in the same way, the point lies on a conic section given in position. It has been demonstrated that to only two lines there corresponds a plane locus. But if more than four lines are given, the point generates loci not presently known, but just called "lines." It is not clear what they are, nor what their properties are. One of them, not the first but the one most manifestly to be seen, has been studied and this has been useful. These however are the propositions concerning them:

If from any point straight lines are drawn making given angles with five straight lines given in position, and if the solid rectangular parallelepiped contained by three of the lines so drawn bears a given ratio to the solid rectangular parallelepiped contained by the other two and any given line whatsoever, the point lies on a "line" given in position. Again, if there are six lines, and if the solid contained by three of the lines bears a given ratio to that contained by the other three lines, this point also lies on a "line" given in position. But if there are more than six lines, we cannot say whether a ratio of something contained by four lines is given to that which is contained by the rest, since there is no figure of more than three dimensions.

Here I beg you to note in passing that the scruple which caused the ancients to use the terms of arithmetic in geometry, which could proceed only from the fact that they did not see clearly enough the relation between the two, caused much obscurity and hindrance in the method with which they explained them. For Pappus proceeds in this way:

For in this are agreed those who formerly interpreted these things, in that they hold that a figure contained by these lines is not understandable in any way. This is permissible, however, both to say and to demonstrate generally by this kind of proportion, and in this way: if from any point straight lines be drawn making given angles with straight lines given in position; and if there be given a ratio compounded of them, that is the ratio that one of the lines drawn has to one, the second has to a second, the third to a third, and so on to the given line if there be seven lines, or if there be eight lines, of the last to a last, the point lies on the lines that are given in position. And similarly, whatever may be the odd or even number, since these, as I have said, correspond in position to the four lines; therefore they have not set forth any method so that a line may be known, etc.

The question, then, which Euclid had begun to solve, and then Apollonius, without anyone having achieved its solution, was such: if we have three, or four, or a greater number of straight lines given in position, we must first of all have a point from which we can draw as many other straight lines, one on each of the given lines, which form given angles with them; and the rectangle contained by two of the lines thus drawn from a single point, must have the given proportion to the square of the third, if there are only three of them; or else with the rectangle of the two others, if there are four. Or again, if there are five of them, the parallelepiped constructed of three of them must have the given ratio to that composed of the two remaining ones, and of another given line. Or, if there are six lines, the parallelepiped constructed of three must have the given ratio to the parallelepiped of the three others. Or, if there are seven of them, the product which is obtained when we multiply four of them by each other must be the given ratio which is produced by the multiplication of the three others, and again of another given line. Or, if there be eight, the product of the multiplication of four must have the given ratio to the product of the four others. And thus this problem can be extended to any number of lines. Then, since there are always an infinite number of points which can fulfill the requirement here, it is always necessary to know and to trace the line in which they are to be found; and Pappus says that, when there are only three or four given straight lines, this line is one of the three conic sections; but he does not undertake to determine it, nor to describe it, nor to do any more than explain those where all these points must be found, when the problem involves a greater number of lines. He only adds that the ancients had recognized one of them which they had shown to be useful, but which seemed the most obvious, and yet was not the most important. This gave me occasion to try and discover whether, through my method, I could go as far as they had gone.

And first of all, I discovered that if this problem is proposed only for three, four, or five lines, we can always discover the required points through simple geometry—that is, through the use of ruler and compasses alone, using nothing but what has been already explained, except when there are five given lines and they are all parallel. In that case, as also in cases when the problem is proposed for six, seven, eight, or nine lines, we can always discover the required points through the geometry of solids, that is, by using some one of the three conic sections; except when there are nine given lines, and they are all parallel. In which case, again, and also for cases of 10, 11, 12, or 13 lines, we can discover the required points by means of a curved line which is a degree higher than the conic sections—except in the case of 13 lines, where they are all parallel; in which case, and for cases of 14, 15, 16, and 17 lines, it is essential to use a curved line of a degree still higher than the preceding: and so on to infinity.

Then I discovered that when there are only three or four given lines, the required points are to be found, not only on one of the three conic sections, but sometimes also on the circumference of a circle or a straight line. And, when there are five, six, seven, or eight of them, all these points are to be found on some one of the lines which are of a degree higher than the conic sections, and it is impossible to conceive any one of these lines which is useful in this problem; but they may also, again, be found on a conic section, or on a circle, or on a straight line, and if there are nine, ten, eleven, or twelve lines, these points may be found on a line which is only one degree higher than the preceding; but all such lines which are of a degree higher may be used for the problem; and so on to infinity.

Finally, the first and simplest line of all, after the conic sections, is that which we can describe by the intersection of a parabola and a straight line, in the way which will presently be explained. Thus I believe I have completely accomplished what Pappus tells us the ancients tried to do in this respect; and I shall try to demonstrate it in a few words, for I am already bored by writing so much about it.

Let AB, AD, EF, GH, etc., be several lines given by position, and let it be required to find a point, such as C, from which we can draw other straight lines (such as CB, CD, CF, and CH)

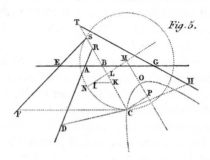

Fig. 5.

on the given ones, in such a way that the angles CBA, CDA, CFE, CHG, etc., are given, and in such a way that the product of the multiplication of one part of these lines is equal to the product of the multiplication of the others—or at least so that these products have some other given ratio, for this does not make the problem more difficult.

First, I assume the problem to be already solved; and in order to avoid the confusion of all these lines, I consider one of the given lines and one of those which it is necessary to find, for example AB and CB, as the principal ones, to which I shall try to relate all the others. Let the segment of the line AB, which is between points A and B, be called x, and let BC be called y; and let all the other given lines be extended until they intersect these two (also extended if necessary), provided that they are not parallel to the principal lines; and you can see here that they cut the line AB at points A, E, G; and BC at points R, S, T. Then, because all the angles of the triangle ARB are given, the ratio between the lines AB and BR is also given, and I represent it as z is to b; so that since AB is x, RB will be $\dfrac{bx}{z}$, and the entire line CR will be $y + \dfrac{bx}{z}$, because point B falls between C and R; for, if R were to fall between C and B, CR would be $y - \dfrac{bx}{z}$, and if C were to fall between B and R, CR would be $-y + \dfrac{bx}{z}$. Again, the three angles of the triangle DRC are given, and consequently the ratio between the sides CR and CD is also known, which I represent as z is to c: so that, if CR is $y + \dfrac{bx}{z}$, CD will be $\dfrac{cy}{z} + \dfrac{bcx}{z^2}$. After this, since the lines AB, AD, and EF are given as to position, the distance between the points A and E is also given, and, if we call it k, we will have EB equal to $k + x$; but this would be $k - x$, if point B were to fall between E and A, and $-k + x$, if E were to fall between A and B. And because the angles of the triangle ESB are all given, the ratio of BE to BS is also given, and I represent it as z to d: so that BS is $\dfrac{dk + dx}{z}$, and the entire line CS is $\dfrac{zy + dk + dx}{z}$; but this would be $\dfrac{zy - dk - dx}{z}$, if point S fell between B and C; and it would be $\dfrac{-zy + dk + dx}{z}$, if C fell between B and S. Moreover, the three angles of the triangle FSC are given, and hence also the ratio of CS to CF, which is the same as z to e; and the entire line CF will be $\dfrac{ezy + dek + dex}{z^2}$. In the same way, AG, which I call l, is given, and BG is $l - x$; also, because of the triangle BGT, the ratio of BG to BT is also given, which is as z to f; and BT will be $\dfrac{fl - fx}{z}$, and CT will equal $\dfrac{zy + fl - fx}{z}$. Then, again, the ratio of TC to CH is given because of the triangle TCH, and, representing it as z to g, we will have CH equal to $\dfrac{gzy + fgl - fgx}{z^2}$.

And thus you can see that no matter how many lines given

in position we may have, all the lines drawn above at given angles from point C, following the tenor of the problem, can always be expressed by three terms, of which one is composed of the unknown quantity y, multiplied or divided by some other known quantity; and another consisting of the unknown quantity x, also multiplied or divided by some other known quantity; and the third consisting of some known quantity. The only exception is the case where the given lines are either parallel to AB, in which case the term containing the quantity x will be zero or else parallel to the line CB, in which case the term containing the quantity y will be zero, and this is too obvious for me to stop to give a demonstration of it. And as to the plus and minus signs attached to these terms, they can be changed in every imaginable fashion.

Then you can also see that, when several of these lines are multiplied by one another, the quantities x and y which are found in the product can each of them have only as many dimensions as there are lines, for the explanation of which they are used, which have been so multiplied. So that they may never have more than two dimensions, when they are produced by the multiplication of two lines, nor more than three, when they are in the product of the multiplication of three lines, and so on to infinity.

Moreover, in order to determine the point C, there is only a single condition required, namely, that the product by multiplication of a certain number of these lines be equal to, or (which is no more difficult) have the given ratio to, the product of the others; we can take at random one of the two unknown quantities x or y, and look for the other through this equation, in which it is evident that when the problem is not posed for more than five lines, the quantity x, which is not used in the expression of the first of the lines, can never have more than two dimensions. So that, taking a known quantity for y, we will have $x^2 \pm ax \pm b^2$; and so we will be able to find the quantity x with ruler and compass, in the manner already explained. Then, taking successively an infinite number of different values for the line y, we will also find an infinite

number of them for the line *x;* and so we will have an infinite
number of different points such as the one marked *C,* by means
of which we will be able to describe the required curved line.

We may also do this when the problem is proposed for six
or a greater number of lines, if, among those that are given,
there are some which are parallel to *BA* or *BC;* in this case,
one of the two quantities *x* or *y* will have only two dimensions
in the equation, and so we will be able to find the point *C*
with ruler and compass. But on the other hand, if they are all
parallel, even though the problem is proposed for but five
lines, we will not be able to find this point *C;* because since
the quantity *x* is not present at all in the equation, it is no
longer permissible to choose a known quantity for that which
is called *y;* instead, it is this which it is essential to find. And
because the term *y* will have three dimensions, we will be able
to find it only by extracting the root of a cubic equation,
which cannot usually be done without using at least one conic
section. And even if there are up to nine lines given, provided
that they are not all parallel, we can always state the equation
so that it shows no more than four dimensions; by means of
which we can always solve it through conic sections, in a way
which I shall explain hereinafter. And although there are up
to thirteen lines given, we can always express the following
equation so that it shows no more than six dimensions; consequently we can solve it by means of a line which is only one
degree higher than the conic sections, in a way which I shall
also explain afterwards. And this is the first part of what I
have to demonstrate here; but, before passing to the second
part, it is necessary that I make some general statements about
the nature of curved lines.

Second Book

Of the Nature of Curved Lines

The ancients knew very well that there are three kinds of problems in geometry: the plane, the solid, and the linear. That is, some can be constructed merely by tracing straight lines and circles, while others cannot be constructed unless we use some conic section, and still others require some other, more complex, line. But I am astonished that they did not distinguish different degrees among these more complex curves besides this, and I am unable to understand why they called these curves mechanical, rather than geometrical. For if we say that they are so called because it is necessary to use a certain instrument to describe them, it is necessary to reject, for the same reason, circles and straight lines, seeing that they can only be described on paper with a compass and ruler, which we can also call instruments. Nor is it because the instruments that are used to trace them, being more complex than the ruler and compass, are therefore not as exact, for were this the case, it would be necessary to exclude them from mechanics, where exactness of works made by hand is desired, rather than from Geometry, where we seek only exactitude of reasoning, which can certainly be as exact with reference to these lines as to simpler ones. Neither shall I say that it was because the ancients did not wish to augment the number of their postulates, but that they were contented that we grant them that they can join two given points by a straight line, and describe from a given center, a circle which passes through a given point: for they had no hesitation about assuming, in their treatment of conic sections, that any given cone can be cut with a given plane. And, in order to trace all the curved lines which I intend to introduce here, we need assume nothing except that two or more lines can be moved through one another, and that their intersections determine other curves—which to me seems no more difficult [than the other two postulates]. It is true that they never completely accepted conic sections in their geometry, and I do not care to undertake to change the names which have been approved through use. But it seems to me that it is very clear that if (as we do) we understand by "geometry" that which is precise and exact, and by "mechanics" that which is not; and if we consider geometry as a science that teaches a general knowledge of the measures of all bodies, we must no more exclude complex lines from it than simple ones, provided that we can conceive them as being described by a continuous movement, or by several successive movements of which the latter are completely determined by those which precede: for by this means, we can always have an exact knowledge of their measure. But perhaps what prevented the ancient geometers from accepting curves more complex than conic sections was that the first ones they considered happened by chance to be the spiral, the quadratrix, and similar curves, which truly belong only to mechanics and are not among the number that I think should be included here; for we can conceive them as being described by two separate movements which have no precisely measurable relation to each other. Yet afterwards they examined the conchoid, the cissoid, and a certain few others which we do accept; nevertheless, perhaps because they did not pay sufficient attention to their properties, they took no more notice of these than of the first. Or else it may have been that—since as yet they knew only a few things about conic sections, and there was even much that they did not know about what could be done with the ruler and compass—they believed they should not approach more difficult material. But because I hope that those who have the skill to use the geometrical calculation here proposed will not find enough to give them pause in plane and solid problems, I believe that I may justly invite them into other investigations, where they will never lack opportunity for practice.

Consider the lines *AB, AD, AF,* and so on, which I assume

to have been described with the aid of an instrument, *YZ*, composed of several rulers. These are so joined that when the one
marked *YZ* is placed on the line *AN*, we can open and close
the angle *XYZ*; and when it is completely closed, the points

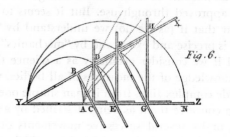

Fig. 6.

B, C, D, E, F, G, H are all assembled at point *A*. But to the
extent that we open it, the ruler *BC*, which is joined at right
angles to *XY* at point *B*, pushes the ruler *CD* toward *Z; CD*
slides along *YZ*, always at right angles to it, and pushes *DE*,
which slides all along *YZ*, remaining parallel to *BC*. Then *DE*
pushes *EF*, *EF* pushes *FG*, *FG* pushes *GH*, etc. And we can
conceive of an infinity of others, which are pushed consecu-
tively in the same way, half of which always maintain the same
angles with *YX* and the others with *YZ*. Now as we thus open
the angle *XYZ*, the point *B* describes the line *AB*, which is a
circle, and the other points *D, F, H,* where the intersections of
the other rulers occur, describe the other curved lines *AD, AF,
AH,* of which the latter are successively more complex than
the first, and thus more complex than the circle. But I can see
nothing to prevent us from conceiving the description of *AD*
as clearly and distinctly as that of the circle, or at least as that
of the conic sections; nor can I see anything which can prevent
us from conceiving the second, and the third, and all the
others that we can describe, as well as the first; nor as a result
can I see why we cannot accept them all in the same way, for
use in the speculations of Geometry.

I could give here many other ways of drawing and conceiving curved lines whose complexity would increase, by degrees,
to infinity. But in order to understand together all curves that

are present in nature, and to classify them by order into certain types, I know of nothing better than to say that all points of those curves which can be called "geometrical"—that is, which fall under some precise and exact measure—necessarily have a certain relation to all the points of a straight line; and this relation can be expressed by a single equation for all the points. And when [no term of] this equation is higher than the rectangle of two undeterminate quantities, or else of the square of a single unknown quantity, the curved line is of the first and simplest class, which comprises only the circle, parabola, hyperbola, and ellipse. But when one or both of the equation's two unknown quantities (for there must be two, in order to explain the relation between two points) reaches the third or fourth degree, the curve is of the second class; and when the equation reaches the fifth or sixth degree, the curve is of the third class; and so on for the others, to infinity.

Let us say, then, that I wish to know to what class the line *EC* belongs, which I imagine to be described by the intersection of the ruler *GL* and the rectilinear plane *CNKL*, whose side *KN* is indefinitely prolonged toward *C*, and which, being moved upon the plane downwards in a straight line—that is, in such a way that its diameter *KL* is always against some part of the line *BA* (prolonged in both directions)—causes this ruler *GL* to move circularly around the point *G*, because the ruler is so joined to the figure *CNKL* that it always passes through the point *L*. I choose a straight line, such as *AB*, in order to relate to its different points all the points of this curved line *EC*, and on this line *AB* I choose a point, such as *A*, at which to begin this calculation. I say that I choose the one and the other, because we are free to choose them however we wish, for although there are many choices which shorten and simplify the equation, nevertheless no matter in what way we choose the straight lines, the curve will always belong to the same class, as is easily demonstrated.

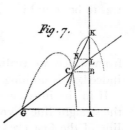

Fig. 7.

After this, taking at random on the curve a point such as *C*, where I assume that the instrument used to describe the curve is applied, I draw from this point *C* the line *CB* parallel to *GA;* and because *CB* and *BA* are two indeterminate and unknown quantities, I name the one *y* and the other *x*. But in order to find the relation between them, I also consider the known quantities which determine the description of this curved line: such as *GA*, which I call *a; KL*, which I call *b;* and *NL* (parallel to *GA*), which I call *c*. Then I say that as *NL* is to *LK*, or *c* to *b*, so *CB*, or *y*, is to *BK*, which consequently is $\frac{b}{c}y$: and *BL* is $\frac{b}{c}y - b$, and *AL* is $x + \frac{b}{c}y - b$. Moreover, as *CB* is to *LB*, or *y* to $\frac{b}{c}y - b$, so *a*, or *GA*, is to *LA*, or $x + \frac{b}{c}y - b$. Thus, multiplying the second by the third, we produce $\frac{ab}{c}y - ab$, equal to $xy + \frac{b}{c}y^2 - by$, which is produced by multiplying the first by the last; and so the equation which was to be found is

$$y^2 = cy - \frac{cx}{b}y + ay - ac,$$

from which we realize that the line *EC* is of the first class; indeed, it is nothing other than a hyperbola.

If in the instrument used to describe the curve we replace the straight line *CNK* by this hyperbola, or some other curved line of the first class terminating the plane *CNKL*, the intersection of this line and the ruler *GL* will describe, instead of the hyperbola *EC*, another curved line, which will belong to the second class. Thus if *CNK* is a circle whose center is *L*, we shall describe the first conchoid of the ancients; and if it is a parabola whose diameter is *KB*, we shall describe the curved line which, as I have already said, is the first and simplest curve required for the problem of Pappus, when there are but five straight lines given in position. But if, instead of one of these curved lines of the first class, we use one of the second, which lies in the plane *CNKL*, we shall describe by its means a curve of the third class; or if [we use] one of the third class, we shall describe a curve of the fourth, and so on indefinitely, as is easy to prove through calculation. And in whatever other way we conceive the description of a curved line, provided this line be among the number of those that I call "geometrical," we will always be able to find an equation to determine all its points in this way.

Now I place curved lines which raise this equation to the fourth degree in the same class as those which raise it to the third degree; and those whose equations are of the sixth degree in the same class as those of the fifth degree,[1] and similarly for the others. The reason for this is that there is a general rule for reducing to a cube all the difficulties of the fourth degree, and to an equation of the fifth degree all equations of the sixth degree, in such a way that we need not consider the higher ones more complex than the lower.

But it is to be noted that among the lines of each class, although for the most part they are all of the same complexity, so that they can be used to determine the same points and construct the same problems, nevertheless there are also some others which are simpler, and more limited in their power. Thus among those of the first class, besides the ellipse, the hyperbola, and the parabola, which are of equal complexity, the circle, which is obviously simpler, is also included. And among those of the second class there is the common conchoid, which takes its origin from the circle; and there are yet some others which, although they do not have as extensive a power as most others of their class, nevertheless cannot be placed in the first class.

---

[1] Literally, ". . . which raise this equation to the square of the square, in the same class as those which raise it only to the cube; and those whose equation goes as high as the square of the cube, in the same class as those in which it goes only as high as the supersolid. . . ."

Now after having so reduced all the curved lines to certain classes, it is easy for me to go on with the demonstration of the answer that I have already given to Pappus' problem. For first, since I showed above that when only three or four straight lines are given, the equation which serves to determine the required points will be of the second degree, it is evident that the curved line where these points are located is necessarily some one of the first class; for this same equation explains the relation of all points on lines of the first class to all those of a straight line. And when no more than eight straight lines are given, this equation is of the fourth degree at most, and thus as a result the required line can be of only the second class, or lower. When there are no more than twelve lines given, the equation can be of the sixth degree at most, and consequently the required curve can only belong to the third class, or lower; and so on for the rest. Now because the position of the given straight lines can vary in every way, and as a result can change many of the known quantities, such as the signs + and − in the equation, in every imaginable way, it is evident that there is no curve of the first class which will not be useful to this problem, when it is proposed in four straight lines; nor any of the second which will not be useful when it is proposed in eight; nor any of the third when it is proposed in twelve; and so on for the rest. So that there is no curved line which is subject to calculation and can be included in Geometry which may not be used for some number of lines.

But here I must more specifically determine and give the method of discovering the required curve which is used in each case, when only three or four straight lines are given. And by this means, we will see that the first class of curved lines contains no others but the three conic sections and the circle.

Look again at the four lines *AB, AD, EF,* and *GH* given above,[2] and let it be required to find another line, in which there are to be found an infinity of points such as *C,* from which, having drawn the four lines *CB, CD, CF,* and *CH,* at

2 See Fig. 5, p. 186.

given angles to the given lines, CB multiplied by CF produces a sum equal to CD multiplied by CH. That is, if we make

$$CB = y,$$

$$CD = \frac{czy + bcx}{z^2},$$

$$CF = \frac{ezy + dek + dex}{z^2},$$

and

$$CH = \frac{gzy + fgl - fgx}{z^2},$$

then the equation is:

$$y^2 = \frac{(cfglz - dekz^2)y - (dez^2 + cfgz - bcgz)xy + bcfglx - bcfgx^2}{ez^3 - cgz^2}.$$

At least this is the equation if we assume that ez is greater than eg; for if it were less, we would have to change all the plus and minus signs. And if the quantity y were found to be zero or less than nothing in this equation, then when we assumed the point C to lie in the angle DAB, we would also have to assume that it lay within the angle DAE, or EAR, or RAG; and the plus and minus signs would have to be changed as necessary to produce this effect. And if in all these four positions the value of y were found to be zero, then the problem would have no solution in the case proposed. But let us here assume the problem to be soluble, and in order to abbreviate its terms, let us write $2m$ in place of the quantities $\frac{cfglz - dekz^2}{ez^3 - cgz^2}$, and $\frac{2n}{z}$ in place of $\frac{dez^2 + cfgz - bcgz}{ez^3 - cgz^2}$. And so we will have

$$y^2 = \frac{2my - \dfrac{2n}{2}xy + bcfglx - bcfgx^2}{ez^3 - cgz^2},$$

whose root is

$$y = m - \frac{nx}{z} + \sqrt{m^2 - \frac{2mnx}{z} \frac{n^2x^2}{z^2} \frac{bcfglx - bcfgx^2}{ez^3 - cgz^2}}.$$

And again in order to abbreviate, let us write o in place of $-\dfrac{2mn}{z} + \dfrac{bcfgl}{ez^3 - cgz^2}$; and in place of $\dfrac{n^2}{z^2} - \dfrac{bcfg}{ez^3 - cgz^2}$, let us write $\dfrac{p}{m}$. For since these quantities are all given, we can name them as we please. And so we have

$$y = m - \frac{n}{z}x + \sqrt{m^2 + ox + \frac{p}{m}x^2},$$

which must give the length of the line BC, leaving AB, or x, undetermined. And it is evident that since the question is proposed for only three or four lines, we shall always have such terms, except that some of them may be zero, and the plus and minus signs may vary.

After this I make KI equal and parallel to BA, so that it cuts away from BC the part BK equal to m, because BC here contains $+ m$; and if it had been $- m$, I should have drawn this line IK on the other side of AB; and if the quantity m had been zero, I would have drawn nothing at all. Then I also draw IL, so that the line IK is to KL as z is to n. That is, if IK is x, KL is $\dfrac{n}{z}x$. And by the same means I also know the ratio of KL to IL, which I pose as that of n to a; so that if KL is $\dfrac{n}{z}x$, IL is $\dfrac{a}{z}x$. And I place the point K between L and C, because it here contains $-\dfrac{n}{z}x$, whereas I would have placed L between K and C, if it had been $+\dfrac{n}{z}x$, and I would not have drawn this line IL at all, if $\dfrac{n}{z}x$ had been zero.

Now this being done, there are only these terms left to me for the line LC:

$$LC = \sqrt{m^2 + ox - \frac{p}{m}x^2},$$

from which I see that if they were zero, this point C would be located in the straight line IL; and that if they were such that their root could be extracted, that is, if m^2 and $\frac{p}{m}x^2$ were both marked with the same plus or minus sign and o^2 were equal to $4pm$, or else if the terms m^2 and ox, or ox and $\frac{p}{m}x^2$ were zero, this point C would be located in another straight line which would be as easy to find as IL. But when this is not the case, this point C is always on one of three conic sections, or on a circle, one of whose diameters is in the line IL, and the line LC is applied in order to this diameter; or on the other hand, LC is parallel to the diameter, to which IL is applied in order. In particular, if the term $\frac{p}{m}x^2$ is zero, this conic section is a parabola; and if it is marked by a plus sign, it is a hyperbola; and finally if it is marked by a minus sign, it is an ellipse. The sole exception occurs when the quantity a^2m is equal to pz^2, and when ILC is a right angle, in which case we have a circle instead of an ellipse. And if this section is a parabola, its right side is equal to $\frac{oz}{a}$, and its diameter is always on the line IL; and to find the point N, which is the vertex, it is necessary to make IN equal to $\frac{am^2}{oz}$, and the point I must be between L and N, if the terms are $+m^2 + ox$; or else the point L must be between I and N, if they are $+m^2 - ox$; or else it would be necessary for N to be between I and L, if the terms were $-m^2 + ox$. But with the terms posed as they are here, m^2 can never be negative. And finally the point N would be identical with the point I if the quantity m^2 were zero. By this means it is easy to find this parabola, according to the first problem of the first book of Apollonius.

But if the required line is a circle, or an ellipse, or a hyperbola, we must first look for the point M, which is its center, and which is always on the straight line IL, where we can find it by taking IM equal to $\frac{aom}{2pz}$ so that if the quantity o is zero, this center is exactly at point I. And if the desired line is a circle or an ellipse, we must take point M on the same side as point L with respect to I, when ox is positive; and when ox is negative, we must take it on the other side. But with the hyperbola, it is just the opposite: if we have $-ox$, this center M must be on the same side of I as L; and if we have $+ox$, it must be on the other side. After this the right side of the figure must be

$$\sqrt{\frac{o^2z^2}{a^2} + \frac{4mpz^2}{a^2}}$$

when m^2 is positive and the required line is a circle or an ellipse, or if m^2 is negative and the line is an hyperbola. And it must be

$$\sqrt{\frac{o^2z^2}{a^2} - \frac{4mpz^2}{a^2}}$$

if the required line is a circle or an ellipse and m^2 is negative, or if it is an hyperbola and the quantity o^2 is greater than $4mp$, m^2 being positive. But if the quantity m^2 is zero, this right side is ox, and if ox is zero, it is

$$\sqrt{\frac{4mpz^2}{a^2}}.$$

Then for the corresponding diameter it is necessary to find a line which is to this right side as a^2m is to pz^2, that is, if this right side is

$$\sqrt{\frac{o^2z^2}{a^2} + \frac{4mpz^2}{a^2}}$$

the diameter is

$$\sqrt{\frac{a^2o^2m^2}{p^2z^2} + \frac{4a^2m^3}{pz^2}}.$$

And in all cases the diameter of the section is the line IM, and LC is the one among those lines which is applied to it in order. So that by making MN equal to half of the diameter and taking it on the same side of point M as is point L, the point N will be the vertex of this diameter. Following this, it is easy to find the section according to the second and third problems of the first book of Apollonius.

But when this section is a hyperbola, and we have $+m^2$,

and if the quantity o^2 is zero or smaller than $4pm$, we must draw the line MOP from the center M parallel to LC, and CP parallel to LM, and make MO equal to

$$\sqrt{m^2 - \frac{o^2 m}{4p}} \; ;$$

while if the quantity ox is zero, we must take MO as equal to m. Then we must consider the point O as the vertex of this hyperbola whose diameter is OP, and consider CP the line which is applied to it in order, and its right side is

$$\sqrt{\frac{4a^4 m^4}{p^2 z^4} - \frac{a^4 o^2 m^3}{p^3 z^4}} \; ,$$

and its diameter is

$$\sqrt{4m^2 - \frac{o^2 m}{p}}$$

—except when ox is zero, for then the right side is $\dfrac{2a^2 m^2}{pz^2}$, and the diameter is $2m$. And so it is easy to discover the required line according to the third problem of the first book of Apollonius.

And the demonstrations of all this are obvious, for, making a sum of the quantities that I have assigned for the right side, the diameter, and the segment of the diameter NL or OP, following the tenets of the eleventh, twelfth, and thirteenth theorems of the first book of Apollonius, we will find all the same terms that compose the square of the line CD or CL, which is applied in order to this diameter. As in this example taking IM, which is $\dfrac{aom}{2pz}$, from NM, which is

$$\frac{am}{2pz}\sqrt{o^2 + 4mp},$$

I have IN; and adding to this IL, which is $\dfrac{a}{z}x$, I have NL which is

$$\frac{a}{z}x - \frac{aom}{2pz} + \frac{am}{2pz}\sqrt{o^2 + 4mp}.$$

And this being multiplied by $\dfrac{z}{a}\sqrt{o^2+4mp}$, which is the right side of the figure, we get

$$x\sqrt{o^2+4mp}-\frac{om}{2p}\sqrt{o^2+4mp}+\frac{mo^2}{2p}+2m^2$$

for the rectangle, from which we must subtract a sum which is to the square of NL as the right side is to the diameter. And this square of NL is

$$\frac{a^2}{z^2}x^2-\frac{a^2om}{pz^2}x+\frac{a^2m}{pz^2}x\sqrt{o^2+4mp}$$

$$+\frac{a^2o^2m^2}{2p^2z^2}+\frac{a^2m^3}{pz^2}-\frac{a^2om^2}{2p^2z^2}\sqrt{o^2+4mp},$$

which must be divided by a^2m and multiplied by pz^2, because these terms explain the ratio between the diameter and the right side. The result is

$$\frac{p}{m}x^2-ox+x\sqrt{o^2+4mp}+\frac{o^2m}{2p}-\frac{om}{2p}\sqrt{o^2+4mp}+m^2.$$

This must be subtracted from the preceding rectangle, and we find $m^2+ox-\dfrac{p}{m}x^2$ for the square of CL, which consequently is the line applied in order in an ellipse, or a circle, to the segment of the diameter NL.

And if we wish to explain all the given quantities numerically, then assume, for example, that $EA=3$, $AG=5$, $AB=BR$, $BS=\frac{1}{2}BE$, $GB=BT$, $CD=\frac{3}{2}CR$, $CF=2CS$, $CH=\frac{2}{3}CT$, the angle $ABD=60°$; and finally, assume that the rectangle of the two CB and CF is equal to the rectangle of the two others CD and CH; for it is essential to have all these things, so that the problem may be entirely determined. Also assume that $AB=x$ and $CB=y$. By the method explained above we shall obtain

$$y^2=2y-xy+5x-x^2, \quad\text{and}\quad y=1-\tfrac{1}{2}x+\sqrt{1+4x-\tfrac{3}{4}x^2};$$

so that BK must be equal to 1, and KL to one-half of KI; and because the angle IKL or ABR is 60°, and KIL, which is equal to half of KIB or IKL, is 30°, ILK is a right angle. And because *IK* or *AB* is called *x*, *KL* is $\frac{1}{2}x$, and *IL* is $x\sqrt{\frac{3}{4}}$, and the quantity which was formerly called *z* is 1, that which was *a* is $\sqrt{\frac{3}{4}}$, *m* is 1, *o* is 4, and *p* is $\frac{3}{4}$; thus *IM* is $\sqrt{\frac{16}{3}}$, *NM* is $\sqrt{\frac{19}{3}}$ and because a^2m (which is $\frac{3}{4}$) is equal to pz^2 here, and the angle *ILC* is a right angle, we find that the curved line *NC* is a circle. And we can easily examine all the others in the same way.

Since all equations which are no higher than the second degree are included in what I have just explained, not only is the problem of the ancients concerning three and four lines completely solved here, but also everything pertaining to what they called the composition of solid loci, and as a result also to that of plane loci, because these are included in the solid. For these loci are nothing but this: when the problem is to find some point lacking one condition for its complete determination (as in this example), any point of a straight line can be taken for the one which is required. And if this line is straight, or circular, we call it a plane locus. But if it is a parabola, or a hyperbola, or an ellipse, we call it a solid locus. And always, in any case, we can arrive at an equation which contains two unknown quantities, and which is analogous to some one of those I have just solved.

But if the line which so determines the needed point is of a more complex degree than the conic sections, we can call it, in the same manner, a supersolid locus, and so for the others. And if two conditions are lacking for the determination of this point, the locus of the point is a surface, which may be completely flat, or spherical, or more complex. But the highest goal of the ancients in this matter was to achieve the composition of solid loci: and it seems that all that Apollonius wrote about conic sections was designed to search for this.

Moreover, we see here that what I have taken as the first class of curved lines can include none but the circle, the parabola, the hyperbola, and the ellipse, which is everything I undertook to prove.

And if the problem of the ancients be proposed in five lines, all parallel, it is clear that the required point will always be in a straight line. But if it is proposed in five lines, four of which are parallel, and the fifth intersecting them at right angles, and even if all the lines drawn from the required point also meet the given lines at right angles, and finally if the parallelepiped composed of three of the lines so drawn on three of the parallel ones is equal to the parallelepiped composed of two lines which are drawn—the one on the fourth of the parallel lines, and the other on that which cuts them at right angles—and of a third line which is given (this is, it seems to me, the simplest case we can imagine, after the preceding one), the required point will be in the curved line described by the movement of a parabola, in the manner explained below.

For example, let the given lines be *AB*, *IH*, *ED*, *GF*, and *GA*, and let the point *C* be required, so that if we draw *CB*,

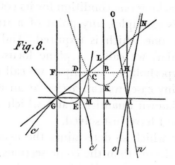

Fig. 8.

CF, *CD*, *CH*, and *CM* at right angles to the given lines, the parallelepiped of the three lines *CF*, *CD*, and *CH* is equal to that of the two others, *CB* and *CM*, and the third, which is *AI*. I posit $CB = y$, $CM = x$, *AI* or *AE* or $GE = a$, in such a way that if point *C* is between the lines *AB* and *DE*, I have $CF = 2a - y$, $CD = a - y$, and $CH = y + a$. And multiplying these three by each other, I have $y^3 - 2ay^2 - a^2y + 2a^3$ equal to the product of the three others, which is *axy*.

After this I consider the curved line *CEG*, which I imagine to be described by the intersection of the parabola *CKN* (which is made to move so that its diameter *KL* is always on the straight line *AB*) and the ruler *GL* (which meanwhile turns about the point *G* in such a way that it always passes through the plane of this parabola at the point L). And I make KL equal to a, and make the principal right side (that is, the one corresponding to the axis of this parabola) also equal to a; and $GA = 2a$, and CB or $MA = y$, and CM or $AB = x$. Then because the triangles GMC and CBL are similar, GM (which is $2a - y$) is to MC (which is x) as CB (which is y) is to BL—which is, as a result, $\dfrac{xy}{2a - y}$. And because LK is a, BK is $a - \dfrac{xy}{2a - y}$, or else $\dfrac{2a^2 - ay - xy}{2a - y}$. And finally, because this same BK is a segment of the diameter of the parabola, BK is to BC (which is its ordinate) as BC is to the right side, which is a; thus calculation shows that $y^3 - 2ay^2 + a^2y + 2a$ is equal to axy, and consequently C is the required point. And it can be taken at any point of the line CEG that we wish to choose, or also on its adjunct $cEGc$, which is described in the same way, except that the vertex of the parabola is turned in the opposite direction; or finally C may lie on their counterparts NIo, nIO, which are described by the intersection of the line GL with the other side of the parabola KN.

Again, if the given parallel lines AB, IH, ED, and GF were not equally distant from each other, and if neither GA nor the lines drawn through C toward the given lines intersected them at right angles: in that case C would not always lie on a curved line of this same nature. And this can sometimes also be the case when none of the given lines are parallel. But suppose there are four parallel lines, and a fifth that traverses them, and the parallelepiped of three of the lines drawn through the required point C (one on the traversing line, and the two others on two of the parallel ones) is equal to that of two lines drawn [through C] to the two other parallel lines and another given line: then the required point C is in a curved line of another nature, namely on a curve such that if all the ordinates to its diameter are equal to those of a conic section, the segments of this diameter, which are between the vertex and the ordinates, have the same ratio to a certain given line that this given line has to the segments of the diameter of the conic section, whose ordinates are equal. And I cannot truly say that this curve is less simple than the preceding one, which I have always believed should be studied first because it is somewhat easier to describe and to calculate.

As for the lines used in the other cases, I shall not stop to classify them by types, because I did not undertake to cover everything and having explained the method of finding an infinite number of points through which these curves pass, I think I have given sufficient means of describing them.

But it is appropriate to note that there is a great difference between this method of finding several points in order to trace a curved line passing through them, and the method used for the spiral and similar curves. For in the latter we do not find all the points of the required line indiscriminately, but only those which can be determined by some process which is simpler than that which is required for composing the curve. And so, strictly speaking, we do not find any one of its points, that is to say, not any one of those which are so properly points of this curve, that they cannot be found except through it; on the other hand, there is no point on the lines that can be used for the proposed problem which cannot be found among those which can be determined through the method just explained. And because this method of drawing a curved line by finding several of its points indiscriminately only extends to those that can also be described by a regular and continuous movement, we need not entirely reject it from geometry.

Nor should we reject the method where we use a string or a loop of cord in order to determine the equality or the difference of two or more straight lines which can be drawn from each point of the required curve to certain other points, or on certain other lines at certain angles, as we did in the *Optics* in order to explain the ellipse and the hyperbola. For although we cannot include in Geometry any lines that are like cords—that is to say, sometimes straight and sometimes curved—because the ratios between straight and curved lines are unknown, and even, I believe, unknowable to men, so that we cannot thereby reach any exact and assured conclusions: nevertheless, because we use cords in these constructions only to determine straight lines whose length we know exactly, we must not entirely reject them.

Now when, from this alone, we know the relation between all the points of a curved line and all those of a straight line, in the way I have explained, it is easy also to find the relation between the points of a curve and all the other given points and lines; and from this to learn the diameters, the axes, the centers, and other lines or points to which each curved line will have some relation, more particular or simple than it will have to the others: and thus to conceive diverse means for describing them, and to choose the easiest of them. And also, we can even discover through this method alone almost everything that can be determined about the magnitude of the space [these curves] comprise, without my having to give any further explanation about it. And finally, as to all the other properties that can be attributed to curved lines, these depend only on the size of the angles that these lines make with certain other lines. But when we can draw straight lines which intersect them at right angles, to the points where they meet those with which they make the angles that we want to measure, or (what I here take to be the same thing) which intersect their contingents, the size of these angles is no more difficult to discover than if the angles were between two straight lines. This is why I believe I shall have given here everything that is required for the elements of curved lines, when I have given a general method of drawing straight lines that fall at right angles on a curve at whichever points on it we wish to choose. And I daresay this problem in geometry is not only the most useful and the most general that I know, but even that I have ever desired to know.

Let *CE* be the given curve, and let it be required to draw through point *C* a straight line which makes a right angle with *CE*. I assume the problem already solved, and that the sought-after line is *CP*; this I extend to point *P*, where it meets the straight line *GA*, which I assume to be the one to which all the points of the line *CE* are to be related. So that making

MA or *CB* = *y*, and *CM* or *BA* = *x*, I have a certain equation that explains the relation between *x* and *y*. Then I make

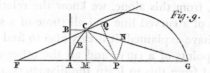

Fig. 9.

PC = *s*, and *PA* = *v*, or *PM* = *v* – *y*; and because *PMC* is a right triangle, I have s^2, which is the square of the hypotenuse, equal to $x^2 + v^2 - 2vy + y^2$, which is the sum of the squares of the two sides. That is, I have

$$x = \sqrt{s^2 - v^2 + 2vy - y^2}$$

or else

$$y = v + \sqrt{s^2 - x^2},$$

and by means of this equation, I eliminate one of the two in-determinate quantities *x* or *y* from the other equation, which explains to me the relation that all the points of the curved line *CE* have to those of the straight line *GA*. This is easy to do by substituting $\sqrt{s^2 - v^2 + 2vy - y^2}$ throughout for *x*, and the square of this sum for x^2, and its cube for x^3, and so on with the others, if it is *x* that I wish to eliminate; or else if it is *y*, [I can do this] by substituting $x + \sqrt{s^2 - x^2}$ for *y*, and the square, the cube, etc., of this sum for y^2, y^3, etc. So that there always remains after this an equation in which there is only one un-known quantity: either *x* or *y*.

For example, if *CE* is an ellipse, and *MA* the segment of its diameter of which *CM* is an ordinate, and which has *r* for its right side and *q* for its transverse axis, we have by the thir-teenth theorem of the first book of Apollonius

$$x^2 = ry - \frac{r}{q}y^2,$$

from which if we take x^2, there remains

$$s^2 - v^2 + 2vy - y^2 = ry - \frac{r}{q}y^2,$$

or else

$$y^2 + \frac{qry - 2qvy + qv^2 - qs^2}{q - r} = 0;$$

for it is better in this case to consider the entire sum together, than to make one of its parts equal to the other.

In the same way, if CE is the curved line described by the movement of a parabola in the manner explained above,[3] and if we have posited b for GA, c for KL, and d for the right side of the diameter KL in the parabola, the equation that explains the relation between x and y is

$$y^3 - by^2 - cdy + bcd + dxy = 0;$$

eliminating x from this, we have

$$y^3 - by^2 - cdy + bcd + dy\sqrt{s^2 - v^2 + 2vy - y^2} = 0.$$

And arranging these terms in order by means of multiplication this becomes

$$y^6 - 2by^5 + (b^2 - 2cd + d^2)y^4 + (4bcd - 2d^2v)y^3$$
$$+ (c^2d^2 - d^2s^2 + d^2v^2 - 2b^2cd)y^2 - 2bc^2d^2y + b^2c^2d^2 = 0,$$

and so for the others.

Even though the points of the curved line are not related to those of a straight line in the manner that I have explained,[4] but in whatever different way we might conceive, nevertheless we can always find such an equation. For example if CE is a line related to the three points F, G, and A in such a way that the straight lines drawn from each of its points, such as C, to the point F, surpass the line FA by a quantity which has a certain given ratio to another quantity, by which GA surpasses the lines drawn from the same points to G. Let us make $GA = b$, $AF = c$; and taking the point C at random on the curve, let the quantity by which CF surpasses FA be to that by which GA surpasses GC, as d is to c, so that if the indeterminate quantity be called z, FC is $c + z$, and GC is $b - \frac{e}{d}z$. Then positing $MA = y$, GM is $b - y$, and FM is $c + y$, and because CMG is a

3 See Fig. 7, p. 193.
4 See Fig. 9, p. 208.

right triangle, taking the square of *GM* from the square of *GC,* we have the square of *CM,* which is

$$\frac{e^2}{d^2} z^2 - \frac{2be}{d} z + 2by - y^2.$$

Then taking the square of *FM* from the square of *FC,* we have again the square of *CM* in other terms, namely,

$$z^2 + 2cz - 2cy - y^2,$$

and since these terms are equal to the preceding ones, they will give us *y,* or *MA,* which is

$$\frac{d^2z^2 + 2cd^2z - e^2z^2 + 2bcdez}{2bd^2 + 2cd^2};$$

and substituting this sum for *y* in the square of *CM,* we find that it is expressed in these terms:

$$(CM)^2 = \frac{bd^2z^2 + ce^2z^2 + 2bcd^2z - 2bcdez}{bd^2 + cd^2} - y^2.$$

Then assuming that the straight line *PC* meets the curve at right angles at point *C,* and making *PC = x* and *PA = v* as before, *PM* is *v − y;* and because *PCM* is a right triangle, we have $s^2 - v^2 + 2vy - y^2$ for the square of *CM;* or again, having substituted for *y* the sum equal to it, we have

$$z^2 + \frac{2bcd^2z - 2bcdez - 2cd^2vz - 2bdevz - bd^2s^2 + bd^2v^2 - cd^2s^2 + cd^2v^2}{bd^2 + ce^2 + e^2v - d^2v} = 0$$

for the required equation.

Now after we have found such an equation, instead of using it to determine the quantities *x, y,* or *z,* which are already given because point *C* is given, we must use it to find *v* or *s,* which determine the required point *P.* And to this end it is necessary to consider that if point *P* is such as we wish it to be, it will be the center of a circle which will pass through point *C,* where it will touch, but not cut, the curved line *CE:* but if this point *P* be ever so little nearer to, or farther from, point *A* than it should be, this circle will cut the curve not only at point *C,* but also necessarily at some other point. Then

it is also necessary to consider that when this circle cuts the
curved line CE, the equation by which we look for the quan-

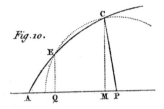

Fig. 10.

tity x or y or another such quantity—assuming PA and PC are
known—necessarily contains two roots, which are unequal. For
if, for example, the circle cuts the curve at the points C and E,
having drawn EQ parallel to CM, the names of the unknown
quantities x and y might be as well used to represent the lines
EQ and QA, as CM and MA; then since PE is equal to PC
because of the circle, if we look for the lines EQ and QA,
through PE and PA that we assume to be given, we will have
the same equation as we would if we were looking for CM and
MA through PC and PA, [assuming the latter to be given].
From this it clearly follows that the value of x or y or any other
such quantity that we may have assumed, will be double in this
equation; that is, there will be two unequal roots in the equation, one of which, if we are looking for the value of x, will
be CM, and the other EQ; or if we are looking for y, one will
be MA, and the other QA; and so for the others. It is true that
if point E is not on the same side of the curve as point C, only
one of these roots will be a true root, and the other will be
reversed, or less than nothing. But the closer the two points
C and E are to one another, the less difference there is between
the two roots; and finally if the two points coincide, the roots
are exactly equal, that is, the circle that passes through C will
touch the curve CE there without cutting it.

In addition, we must observe that when there are two equal
roots in one equation, its form is necessarily the same as if we
were to multiply by itself the unknown quantity less the
known quantity equal to it; and after this, if this last equation

is not of as high a degree as the preceding one, we multiply it by another equation having as many dimensions as the second equation lacks, so that each of the terms of the one equation will correspond to each of the terms of the other.

Thus, for example, I say that the first equation found above, namely,

$$y^2 + \frac{gry - 2qvy + qv^2 - qs^2}{q - r},$$

must have the same form as the equation produced by making e equal to y, and multiplying $y - e$ by itself, from which we get $y^2 - 2ey + e^2$, so that we may compare each of their terms separately, and say that since the first, which is y^2, is the same in each, the second term in the one equation $\frac{qry - 2qvy}{q - r}$ is equal to the second term of the other equation, which is $-2ey$; from which, if we are seeking the quantity v which is the line PA, we have

$$v = e - \frac{r}{q}e + \tfrac{1}{2}r;$$

or else, because we have assumed $e = y$, we have

$$v = y - \frac{r}{q}y + \tfrac{1}{2}r.$$

And thus we can find s through the third term $e^2 = \frac{qv^2 - qs^2}{q - r}$; but because the quantity v sufficiently determines the point P, which is all that is required, there is no need to go further.

In the same way the second equation found above, namely

$$y^6 - 2by^5 + (b^2 - 2cd + d^2)y^4 + 4bcd - 2d^2v)y^3 \\ + (c^2d^2 - 2b^2cd + d^2v^2 - d^2s^2)y^2 - 2bc^2d^2y + b^2c^2d^2,$$

must have the same form as the expression that is produced when we multiply

$$y^2 - 2ey + e^2 \quad \text{by} \quad y^4 + fy^3 + g^2y^2 + h^3y + k^4,$$

which is

$$y^6 + (f - 2e)y^5 + (g^2 - 2ef + e^2)y^4 + (h^3 - 2eg^2 + e^2f)y^3 \\ + (k^4 - 2eh^3 + e^2g^2)y^2 + (e^2h^3 - 2ek^4)y + e^2k^4.$$

So that from these two equations I can derive six others, which may be used to find the six quantities of f, g, h, k, o, and s. From this it is easy to understand that to whatever class the proposed curve belongs, by this procedure there will always be as many equations as we are obliged to assume there are unknown quantities. But in order to solve these equations in order, and finally to find the quantity v—which is the only one we need, and which is the occasion of our looking for the others—we must first look for the value of f, the first of the unknown quantities of the last expression, through the second term, and we find that $f = 2e - 2b$. Then through the latter we must find k, the last of the unknown quantities of the same expression, and we find that $k^4 = \dfrac{b^2c^2d^2}{c^2}$. Then through the third term we must look for g, the second quantity, and we have

$$g^2 = 3e^2 - 4be - 2cd + b^2 + d^2.$$

Then with the penultimate term we must find h, the penultimate quantity, which is

$$h^3 = \frac{2b^2c^2d^2}{e^3} - \frac{2bc^2d^2}{e^2}$$

and thus we would have to continue following this same order right up to the last, if there are any more in this expression; for it is something we can always do in the same manner.

Then from the term that follows in this same order, which is here the fourth, it is necessary to find the quantity v, and we have

$$v = \frac{2e^3}{d^2} - \frac{3be^2}{d^2} + \frac{b^2e}{d^2} - \frac{2ce}{d} + e + \frac{2bc}{d} + \frac{bc^2}{e^2} - \frac{b^2c^2}{e^3};$$

or substituting y for e, which is equal to it, we have

$$v = \frac{2y^3}{d^2} - \frac{3by^2}{d^2} + \frac{b^2y}{d^2} - \frac{2cy}{d} + y + \frac{2bc}{d} + \frac{bc^2}{y^2} - \frac{b^2c^2}{y^3}$$

for the line AP. And so the third equation,[5] which is

[5] See Fig. 7, p. 193.

$$z^2 + \cfrac{\begin{array}{c}2bcd^2z - 2bcdez - 2cd^2vz - 2bdevz \\ - bd^2s^2 + bd^2v^2 - cd^2s^2 + cd^2v^2\end{array}}{bd^2 + ce^2 + e^2v - d^2v},$$

has the same form as $z^2 - 2fz + f^2$, assuming that $f = z$; so that again $- 2f$ or $- 2z$ must be equal to

$$\frac{2bcd^2 - 2bcde - 2cd^2v - 2bdev}{bd^2 + ce^2 + e^2v - d^2v},$$

from which we learn that the quantity v is

$$\frac{bcd^2 - bcde + bd^2z + ce^2z}{cd^2 + bde - e^2z + d^2z}.$$

That is why if we compose the line AP [6] from this expression equal to v, all of whose quantities are known, and if we draw from point P, which we found in this way, a straight line toward C, this line will cut the curve CE at right angles at C, which is what was required. And I see no reason why we cannot extend this solution in the same way to all [problems concerning] curved lines, which fall within the calculations of geometry.

But concerning the latter expression, which we take at random to complete the number of dimensions in the other expression when some of them are missing there, as we just now took $y^4 + fy^3 + g^2y^2 + h^3y + k^4$: we should note that the signs $+$ and $-$ can be assumed to be however we wish, without this causing any difference in the line v, or AP, as you can easily see through experiment. For if I had to stop to demonstrate all the theorems I mention, I would be forced to write a much larger volume than I wish. But I should like to inform you, in passing, that the invention of assuming two equations of the same form, in order to compare separately all the terms of the one with those of the other, and so to get several equations from one (of which you have seen an example here), can be used in an infinity of other problems, and is not one of the lesser inventions of the method I am using.

I do not add the constructions by means of which we can

[6] See Fig. 9, p. 208.

describe the required tangents or perpendiculars, following the
calculation I have just explained; for it is always easy to find
them although we often need a bit of ingenuity in order to
render them short and simple.

For example, let *DC* be the first conchoid of the ancients,
and *A* is its pole and *BH* its ruler, so that all the straight

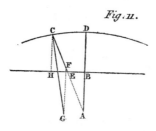

Fig. 11.

lines—such as *DB* and *CE*—which converge toward *A* and are
included between the curve *CD* and the straight line *BH* are
equal: and assume we want to find the line *CG* which cuts [the
conchoid] at point *C*, at right angles. In searching for the point
in the line *BH* through which this line *CG* must pass, according to the method here explained, we would have to be engaged in a calculation as long as, or longer than, any of the
preceding. But nevertheless, the construction which would
afterwards be deduced from it is very simple. For we have only
to take *CF* in the straight line *CA*, and make it equal to *CH*
which is perpendicular to *HB*; then from point *F* draw *FG*,
parallel to *BA*, and equal to *EA*, by which means we get the
point *G*, through which the required line *CG* must pass.

For the rest, so that you may be aware that considering the
curved lines here proposed is not without usefulness, and that
they have diverse properties, which concede nothing [in value]
to those of conic sections, I wish to add here an explanation
of certain ovals, that you will see to be very useful for the
theory of optics. Here is the way in which I describe them.

First, having drawn the straight lines *FA* and *AR*, which
intersect at point *A* (at what angle it does not matter), I take

on one of them the point *F* at random—that is, more or less
removed from the point *A* according as I want to make these
ovals greater or smaller—and from this point *F* as center I

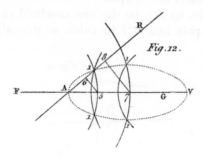

Fig. 12.

describe a circle which cuts *FA* at a point a little beyond *A,*
such as at point *5.* Then from this point *5,* I draw the straight
line *56,* which cuts the other line at point *6,* so that *A6* is less
than *A5* in any given ratio we may wish (such as that which
measures refractions if we wish to use the oval in optics). After
this I also take point *G* in the line *FA,* on the same side as
point *5,* and at random—that is, by making the lines *AF* and
GA have between them any given ratio I might want. Then I
make *RA* equal to *GA* in the line *A6,* and from the center *G,*
I describe a circle whose radius is equal to *R6.* This circle will
cut the other at the two points [marked] *1,* through which the
first of the required ovals must pass. Then again from the
center *F* I describe a circle which passes through *FA* a bit
nearer to or farther from point *5*—for example, at point *7*—
and having drawn the straight line *78* parallel to *56,* from the
center *G* I describe another circle, whose radius is equal to the
line *R8,* and this circle cuts the one that passes through point
7 at the points *1, 1,* which are again points of the same oval.
And thus we can find as many other points as we may wish,
by again taking other lines parallel to *78,* and other circles
with *F* and *G* as centers.

For the second oval there is no difference, except that instead of *AR* it is necessary to take *AS*, from the other side of point *A*, as equal to *AG*, and that, in order for the radius of the circle described from the center *G* to cut the one described

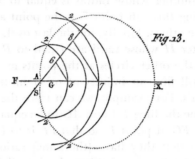

Fig.13.

from the center *F*, which passes through point *5*, this radius must be equal to the line *S6;* or else it must be equal to *S8*, if it is to cut the circle that passes through point *7;* and so for the others. By this means, these circles intersect at the points marked *2, 2*, which are those of this second oval *A2X*.

For the third and fourth, instead of taking *AG*, it is necessary to take *AH* on the other side of *A*, that is, on the same side as *F*. And here it is to be observed that this line *AH* must be greater than *AF* (which may even be zero); so that the points *F* and *A* coincide in the description of all these ovals. After this, since the lines *AR* and *AS* are equal to *AH*, in

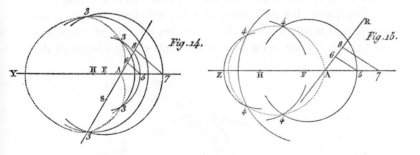

Fig.14.

Fig.15.

order to describe the third oval, *A3Y,* I draw from the center
H a circle whose radius is equal to *S6,* which cuts at point *3*
the circle around the center *F,* which passes through point *5;*
and [I draw] another whose radius is equal to *S8,* which cuts
the circle passing through point *7* at the point also marked *3,*
and so with the others. Finally, for the last oval, I draw circles
about the center *H* whose radii are equal to *R6, R8,* and so
on, which cut the other circles at the points marked *4.*

We could still find an infinity of other means to describe
these same ovals. For example, we can trace the first one *AV,*
when we assume the lines *FA* and *AG* to be equal, if we divide
the entire line *FG* at point *L,* so that *FL* is to *LG* as *A5* is to
A6: that is, so that they have [the same] ratio as [the one]
which measures refractions.[7] Then, having divided *AL* into
two equal parts at point *K,* we cause a ruler, such as *FE,* to
turn about point *F,* by pressing the cord *EC* with the finger
at *C;* this cord, being attached to the end of the ruler at *E,*
passes from *C* toward *K,* then from *K* again toward *C,* and
from *C* to *G,* where its other end is attached, so that the length
of this cord is composed of *GA* plus *AL* plus *FE* minus *AF.*
And the movement of point *C* will describe this [first] oval in a
manner similar to that in which the ellipse and the hyperbola
have been described in the *Optics.* But I do not wish to pause
any longer over this subject.

Now although all these ovals appear to be of almost the
same nature, nevertheless they are of four different kinds, each
of which contains an infinity of other subclasses, which again
contain as many different classes as does the class of ellipses or
of hyperbolas: for according as the ratio changes between the

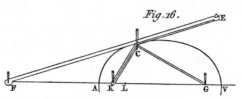

Fig. 16.

---

[7] That is, the ratio that corresponds to the index of refraction.

lines *A5* and *A6,* or other like lines, so do the subclasses of
these ovals. Then according as the ratio between the lines *AF*
and *AG,* or *AH,* is changed, the ovals of each subclass change
in kind. And according as *AG* or *AH* is longer or shorter, the
ovals differ in size. And if the lines *A5* and *A6* are equal, in
place of the ovals of the first or third classes we will describe
only straight lines; while in place of those of the second class
we will have all possible hyperbolas, and in place of those of
the fourth class, we will have all possible ellipses.

Besides this, for each of these ovals we must consider two
parts, which have different properties: in the first oval, the
part toward *A* [8] causes rays passing through the air from *F* to
converge toward point *G,* when they encounter the convex
surface *1A1* of a lens which, in accordance with what was said
in the *Optics,* has refractions such that they can all be measured by the ratio between the lines *A5* and *A6,* or similar ones,
through the aid of which we described this oval.

But the part that is toward *V* causes all the rays coming
from point *G* to be reflected toward *F,* when they meet at *G*
the concave surface of a mirror of the shape of *1V1,* which is
of a material such that it diminishes the force of these rays according to the ratio between the lines *A5* and *A6:* for from
what has been proven in the *Optics,* it is evident that as here
pointed, the angles of reflection will be inequal, as will be the
angles of refraction, and can be measured in the same way.

In the second oval the part *2A2* [9] serves again for the reflections whose angles may be assumed to be unequal. For since
it is on the surface of a mirror composed of the same material
as the preceding one, it would so reflect all the rays coming
from point *G,* that they would seem afterwards to come from
point *F.* And it is to be noted that since we have made the line
AG much longer than *AF,* this mirror would be convex in the
middle toward *A,* and concave at the edges; for such is the
shape of this line, which in this respect resembles a heart
rather than an oval.

[8] See Fig. 12, p. 216.
[9] See Fig. 13, p. 217.

But its other part, *X2,* is useful for refractions, and causes rays passing through the air toward *F* to be refracted by passing through the surface of a lens which has this form.

The third oval is useful only for refractions, and causes the rays which tend in the air toward *F* [10] to turn toward *H* in the lens, after they have passed through its surface, whose shape is *A3Y3,* which is convex everywhere except toward *A,* where it is a bit concave, so that it has the shape of a heart as does the preceding one. And the difference between the two parts of this oval consists in the fact that point *F* is nearer to the one than is point *H,* and *F* is farther away from the other than is *H.*

In the same way the fourth oval is useful only for reflections, and it causes all the rays coming from point *H,*[11] which would meet the concave surface of a mirror of the same material as the preceding ones, and whose shape is *A4Z4,* to be reflected toward *F.*

So that we can name the points *F* and *G,* or *H,* the burning points of these ovals, after the example of those of the ellipses and hyperbolas, which were so named in the *Optics.*

I omit many other refractions and reflections which are caused by these same ovals: for being but the converse, or contrary, [effects] of these here, they can easily be deduced. But there is no need for me to omit the demonstration of what I have already said, and for this purpose, let us take point *C,* for example, at random in the first section of the first of these ovals; then let us draw the straight line *CP,* which cuts the curve at right angles at point *C,*[12] which can be easily accomplished through the preceding problem. For, taking $b = AG$, $c = AF$, $c + z = FC$; and assuming that the ratio between d and e (which I shall always take here to be that which measures the refractions of the lens being considered) to represent also the ratio between the lines *A5* and *A6,* or similar ones, used to

[10] See Fig. 14, p. 217.
[11] See Fig. 15, p. 217.
[12] See Figs. 9 and 12, pp. 208 and 216.

describe this oval, then we have $b - \dfrac{e}{d}z = GC;$ and we find that the line AP is

$$\frac{bcd^2 - bcde + bd^2z + ce^2z}{bde + cd^2 + d^2z - e^2z}$$

in the same way as has been demonstrated above. Moreover, from point P, having drawn PQ at right angles on the straight line FC, and PN also at right angles on GC, let us consider that if PQ is to PN as d is to e, that is, [if they have the same ratio] as the lines which measure the refraction of the convex lens AC, then the ray that passes from point F to C must curve there, upon entering this lens, in such a way that it turns afterwards toward G. This is quite evident from what was said in the *Optics*. Then finally let us see by means of calculation if it is true that PQ is to PN as d is to e. The right triangles PQF and CMF are alike; whence it follows that CF is to CM as FP is to PQ, and consequently that if FP is multiplied by CM and divided by CF, it equals PQ. In the same way the right triangles PNG and CMG are similar, whence it follows that GP multiplied by CM and divided by CG is equal to PN. Then because the multiplying or dividing of two terms by the same term does not change the ratio between them, if

$$\frac{FP \cdot CM}{CF} : \frac{GP \cdot CM}{CG} = d : e,$$

then, dividing each term of the ratio by CM, and then multiplying each of them by CF, and again by CG, there remains $FP \cdot CG : GP \cdot CF = d : e$. Or by construction

$$FP = c + \frac{bcd^2 - bcde + bd^2z + ce^2z}{cd^2 + bde - e^2z + d^2z},$$

or else,

$$FP = \frac{bcd^2 + c^2d^2 + bd^2z + cd^2z}{cd^2 + bde - e^2z + d^2z}$$

and

$$CG = b - \frac{e}{d}z.$$

Thus, multiplying FP by CG we get

$$\frac{b^2cd^2 + bc^2d^2 + b^2d^2z + bcd^2z - bcdez - c^2dez - bdez^2 - cdez^2}{cd^2 + bde - e^2z + d^2z}.$$

Then

$$GP = b - \frac{bcd^2 - bcde + bd^2z + ce^2z}{cd^2 + bde - e^2z + d^2z};$$

or

$$GP = \frac{b^2de + bcde - be^2z - ce^2z}{cd^2 + bde - e^2z + d^2z}$$

and

$$CF = c + z;$$

so that multiplying GP by CF, we get

$$\frac{b^2cde + bc^2de + b^2dez + bcdez - bce^2z - c^2e^2z - be^2z^2 - ce^2z^2}{cd^2 + bde - e^2z + d^2z}.$$

And because the first of these sums divided by d is the same as the second divided by e, it is manifest that FP multiplied by CG is to GP multiplied by CF (i.e., PQ is to PN) as d is to e, which is what was to be demonstrated.

And you should understand that this same demonstration extends to everything that has been said of the other refractions or reflections which are brought about in the ovals under consideration, without our having to change anything but the values of the plus and minus signs of the calculation. This is why each of them may be easily determined of itself, without my having to stop to do it here.

But it is now necessary that I make up for what I omitted in the *Optics;* there, I remarked that there can be lenses of diverse shapes, each equally capable of making the rays coming from one single point of the object to assemble at another point after having passed through them; and that among these lenses, those that are convex on one side and concave on the other have more burning force than those that are equally convex on two sides, whereas on the contrary, these latter are better for telescopes. I contented myself with explaining only

those that are better in practice, by examining the difficulties
which artisans may have cutting them. This is why, so that
there may be nothing wanting concerning the theory of this
science, I shall now have to explain here again the shape of
lenses which, having one of their surfaces as convex or concave
as we might wish, nevertheless cause all the rays which come
toward them from a single point, or parallel, to converge after
having passed through them at another given point. And
[I shall also explain] the shape of lenses which cause similar
effects, but are equally convex on two sides, or else are such
that the convexity of one of their surfaces has a given ratio to
that of the other.

Let us posit, for the first case, that the points G, Y, C, and F
are given, and that the rays coming from point G, or else parallel to GA, must converge at point F after having passed through

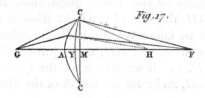

Fig. 17.

a concave lens. Let Y be the middle of the interior surface [of
this lens], and C its edge, so that the cord CMC and the alti-
tude YM of the arc CYC are given. The first question we must
consider is: given the surface of the lens YC, which shape,
among the ovals already explained, must it have in order to
cause the rays which, while they were inside, tended toward a
point such as H, not yet known, to tend toward another point,
say F, after having left the lens? For there is no effect upon
the rays' interrelation, altered by reflection or refraction from
one point to another, which cannot be brought about by some
one of these ovals; and we can easily see that this particular
result can be achieved through the part of the third oval which
earlier we marked $3A3$,[13] or by the part of the same oval

[13] See Fig. 14, p. 217.

marked *3Y3,* or finally by the section of the second oval which has been marked *2X2.*[14] And because these three fall under the same calculation, we must in each case take *Y* for their vertex, *C* for the point on their circumference, and *F* for one of their burning points. After which it remains for us only to find the point *H,* which must be the other burning point. And we can find it by considering that the difference between the lines *FY* and *FC* is to the difference between *HY* and *HC* as *d* is to *e;* that is, as the greater of the lines that measure the refractions of the proposed lens is to the lesser; this is manifest from the description of these ovals. And because the lines *FY* and *FC* are given, their difference is also given, and from this we know the difference between *HY* and *HC,* because the ratio between these two differences is given. And moreover, because *YM* is given, the difference between *MH* and *HC* is also given; and finally because *CM* is given, there remains to be found only *MH,* the side of the right triangle *CMH,* whose other side *CM* we know. We also know the difference between *CH,* the hypotenuse, and *MH,* the required side. So we can easily find *MH.* For if we take *k* for the quantity by which *CH* exceeds *MH,* and *n* for the length of the line *CM,* we will have $\frac{n^2}{2k} - \frac{1}{2}k$ for *MH.* And after thus finding point *H,* if it is found to be farther from point *Y* than is point *F,* the line *CY* must be the first part of the third class of oval, which has already been named *3A3.* But if *HY* is less than *FY,* or else if *HY* is so much greater than *HF* that the ratio of their difference to the entire line *FY* is greater than the ratio of *e,* the smaller of the lines which measure the refractions, to *d,* the larger (i.e., so much greater that if we make *HF = c* and *HY = c + h, dh* is greater than *2ce + eh*)—then *CY* must be the second part of the same oval of the third class, which has already been named *3Y3.* Or else, if *dh* is equal to or less than *2ce + eh,* then *CY* must be the second part of the oval of the second class, which above was called *2X2.* And finally if point *H* is

14 See Fig. 13, p. 217.

identical with point *F,* which only happens when *FY* and *FC* are equal, this line *CY* is a circle.

After this it is necessary to look for *CAC,* the other surface of this lens, which, if we assume the rays falling on it to be parallel, must be an ellipse whose burning point is *H;* and then it is easy to find the form. But if we assume that the rays come from point *G,* this lens must have the form of the first part of an oval of the first class, whose two burning points are *G* and *H,* and which passes through point *C;* from this we discover the point *A* as the vertex of this oval, by noting that the amount by which *GC* exceeds *GA* is to that by which *HA* exceeds *HC,* as *d* is to *e.* For, having taken *k* as the difference between *CH* and *HM,* if we assume that *AM* = *x,* we will have *x* – *k* as the difference between *AH* and *CH;* then if we let *g* represent the difference between *GC* and *GM,* which are given, we will have *g* + *x* as the difference between *GC* and *GA.* And because *g* + *x* is to *x* – *k* as *d* is to *e,* we have *ge* + *ex* = *dx* – *dk,* or $\frac{ge + dk}{d - e}$ for the line *X,* or *AM,* by means of which we determine the required point *A.*

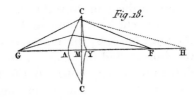

Fig. 18.

Now let us posit that for the other case, only the points *G, C,* and *F* and the ratio between the lines *AM* and *YM,* are given, and that it is required to find the lens *ACY* which causes all the rays coming from point *G* to converge at point *F.*

Here again we can use two ovals; one of these, *AC,* has *G* and *H* for its burning points, and the other, *CY,* has *F* and *H* for its burning points. And to determine these, let us first assume that *H,* which is common to both, is known. Then I look for *AM* by means of the three points *G, C, H,* in the way that I just now explained: that is, if I take k as the difference between CH and HM, and g as the difference between GC and GM, and if AC is the first part of the oval of the first class, I have $AM = \dfrac{ge + dk}{d - e}$. Then I also look for MY by means of the three points F, C, H, so that CY is the first part of an oval of the third class; and taking y as MY, and f as the difference between CF and FM, I have $f + y$ as the difference between CF and FY. Then since I already have k as the difference between CH and HM, I have $k + y$ for the difference between CH and HY; and this difference must be to $f + y$ as e is to d, because the oval is of the third class; thus I find that y or MY is $\dfrac{fe - dk}{d - e}$. Then, joining together the two quantities found for AM and MY, I find that the entire line AY is equal to $\dfrac{ge + fe}{d - e}$; from this it follows that on whatever side point H is [to lie], this line AY is always composed of a quantity which is to the quantity by which $GC + CF$ exceeds GF, as e, the lesser of the two lines used to measure the refractions of the proposed lens, is to $d - e$, the difference between these two lines: which is a rather elegant theorem. Now thus having the entire line AY, it is necessary to cut it according to the ratio which its parts AM and MY must have; by this means, since we already have point M, we also can find the points A and Y, and then point H, through the preceding problem. But first we must see if the line AM so discovered is greater or smaller than or equal to, $\dfrac{ge}{d - e}$. For if it is greater, we can gather from this that AC must be the first part of an oval of the first class, and CY the first part of an oval of the third class, as we have assumed them to be here. Whereas if it is smaller, this shows that CY must be the first part of an oval of the first class, and that AC must be the first part of one of the third class. Finally, if $AM = \dfrac{ge}{d - e}$, the two curves AC and CY must be hyperbolas.

We can extend these two problems to an infinity of other cases, which I shall not stop to deduce here, since they have had no usefulness to optics.

I could also go further, and tell you, when one surface of a lens is given—provided that it be neither completely flat nor composed of conic sections or circles—how we must make its other surface so that it may transmit all the rays from one given point to another point, also given. For this is no more difficult than what I have just explained; or rather, it is easier, because the way is now open. But I would rather others tried to solve this; for if they still have a little difficulty in finding it, then they will have more esteem for the invention of the things demonstrated here.

For the rest, in all this discussion I have spoken only of curved lines which we can describe on a flat surface. But it is easy to relate what I have said to all those curves which can be conceived to be formed by the regular movement of the points of a body in a three-dimensional space, namely, by drawing two perpendiculars from each point of the curved line we wish to consider onto two planes which intersect at right angles, one perpendicular on the one plane, the other on the other. For the ends of these perpendiculars will describe two other curves, one on each of these planes, from which, in the way explained above, we can determine all the points, and relate them to those of the straight line that is common to these two planes; and by means of these the points of the three-dimensional curve will be completely determined. Even if we wish to draw a straight line cutting this curve at right angles at the given point, it is necessary only to draw two other straight lines in the two planes, one in each, which cut at right angles the two curved lines which are at the two points where the perpendiculars which come from this given point fall. For having constructed two other planes, one on each of these straight lines, which cut the planes containing them at right angles, we will have the intersection of these two planes as the required straight line. And thus, I believe, I have omitted nothing that is necessary to the understanding of curved lines.

Third Book

Of the Construction of Solid and Supersolid Problems

Although all curved lines which can be described by some regular motion ought to be included in geometry, this does not mean that we are permitted to make indiscriminate use of the first one we encounter in the construction of any problem; instead, we must be careful always to choose the simplest curve through which the problem can be solved. And it should be noted that by "the simplest," we must understand, not only those that are the easiest to describe, nor those that most facilitate the construction or demonstration of the proposed problem, but principally those that are of the simplest class which can be used to determine the required quantity.

For example, I do not believe there is any easier or more clearly demonstrated method for finding however many mean

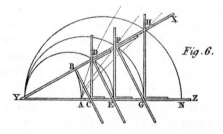

Fig. 6.

proportionals you might wish, than to use the curved lines described by the instrument *XYZ*, explained above. For if we wish to find two mean proportionals between *YA* and *YE*, we have only to describe a circle whose diameter is *YE;* and because this circle cuts the curve *AD* at point *D, YD* is one of the required mean proportionals. The demonstration is obvious to the eye, merely by applying this instrument to the line *YD:* for, as *YA,* or *YB* which is equal to it, is to *YC,* so *YC* is to *YD,* and *YD* to *YE.*

In the same way, in order to find four mean proportionals between *YA* and *YG,* or to find six of them between *YA* and *YN,* it is only necessary to trace the circle *YFG,* which, intersecting *AF* at point *F,* determines the straight line *YF,* which is one of these four proportionals; or [else to trace] *YHN,* which, intersecting *AH* at point *H,* determines *YH,* one of the six; and so with the others.

But because the curved line *AD* is of the second class, and we can find two mean proportionals by using conic sections, which are of the first class; and also because we can find four or six mean proportionals by using lines of classes not as complex as *AF* and *AH,* it would be a mistake in geometry to use these curves. And, on the other hand, it would also be a mistake to work uselessly to construct some problem through a class of lines simpler than its nature permits.

Now in order that I may give some rules for avoiding both the one mistake and the other, I must say something in general about the nature of equations—that is, about sums composed of many terms, partly known and partly unknown, some of which are equal to others, or rather, all of which taken together are equal to nothing, for it is often best to consider them in this way.

Understand, then, that in each equation there can be as many different roots (that is, values of the unknown quantity), as the unknown quantity has dimensions. For example, if we assume *x* equal to 2, or else *x* – 2 equal to zero; and again $x = 3$, or else $x - 3 = 0$, then by multiplying these equations, $x - 2 = 0$ and $x - 3 = 0$, by each other, we will have $x^2 - 5x + 6 = 0$, or else $x^2 = 5x - 6$, which is an equation in which *x* has the value 2, and simultaneously has the value 3. And if again we make $x - 4 = 0$, and multiply this by $x^2 - 5x + 6 = 0$, we will have $x^3 - 9x^2 + 26x - 24 = 0$, which is another equation in which *x*, having three dimensions, also has three values, which are 2, 3, and 4.

But often it happens that some of these roots are negative,

or less than nothing. For example, if we assume that x also designates the defect of a quantity which is 5,[1] we have $x + 5 = 0$; and this, when it is multiplied by $x^3 - 9x^2 + 26x - 24 = 0$, gives $x^4 - 4x^3 - 19x^2 + 106x - 120 = 0$, as an equation in which there are four roots—three true roots, 2, 3, and 4; and one negative root, 5.

And we see clearly from this that the sum of an equation containing many roots can always be divided by a binomial composed of the unknown quantity, minus the value of one of the true roots, whatever it may be, or plus the value of one of the negative roots, whereby we can diminish the dimensions of the equation.

And reciprocally, if the sum of an equation cannot be divided by a binomial composed of the unknown quantity, plus or minus some other quantity, this shows that the latter quantity is not the value of any of the equation's roots. Thus, this last equation

$$x^4 - 4x^3 - 19x^2 + 106x - 120 = 0$$

can be divided by $x - 2$, $x - 3$, $x - 4$, and $x + 5$, but not by x plus or minus any other quantity, which shows that it can only have the four roots 2, 3, 4, and 5.

We can also know from this how many true and how many negative roots there can be in each equation, namely, there can be as many true roots as the number of times the plus and minus signs change; and as many negative roots as the number of times there are two plus or two minus signs in succession. Thus, in the last equation, since $+ x^4$ is followed by $- 4x^3$, which is a change from the plus sign to the minus, and $- 19x^2$ is followed by $+ 106x$, and $+ 106x$ by $- 120$, which are two more changes, we know that there are three true roots; and because the two minus signs of $4x^3$ and $19x^2$ follow one another, we know there is one negative root.

Moreover, in the same equation, it is easy to make all the roots which were negative become true ones, and by the same means, to make all the previously true roots become negative.

[1] That is, $x = -5$, and -5 is the remainder when 5 is taken from 0.

We can do this by changing all the plus and minus signs of the second, fourth, sixth, or other even numbers, while leaving those of the first, third, fifth, and all the other odd terms unchanged. Thus, if in place of

$$x^4 - 4x^3 - 19x^2 + 106x - 120 = 0$$

we write

$$x^4 + 4x^3 - 19x^2 - 106x - 120 = 0,$$

we have an equation in which there is only one true root, 5, and three negative roots, 2, 3, and 4.

And if, without knowing the value of the roots of an equation, we wish to increase or diminish it by some known quantity, it is only necessary to assume, in the place of the unknown quantity, another which is greater or lesser than this same quantity by the given number, and to substitute it throughout the equation in place of the first. Thus, if we desire to increase by 3 the root of this equation:

$$x^4 + 4x^3 - 19x^2 - 106x - 120 = 0,$$

we must substitute y for x, and assume that y is greater than x by 3, so that $y - 3 = x$; and in place of x^2, we must put the square of $(y - 3)$, or $y^2 - 6y + 9$; and for x^3, we put its cube, which is $y^3 - 9y^2 + 27y - 27$; and finally in place of x^4 we must put its fourth power, which is $y^4 - 12y^3 + 54y^2 - 108y + 81$. And so, describing the preceding sum by substituting y for x throughout, we have

$$
\begin{array}{r}
y^4 - 12y^3 + 54y^2 - 108y + 81 \\
+ 4y^3 - 36y^2 + 108y - 108 \\
- 19y^2 - 114y - 171 \\
- 106y - 318 \\
- 120 \\
\hline
y^4 - 8y^3 - y^2 + 8y = 0,
\end{array}
$$

or else,

$$y^3 - 8y^2 - y + 8 = 0,$$

where the true root, which was 5, is now 8, because the number 3 was added to it.

But if we wish, on the contrary, to diminish the root of the same equation by three, we must make $y + 3 = x$, and $y^2 + 6y + 9 = x^2$, and so with the others: so that in place of $x^4 + 4x^3 - 19x^2 - 106x - 120 = 0$, we put

$$
\begin{array}{l}
y^4 + 12y^3 + 54y^2 + 108y + 81 \\
 + 4y^3 + 36y^2 + 108y + 108 \\
 - 19y^2 - 114y - 171 \\
 - 106y - 318 \\
 - 120 \\
\hline
y^4 + 16y^3 + 71y^2 - 4y - 420 = 0,
\end{array}
$$

And it should be noted that in augmenting the true roots of an equation, we diminish the negative roots by the same quantity, whereas, on the contrary, in diminishing the true, we augment the negative; and if we diminish either true or negative roots by an amount that is equal to them, they become zero, and diminishing them by a quantity which is greater than they are makes a true root negative and a negative one true. Thus in this case, by augmenting by 3 the true root, which was 5, we have diminished each of the negative roots by 3, so that the one which was 4 is now only 1, and that which was 3 is zero, and that which was 2 is now a true root equal to 1, because $-2 + 3 = +1$. This is why, in the equation

$$y^3 - 8y^2 + 1y + 8 = 0,$$

there are no more than three roots, among which there are two true roots, 1 and 8, and one negative, which is also 1. And in the other equation

$$y^4 + 16y^3 - 71y^2 - 4y - 420 = 0,$$

there is only one true root, which is 2, because $5 - 3 = 2$, and three negative roots, which are 5, 6, and 7.

Now by this method of changing the value of the roots of an equation without knowing them, we can do two things which will have, hereinafter, some use. The first is that we can always remove the second term of the equation we are examining, by diminishing its true roots by the known quantity of the second term, divided by the number of dimensions of the first term, if one of these terms is marked +, and the other −;

or else by augmenting the roots by the same quantity, if they are both marked by the same sign. Thus, in order to remove the second term of the last equation, which is $y^4 - 16y^3 + 71y^2 - 4y - 420 = 0$, having divided 16 by 4, because of the four dimensions of the term y^4, it again becomes 4. This is why I make $z - 4 = y$, and I write

$$\begin{array}{r} z^4 - 16z^3 + 96z^2 - 256z + 256 \\ + 16z^3 - 192z^2 + 768z - 1024 \\ + 71z^2 - 568z + 1136 \\ - 4z + 16 \\ - 420 \\ \hline z^4 \qquad - 25z^2 - 60z - 36 = 0; \end{array}$$

where the true root, which was 2, is now 6, because it is augmented by 4, and the negative roots, which were 5, 6, and 7, are only 1, 2, and 3, because they are each diminished by 4.

In the same way, if we want to remove the second term of $x^4 - 2ax^3 + (2a^2 - c^2)x^2 - 2a^3x + a^4 = 0$, since $2a$ divided by 4 is $\frac{1}{2}a$, we must make $z + \frac{1}{2}a = x$, and write

$$\begin{array}{r} z^4 + 2az^3 + \frac{3}{2}a^2z^2 + \frac{1}{2}a^3z + \frac{1}{16}a^4 \\ - 2az^3 - 3a^2z^2 - \frac{3}{2}a^3z - \frac{1}{4}a^4 \\ + 2a^2z^2 + 2a^3z + \frac{1}{2}a^4 \\ - c^2z^2 - ac^2z - \frac{1}{4}a^2c^2 \\ - 2a^3z - a^4 \\ + a^4 \\ \hline z^4 + (\frac{1}{2}a^2 - c^2)z^2 - (a^3 + ac^2)z + \frac{5}{16}a^4 - \frac{1}{4}a^2c^2 = 0. \end{array}$$

And if after this we find the value of z, we will have the value of x by adding $\frac{1}{2}a$ to z.

The second thing which will be useful hereinafter is that if we augment the value of the true roots by a quantity greater than any of the negative roots, we can always make all the roots become true ones, so that there will be no two consecutive plus or minus terms; and besides this, the known quantity of the third term will be greater than the square of half that of the second term. For, although this is done when these negative roots are unknown, it is nevertheless easy to judge their approximate size, and then take a quantity which exceeds the roots by as much or more than is required for this result. Thus, if we have

$$x^6 + nx^5 - 6n^2x^4 + 36n^3x^3 - 216n^4x^2 + 1296n^5x - 7776n^6 = 0,$$

by making $y - 6n = x$, we will have

$$
\begin{array}{l}
y^6 - 36n\Big) \\
\quad + n\Big)
\end{array}
\begin{array}{l}
y^5 + 540n^2\Big) \\
\quad - 30n^2\Big\} \\
\quad - 6n^2\Big)
\end{array}
\begin{array}{l}
y^4 - 4320n^3\Big) \\
\quad + 360n^3\Big\} \\
\quad + 144n^3\Big(\\
\quad + 36n^3\Big)
\end{array}
\begin{array}{l}
y^3 + 19440n^4\Big) \\
\quad - 2160n^4\Big(\\
\quad - 1296n^4\Big\} \\
\quad - 648n^4\Big(\\
\quad - 216n^4\Big)
\end{array}
\begin{array}{l}
y^2 - 46656n^5\Big) \\
\quad + 6480n^5\Big(\\
\quad + 5184n^5\Big\rangle \\
\quad + 3888n^5\Big(\\
\quad + 2592n^5\Big(\\
\quad + 1296n^5\Big)
\end{array}
\begin{array}{l}
y + 46656n^6 \\
\quad - 7776n^6 \\
\quad - 7776n^6 \\
\quad - 7776n^6 \\
\quad - 7776n^6 \\
\quad - 7776n^6 \\
\quad - 7776n^6
\end{array}
$$

$$y^6 - 35ny^5 + 504n^2y^4 - 3780n^3y^3 + 15120n^4y^2 - 27216n^5y = 0.$$

From this it is manifest that $504n^2$, which is the known quantity of the third term, is greater than the square of $\dfrac{35n}{2}$, which is half that of the second term. And there is no case where the quantity by which we increase the true roots need be, for this effect, larger in proportion to those given, than for this one here.

But if the last term is zero, and we do not desire that it be so, we must again augment by a little bit the value of the roots, but not by so little that it is not sufficient for this effect. Similarly, if we want to raise the number of dimensions of some equation, and insure that all the places of its terms be filled—if, for example, instead of $x^5 - b = 0$, we wish to have an equation in which none of the terms are zero—we must first, for $x^5 - b = 0$, write $x^6 - bx = 0$; then, having made $y - a = x$, we will have

$$y^6 - 6ay^5 + 15a^2y^4 - 20a^3y^3 + 15a^4y^2 - (6a^5 + b)y + a^6 + ab = 0.$$

Whence it is obvious that, however small we assume the quantity a to be, all the places of the equation are nevertheless filled.

In addition, without knowing the value of the true roots of an equation, we can multiply or divide them all by any known quantity we want. This is done by assuming that the unknown quantity, when multiplied or divided by the quantity by which the root is to be multiplied or divided, is equal to another unknown quantity; then multiplying or dividing the known quantity of the second term by this given quantity, and the known quantity of the third term by the square of the given quantity, and that in the fourth term by the cube of the given quantity, and so on to the end.

This can be useful in reducing fractions—and often also the surds in an equation—to whole and rational numbers. Thus, if we have

$$x^3 - \sqrt{3}x^2 + \frac{26}{27}x - \frac{8}{27\sqrt{3}} = 0,$$

and we want to have another equation instead, in which all the terms are expressed in rational numbers, we must assume $y = x\sqrt{3}$, and multiply by $\sqrt{3}$ the known quantity of the second term, which is also $\sqrt{3}$; and the third term which is $\frac{26}{27}$, by the cube of $\sqrt{3}$, which is 3; and the last term, which is $\frac{8}{27\sqrt{3}}$ by the cube of $\sqrt{3}$, which is $3\sqrt{3}$. This gives

$$y^3 - 3y^2 + \frac{26}{9}x - \frac{8}{9} = 0.$$

Then, if we want again to replace the equation by another whose known quantities are expressed only by whole numbers, we must assume $z = 3y$, and multiplying 3 by 3, 26/9 by 9, and 8/9 by 27, we find:

$$z^3 - 9z^2 + 26z - 24 = 0,$$

and since the roots of this equation are 2, 3, and 4, we know from this that the roots of the preceding equation were 2/3, 1, and 4/3, and that those of the first were $\frac{2}{9}\sqrt{3}$, $\frac{1}{3}\sqrt{3}$, and $\frac{4}{9}\sqrt{3}$.

This operation can also be used to make the known quantity of any term of the equation equal to some other given term. Thus, if we have

$$x^3 - b^2x - c^3 = 0,$$

and we wish to replace it with another equation in which the known quantity of the term which occupying the third place [2]

---

[2] In the original, the equation is $x^3 * - b^2x + c^3 = 0$. Descartes uses the asterisk to indicate that a term is missing; thus, "third place."

in the equation, namely b^2, is replaced by $3a^2$, we must assume

$$y = x \sqrt{\frac{3a^2}{b^2}},$$

and then write

$$y^3 - 3a^2 y + \frac{3a^3 c^3}{b^3} \sqrt{3} = 0.$$

For the rest [note that] the true roots, as well as the negative ones, are not always real, but sometimes only imaginary; that is, while we can always conceive as many roots for each equation as I have stated, still there is sometimes no quantity corresponding to those we conceive. Thus, although we can conceive three roots in the equation

$$x^3 - 6x^2 + 13x - 10 = 0$$

there is nevertheless only one real root, 2, and no matter how we may augment, diminish, or multiply the other two, in the way just explained, they will still be imaginary.

Now, when in order to find the construction of some problem, we come to an equation in which the unknown quantity has three dimensions, we must first, if the known quantities in the equation contain some fractions,[3] reduce them to other whole numbers by the multiplication already explained. And if they contain surds, we must reduce these, too, to other rational numbers, as much as possible, either by this same multiplication or by various other means which are easy enough to find. Then, examining in order all the quantities by which the last term can be divided with no remainder, we must see if some one of them, joined to the unknown quantity by a plus or minus sign, can compose a binomial by which the entire sum can be divided. And if this is the case, the problem is plane, that is, it can be constructed with ruler and compass. For either the known quantity of this binomial is the required root, or else the equation, when divided by it, is reduced to two dimensions, so that we can afterwards find its root, through what was explained in the first book.

[3] *Nombres rompus*, literally. "broken numbers."

For example, if we have $y^6 - 8y^4 - 124y^2 - 64 = 0$, the last term, 64, can be divided without remainder by 1, 2, 4, 8, **16, 32,** and 64. This is why it is necessary to examine, by order, to see if this equation can be divided by any of the binomials, $y^2 - 1$, $y^2 + 1$, $y^2 - 2$, $y^2 + 2$, $y^2 - 4$, and so on; and we find that it can be divided by $y^2 - 16$, in this way:

$$
\begin{array}{l}
+ \ y^6 - \ \ 8y^4 - 124y^2 - 64 = 0 \\
- \ y^6 - \ \ 8y^4 - \ \ \ 4y^2 - 16 \\
\hline
\ \ 0 \ \ - 16y^4 - 128y^2 \\
\ \ \ \ \ \ \ - 16 \ \ - \ \ 16 \\
\hline
\ \ \ \ \ + \ \ y^4 + \ \ \ 8y^2 + \ \ 4 = 0.
\end{array}
$$

I begin with the last term, and divide $- 64$ by $- 16$, which gives $+ 4$, which I write in the quotient. Then I multiply $+ 4$ by $+ y^2$, which gives $+ 4y^2$, and this is why I write $- 4y^2$ in the dividend, for it is always necessary to write the opposite plus or minus sign than that which the multiplication produces. And adding $- 124y^2$ to $4y^2$, I have $128y^2$, which I again divide by $- 16$, and I have $8y^2$ to put in the quotient. And multiplying it by y^2, I have $- 8y^4$ to be added to the dividend, which is also $- 8y^4$; and these two together are $- 16y^4$, which I divide by $- 16$. This gives $+ 1y^4$ for the quotient, and $- 1y^6$ to join with $+ 1y^6$: which equals zero, and shows that the division is finished. But if there were a remainder, or if there were some of the preceding terms which we had not been able to divide by 16, then we would have had to recognize from that that it could not be done.

In the same way, if we have

$$
\left. y^6 + \begin{array}{c} a^2 \\ -2c^2 \end{array} \right\} y^4 - \begin{array}{c} a^4 \\ +c^4 \end{array} \right\} y^2 - \left. \begin{array}{c} a^6 \\ -2a^4c^2 \\ -a^2c^4 \end{array} \right\} = 0,
$$

the last term can be divided, without remainder, by a, a^2, $a^2 + c^2$, $a^3 + ac^2$, and the like. But there are only two of them we need consider, namely a^2 and $a^2 + c^2$; for the others, giving more or fewer dimensions in the quotient than there are in the known quantity of the penultimate term, will prevent the division from being done. And note that I here count y^6 as having only three dimensions,[4] because there is no y^5, y^3, or y, in the whole equation. Now by examining the binomial

$$y^2 - a^2 - c^2 = 0,$$

we find that the division can be performed by means of it in this way:

$$
\left.
\begin{array}{l}
+y^6 + a^2 \\
-y^6 - 2c^2
\end{array}
\right\} y^4
\left.
\begin{array}{l}
- a^4 \\
+ c^4
\end{array}
\right\} y^2
\left.
\begin{array}{l}
- a^6 \\
- 2a^4c^2
\end{array}
\right\} = 0
$$

$$
\frac{
\left.
\begin{array}{l}
0 - 2a^2 \\
+ c^2
\end{array}
\right\} y^4
\left.
\begin{array}{l}
- a^4 \\
- a^2c^2
\end{array}
\right\} y^2
\left.
\begin{array}{l}
- a^2c^4 \\
\end{array}
\right.
}{
-a^2 - c^2 \qquad -a^2 - c^2 \qquad - \quad a^2 - c^2
}
$$

$$
+y^4 \qquad
\left.
\begin{array}{l}
+ 2a^2 \\
- c^2
\end{array}
\right\} y^2
\left.
\begin{array}{l}
+ a^4 \\
+ a^2c^2
\end{array}
\right\} = 0;
$$

this shows that the required root is $a^2 + c^2$, which can be proven easily by multiplication.

But when we can find no binomial into which the entire sum of the proposed equation can be divided, it is certain that the problem which depends upon it is solid. And it is then no less mistaken to try to construct it by using only circles and straight lines, as it would be to use conic sections to construct those problems which need only circles; because, in a word, anything that attests to ignorance is called a mistake.

And if we have an equation in which the unknown quantity has four dimensions, in the same way, after we have removed the fractions and surds, if there are any, we must see if we can find a binomial divisor for the entire sum, by composing it of one of the quantities into which the last term can be divided without remainder. And if we find one of them, either the known quantity of this binomial is the required root, or at least, after this division, there will remain only three dimensions in the equation, after which it will again be necessary to examine it in the same way. But when no such binomial is to be found, we must eliminate the second term of the sum by augmenting or diminishing the value of the root, in the manner already explained; and afterwards, we must reduce it to another sum containing only three dimensions. This is done

[4] Or as we would now say, "I count y^6 as of the third degree."

as follows: in place of

$$x^4 \pm px^2 \pm qx \pm r = 0,$$

we must write

$$y^6 \pm 2py^4(p^2 \pm 4r)y^2 - q^2 = 0.$$

And for the plus or minus signs, which I have left out, if there had been $+p$ in the first equation, it would be necessary to put $+2p$ in the second; or if it had been $-p$ in the first, then $-2p$ in the second. And on the other hand, if it had been $+r$ in the first, it would be $-4r$ in the second, or if $-r$, then $+4r$; but whether it was $+q$ or $-q$ in the first equation, it is always necessary to write $-q^2$ and $+p^2$ in the second, provided that x^4 and y^6 are marked with the plus sign, for if they were marked with a minus sign, we would write $+q^2$ and $-p^2$.

For example, if we have

$$x^4 - 4x^2 - 8x + 35 = 0$$

we must write in its place

$$y^6 - 8y^4 - 124y^2 - 64 = 0.$$

For since the quantity that I have called p is equal to -4, we must substitute $-8y^4$ for $2py^4$; and since the quantity I have called r is equal to 35, we must replace $(p^2 - 4r)y^2$ by $(16 - 140)y^2$; that is, by $-124y^2$. And finally since q is equal to 8, we must substitute -64 for $-q^2$. In the same way, instead of

$$x^4 - 17x^2 - 20x - 6 = 0,$$

we must write

$$y^6 - 34y^4 + 313y^2 - 400 = 0.$$

For 34 is twice 17, and 313 is the square of 17 added to four times 6, and 400 is the square of 20.

In the same way, also, in place of

$$z^4 + (\tfrac{1}{2}a^2 - c^2)z^2 - (a^3 + ac^2)z - \tfrac{1}{16}a^4 - \tfrac{1}{4}a^2c^2 = 0,$$

we must write

$$y^6 + (a^2 - 2c^2)y^4 + (c^4 - a^4)y^2 - a^6 - 2a^4c^2 - a^2c^4 = 0;$$

for p equals $\frac{1}{2}a^2 - c^2$, and p^2 equals $\frac{1}{4}a^4 - a^2c^2 + c^4$, and $4r$ equals $-\frac{5}{4}a^4 + a^2c^2$, and finally $-q^2$ equals $-a^6 - 2a^4c^2 - a^2c^4$.

When the equation is thus reduced to three dimensions, we must look for the value of y^2 through the method already explained. And if this cannot be found, there is no need to go further, for it follows inevitably from this that the problem is solid. But if we find it, by that means we can divide the preceding equation into two others, each of which has an unknown quantity of only two dimensions, and has roots that will be the same as those of the original equation. That is, in place of

$$x^4 \pm px^2 \pm qx \pm r = 0,$$

we must write these two other equations:

$$x^2 - yx + \tfrac{1}{2}y^2 \pm \tfrac{1}{2}p \pm \frac{q}{2y} = 0,$$

and

$$x^2 + yx + \tfrac{1}{2}y^2 \pm \tfrac{1}{2}p \pm \frac{q}{2y} = 0.$$

And as for the plus and minus signs which I have omitted, if there is $+p$ in the preceding equation, it is necessary to put $+\frac{1}{2}p$ in each of the two substitutes, and $-\frac{1}{2}p$ when p has a negative sign. But it is necessary to put $+\frac{q}{2y}$ when we have $-yx$, and $-\frac{q}{2y}$ when we have $+yx$, when there is $+q$ in the first equation. But on the contrary if $-q$ is in the first equation, we must put $-\frac{q}{2y}$ in the one where we have $-yx$, and $+\frac{q}{2y}$ in the one where we have $+yx$. Following this, it is easy to know all the roots of the proposed equation, and consequently to construct the problem whose solution it contains, without using anything but circles and straight lines.

For example, because by substituting

$$y^6 - 34y^4 + 313y^2 - 400 = 0$$

for

$$x^4 - 17x^2 - 20x - 6 = 0,$$

we find that $y^2 = 16$, in place of the equation

$$x^4 - 17x^2 - 20x - 6 = 0,$$

we must write these two others:

$$x^2 - 4x - 3 = 0, \quad \text{and} \quad x^2 + 4x + 2 = 0.$$

For y equals 4, $\frac{1}{2}y^2$ equals 8, p equals 17, and q equals 20; so that

$$\tfrac{1}{2}y^2 - \tfrac{1}{2}p - \frac{q}{2y} = -3,$$

and

$$\tfrac{1}{2}y^2 - \tfrac{1}{2}p + \frac{q}{2y} = +2.$$

And extracting the roots of these two equations, we find the same results as if we had extracted the roots of the equation with x^4; that is, we find one true root $\sqrt{7+2}$, and three negative ones, $\sqrt{7-2}$, $2 + \sqrt{2}$, and $2 - \sqrt{2}$. Thus if we have

$$x^4 - 4x^2 - 8x + 35 = 0,$$

because the root of

$$y^6 - 8y^4 - 124y^2 - 64 = 0$$

is once again 16, we must write

$$x^2 - 4x + 5 = 0, \quad \text{and} \quad x^2 + 4x + 7 = 0.$$

For here $+\frac{1}{2}y^2 - \frac{1}{2}p - \dfrac{q}{2y}$ equals 5, and $\frac{1}{2}y^2 - \frac{1}{2}p + \dfrac{q}{2y} = 7$.

And because we can find no root, either true or negative, in these latter two equations, we know from this that the four roots of the equation from which they proceed are imaginary; and that the problem for which we discovered this equation is plane by nature, but that it cannot in any way be constructed, because the given quantities cannot be added.

In the same way, if we have

$$z^4 + (\tfrac{1}{2}a^2 - c^2)z^2 - (a^3 + ac^2)z + \tfrac{5}{16}a^4 - \tfrac{1}{4}a^2c^2 = 0,$$

because we find that y^2 is $a^2 + c^2$, we must write

$$z^2 - \sqrt{a^2 + c^2}\,z + \tfrac{3}{4}a^2 - \tfrac{1}{2}a\sqrt{a^2 + c^2} = 0,$$

and

$$z^2 + \sqrt{a^2 + c^2}\,z + \tfrac{3}{4}a^2 + \tfrac{1}{2}a\sqrt{a^2 + c^2} = 0;$$

for y equals $\sqrt{a^2 + c^2}$ and $\tfrac{1}{2}y^2 + \tfrac{1}{2}p$ equals $\tfrac{3}{4}a^2$, and $\dfrac{q}{2y}$ equals $\tfrac{1}{2}a\sqrt{a^2 + c^2}$. From this we learn that the value of z is

$$\tfrac{1}{2}\sqrt{a^2 + c^2} + \sqrt{-\tfrac{1}{2}a^2 + \tfrac{1}{4}c^2 + \tfrac{1}{2}a\sqrt{a^2 + c^2}},$$

or

$$\tfrac{1}{2}\sqrt{a^2 + c^2} - \sqrt{-\tfrac{1}{2}a^2 + \tfrac{1}{4}c^2 + \tfrac{1}{2}a\sqrt{a^2 + c^2}}.$$

And, because above we made $z + \tfrac{1}{2}a = x$, we learn that the quantity x, which we performed all these operations in order to know, is

$$\tfrac{1}{2}a + \sqrt{\tfrac{1}{4}a^2 + \tfrac{1}{4}c^2 - \sqrt{\tfrac{1}{4}c^2 - \tfrac{1}{2}a^2 + \tfrac{1}{2}a\sqrt{a^2 + c^2}}}.$$

But in order for us better to understand the utility of this rule, I must apply it to some problem.

If the square AD and the line BN are given, we must extend the side AC to E, so that EF, drawn from E toward B, is equal

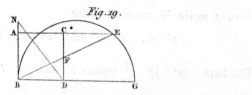

Fig. 29.

to NB. We learn from Pappus that if we first extend BD to G, so that DG is equal to DN, and if we describe a circle whose diameter is BG, then if we extend the straight line AC, it will meet the circumference of this circle at the point E which was required. But for those who do not know of this construction, it would not be easy to hit upon it, and by looking for it by means of the method here proposed, they would never think to take DG as the unknown quantity, but rather CF or FD, because those are the ones which lead most easily to the equation. And thus they would find an equation which would not be easy to solve, without the rule I have just explained. For, positing a for BD or CD, and c for EF, and x for DF, we have $CF = a - x$; and CF, or $a - x$, is to FE, or C, as FD, or x, is to BF, which is as a result $\dfrac{cx}{a - x}$. Then, because BDF is a right triangle, whose sides are x and a, their squares, x^2 and a^2, are equal to the square of the hypotenuse, which is $\dfrac{c^2x^2}{x^2 - 2ax + a^2}$; thus multiplying the whole by $x^2 - 2ax + a^2$, we find that the equation is

$$x^4 - 2ax^3 + 2a^2x^2 - 2a^3x + a^4 = c^2x^2,$$

or

$$x^4 - 2ax^3 + (2a^2 - c^2)x^2 - 2a^3x + a^4 = 0.$$

And if we posit BF or CE or BE as the unknown quantity, we again get an equation which has four dimensions, but which is much simpler to solve, and we come by the equation rather easily; if DG were to be used, on the other hand, the equation would be much more difficult to arrive at, but very simple to solve. I put this here to advise you that when the proposed problem is not solid, if we arrive at a very complex equation when looking for it through one method, we can ordinarily arrive at a much simpler one if we look for it through another method.

I could still add different rules for solving cubic or biquadratic equations, but they would be superfluous, for as long as the problems are plane, you can always find the construction through the methods given here.

I could also add other rules for equations which go as high as the supersolid, or the sixth dimension, or higher; but I prefer to include them in one rule, and say in general that, when we have tried to reduce the given equations to the same form as those having as many dimensions as the product of two other equations of lower degree, and if, once we enumerate all the means through which such a multiplication is possible, none turns out to be successful, then we may be assured that the given equations cannot be reduced to simpler ones. So that if the unknown quantity has three or four dimensions, the problem in which we are seeking it is solid; and if it has five or six dimensions, it is one degree more complex, and so with the others.

Finally, I have not demonstrated here most of what I have said, because the demonstrations seem to me so simple that, provided you take the pains to see methodically whether I have been mistaken, they will present themselves to you; and it will be of much more value to you to learn them this way than by reading them.

Now when we are sure that the proposed problem is solid, whether the equation through which we seek its solution is of the fourth degree or only of the third, we can always find its root with one of the three conic sections, whichever it be—or even with some part of one of them, however small—using nothing else but straight lines and circles. But I shall be content here to give a general rule for finding them all by means of a parabola, because it is, in some respects, the simplest of curves.

First, we must eliminate the second term of the equation, if it is not already zero, and thus reduce the equation to a form such as $z^3 = \pm apz \pm a^2q$, if the unknown quantity has but three dimensions; or else a form such as $z^4 = \pm apz^2 \pm a^2qz \pm a^3r$, if it has four dimensions. Or, by taking a as unity, the first becomes $z^3 = \pm pz \pm q$ and the latter $z^4 = \pm pz^2 \pm qz \pm r$.

After this, assuming that the parabola FAG has already been described, and that its axis is $ACDKL$, and that its right side is a or 1, of which AC is half; and finally assume that point C is inside the parabola, and A is the vertex. We must make $CD = \frac{1}{2}p$, and take it on the same side as point A, relative to C, if the equation contains $+ p$; but if it contains $- p$,

we must take it on the other side. Then from point *D*—or, if
the quantity *p* is zero, from *C*—it is necessary to raise a perpen-

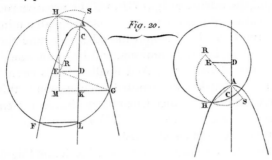

Fig. 20.

dicular to *E*, so that this line is equal to $\frac{1}{2}q$. And finally, from
the center *E*, it is necessary to describe the circle *FG*, whose
radius is *AE* if the equation is cubic, so that the quantity *r* is

zero. But when the equation contains
+ *r*, on the extension of this line *AE*
produced, we must on one side take *AR*
equal to *r*, and on the other take *AS*
equal to the right side of the parabola,
which is 1. And when we have described
a circle whose diameter is *RS*, we must
draw *AH* perpendicular to *AE*, and *AH*
will meet this cricle *RHS* at point *H*,
through which the other circle *FHG*
must pass. And when – *r* is in the equation, after we have so found the line
AH, we must inscribe *AI*, which is equal
to it, in another circle whose diameter
is *AE*; and then *FIG*, the first required
circle, must pass through this point *I*.
Now this circle *FG* may intersect or
touch the parabola at one, two, three,
or four points; if from these we draw
perpendiculars to the axis, we have all

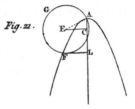

Fig. 21.

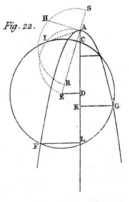

Fig. 22.

the roots of the equation, true as well as negative. That is, if
the quantity *q* is marked with a plus sign, the true roots will

be those among these perpendiculars, such as *FL,* which will be on the same side of the parabola as *E,* the center of the circle; and the others, such as *GK,* will be negative roots. But on the contrary, if this quantity *q* is marked with a minus sign, the true roots will be those on the other side, and those that are negative, or less than nothing, will be on the same side as *E,* the center of the circle. And finally, if this circle neither intersects nor touches the parabola at any point, this shows that there is no root, either true or negative, in the equation, and that they are all imaginary. Thus this rule is as general and as complete as one could wish.

And its demonstration is very easy. For if the line *GK,* discovered through this construction, is called *z, AK* will be z^2, because of the parabola in which *GK* must be the mean proportional between *AK* and the right side, which is 1. Then, if from *AK* I take *AC,* which is $\frac{1}{2}$, and *CD,* which is $\frac{1}{2}p$, there remains *DK* or *EM,* which is $z^2 - \frac{1}{2}p - \frac{1}{2}$, whose square is

$$z^4 - pz^2 - z^2 + \tfrac{1}{4}p^2 + \tfrac{1}{2}p + \tfrac{1}{4};$$

and because *DE* or *KM* equals $\frac{1}{2}q$, the whole of *GM* is equal to $z + \frac{1}{2}q$, whose square is

$$z^2 + qz + \tfrac{1}{4}q^2;$$

and adding these two squares we have

$$z^4 - pz^2 + qz + \tfrac{1}{4}q^2 + \tfrac{1}{4}p^2 + \tfrac{1}{2}p + \tfrac{1}{4}$$

for the square of the line *GE,* because it is the hypotenuse of the right triangle *EMG.*

But, because this same line *GE* is the radius of the circle *FG,* it can be explained in still other terms; namely, if *ED* is equal to $\frac{1}{2}q$, and *AD* is $\frac{1}{2}p + \frac{1}{2}$, *EA* is

$$\sqrt{\tfrac{1}{4}q^2 + \tfrac{1}{4}p^2 + \tfrac{1}{2}p + \tfrac{1}{4}},$$

because *ADE* is a right angle. Then, if *HA* is the mean proportional between *AS,* which is 1, and *AR,* which equals *r,* it is equal to $\sqrt{r}$; and because *EAH* is a right angle, the square of *HE* or *FG* is $\frac{1}{4}q^2 + \frac{1}{4}p^2 + \frac{1}{2}p + \frac{1}{4} + r$. Thus there is an equation between this sum and the preceding one, which is the same as

$z^4 = pz^2 - qz + r$; and as a result, the discovered line GK, which has been called z, is the root of this equation, which was what was to be demonstrated. And if you apply this same method of calculation to all the other cases of this rule, changing the plus and minus signs appropriately, you will find satisfaction in the same way, without my needing to pause over it here.

If then, following this rule, we wish to find two mean proportionals between the lines a and q,[5] it is clear to everyone that if we represent one of the proportionals by z, then a is to z as $\dfrac{z^2}{a}$ is to $\dfrac{z^3}{a^2}$. Thus there is an equation between q and $\dfrac{z^3}{a^2}$, that is to say, $z^3 = a^2q$. And when the parabola FAG is described, along with part of its axis AC, which is equal to $\frac{1}{2}a$, or half the right side, we must at point C erect the perpendicular CE equal to $\frac{1}{2}q$; and by describing the circle AF from the

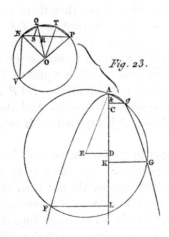

Fig. 23.

center E, through A, we find FL and LA as the two required mean proportionals.

In the same way, if we wish to divide the angle NOP—or rather the arc, or portion of the circle, $NQTP$—into three equal parts, we take $NO = 1$ for the radius of the circle, and $NP = q$ for the chord subtending the given arc, and $NQ = z$ for the chord subtending a third of that arc, we get the equation

$$z^3 = 3z - q.$$

For, if we draw the lines NQ, OQ, and OT, and make QS parallel to TO, we see that as NO is to NQ, so NQ is to QR, and QR to RS: so that if NO is 1, and NQ is z, then QR equals z^2 and RS equals z^3. And because only RS, or z^3, is lacking in order for the line NP, which is q, to be triple NQ, which is z, we have $q = 3z - z^3$, or else $z^3 = 3z - q$.

Then, if we describe the parabola FAG, and if CA, the half of its principal right side, is $\frac{1}{2}$; and then if we take $CD = \frac{3}{2}$, and the perpendicular $DE = \frac{1}{2}q$, and if, from the center E we describe the circle $FAgG$ through A, it will cut this parabola at the three points F, g, and G, not counting point A, which is the vertex. This shows that there are three roots in this equation, namely, the two true roots GK and gk, and the third, FL, which is negative. And of these two true roots, it is the smallest, gk, which must be taken for the line NQ, which was required. For the other, GK, is equal to NV, the subtending chord of the third part of the arc NVP which, with the other arc NQP, completes the circle. And the negative root, FL, is equal to QN and NV together, as is easy to see through the calculation.

It would be superfluous for me to stop here to give more examples; for all problems that are merely solid can be reduced to such a point that we do not need this rule for constructing them—except insofar as it serves to find two mean proportionals, or else to divide an angle into three equal parts. Thus you can see, by considering that the difficulties of these problems can always be expressed by equations that go no higher than the third or fourth degree, that all equations of the fourth degree can be reduced to those of the second, by means of certain others no higher than the third degree; and finally, that we can eliminate the second term of these equations so that there are none that cannot be reduced to some one of these three forms:

$$z^3 = -pz + q,$$
$$z^3 = +pz + q,$$
$$z^3 = +pz - q.$$

Now, if we have $z^3 = -pz + q$, the rule that Cardan attributes to a man named Scipio Ferreus tells us that the root is:

$$\sqrt[3]{+\tfrac{1}{2}q + \sqrt{\tfrac{1}{4}q^2 + \tfrac{1}{27}p^3}} - \sqrt[3]{-\tfrac{1}{2}q + \sqrt{\tfrac{1}{4}q^2 + \tfrac{1}{27}p^3}};$$

as also, when we have $z^3 = +pz + q$, where the square of half the last term is greater than the cube of one-third of the known quantity of the penultimate term, a corresponding rule tells us that the root is

$$\sqrt[3]{+\tfrac{1}{2}q + \sqrt{\tfrac{1}{4}q^2 - \tfrac{1}{27}p^3}} + \sqrt[3]{+\tfrac{1}{2}q - \sqrt{\tfrac{1}{4}q^2 - \tfrac{1}{27}p^3}}.$$

It appears from this that we can construct all problems whose difficulties can be reduced to one of these two forms, without using conic sections for anything other than extracting the cubic roots of certain given quantities; that is, for finding two mean proportionals between these quantities and unity.

Then, if we have $z^3 = +pz + q$, and if the square of half of the last term is not greater than the cube of one-third of the known quantity of the penultimate term, by assuming the circle $NQPV$, whose radius NO is $\sqrt{\tfrac{1}{3}p}$, that is, the mean proportional between one-third of the given quantity p and unity; and also assuming the line NP, inscribed in this circle, to be $\dfrac{3q}{p}$—that is, such that it is to q, the other known quantity, as unity is to $\tfrac{1}{3}p$; then we have only to divide each of the two arcs NQP and NVP into three equal parts, and we will have NQ, the subtending chord of one-third of the first arc, and NV, the subtending chord of one-third of the other; and when we add these two together, they comprise the required root.

Finally, if we have $z^3 = pz - q$, by assuming once again the circle $NQPV$, whose radius NO is equal to $\sqrt{\tfrac{1}{3}p}$, and assuming

NP, which is equal to $\dfrac{3q}{p}$, inscribed in it, then *NQ*, the sub-tending chord of one-third of the arc *NQP*, will be one of the required roots, and *NV*, the subtending chord of one-third of the other arc, will be the other. At least, this will be so if the square of half of the last term is not greater than the cube of one-third of the known quantity of the penultimate term; for, if it were greater, the line *NP* could not be inscribed in the circle, because it would be longer than the diameter. In that case the two true roots of this equation would be only imaginary, and the only real root would be the negative one, which, following the rule of Cardan, would be

$$\sqrt[3]{\tfrac{1}{2}q + \sqrt{\tfrac{1}{4}q^2 - \tfrac{1}{27}p^3}} + \sqrt[3]{\tfrac{1}{2}q - \sqrt{\tfrac{1}{4}q^2 - \tfrac{1}{27}p^3}}.$$

Moreover, it should be noted that this method of expressing the value of roots through their relation to the sides of certain cubes, of which only the areas are known, is no more intelligible, nor more simple, than that of expressing them through their relation to the subtending chords of certain arcs, or portions of circles, whose triples are given. Thus, all the cubic equations that cannot be expressed by Cardan's rules can be expressed as clearly, or more so, through the method here proposed.

If, for example, we believe we can know the root of the equation $z^3 = +pz + q$, because we know that it is composed of two lines, one of which is the side of a cube whose area is $\tfrac{1}{4}q^2 - \tfrac{1}{27}p^3$, and the other is the side of another cube whose volume is the difference between $\tfrac{1}{2}q$ and the side of a square whose area is $\tfrac{1}{4}q^2 - \tfrac{1}{27}p^3$ (which is all we can learn about it through Cardan's rule): there is no doubt that we can know the root of the equation $z^3 = +qz - p$ as clearly, or even more so, by considering it inscribed in a circle whose radius is $\sqrt{\tfrac{1}{3}p}$, in which we know it is the subtending chord of an arc which is one-third the arc whose subtending chord is $\dfrac{3q}{p}$. These terms are even much less cumbersome than the others, and they will be found much more economical, if we wish to use some particular symbol for expressing these subtending chords, as we used the symbol $\sqrt{C}.$ to express the side of a cube.

And we can also, following the rules explained here, express the roots of all biquadratic equations; therefore, I know of nothing further to be desired in this matter, because, in short, the nature of these roots does not permit us to express them in simpler terms, nor can we determine them through any construction that is both more general and easier.

It is true that I have not yet said on the basis of what reasons I venture so to assure you that a thing is or is not possible. But if you take note that, with the method I use, everything falling under the geometer's consideration can be reduced to a single class of problem—namely, that of looking for the value of the roots of a certain equation—you will clearly see that it is not difficult to enumerate all the ways through which they can be found, which is sufficient to prove that the simplest and the most general one has been chosen. And particularly for solid problems, which I have said cannot be constructed without using some [curved] line that is more complex than the circle, this is something you can easily discover from the fact that they are all reducible to two constructions. In one of these, it is necessary to have both of the two points which determine two mean proportionals between two given lines; and in the other, the two points which divide a given arc into three equal parts. For inasmuch as the curvature of the circle depends only upon a simple relation between its center and all of its parts, we can use it only to determine a single point between two extremes, as in finding a mean proportional between two given straight lines, or dividing a given arc into two parts. The curvature of conic sections, on the other hand, because it always depends on two different things, can be used to determine two different points as well.

But for this same reason, it is impossible that any problem which is of a more complex degree than solid ones, and which presupposes the invention of four mean proportionals or the division of an angle into five equal parts, can be constructed by any of the conic sections. This is why I shall believe I have accomplished all that is possible in this matter, if I can give a general rule for constructing them through the use of a curved line which is described by the intersection of a parabola and a straight line, in the manner explained above. For I venture to be certain that there is no simpler rule in nature that can be used for this purpose, and you have seen how this curve comes immediately after the conic sections in that question the ancients examined so, whose solution teaches in order all the curved lines which must be included in geometry.

You already know how, when we are looking for the quantities required for the construction of these problems, we can always reduce them to some equation of no higher degree than the sixth or the supersolid. And you also know how, by augmenting the value of the roots of this equation, we can always make them into true roots and, at the same time, make the known quantity of the third term greater than the square of half that of the second. And finally, [you know] how, if the equation is of a degree no higher than the supersolid, we can raise it to the sixth degree, and insure that each of its terms are filled. Now in order to resolve by a single rule all the difficulties that are here in question, I would have us do all these things, and thereby reduce them to an equation of the form

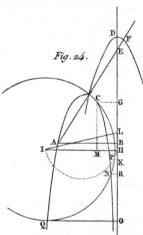

Fig. 24.

$$y^6 - py^5 + qy^4 - ry^3 + sy^2 - ty + u = 0,$$

in which the quantity called q is greater than the square of one-half that which is called p.

Then, having extended BK indefinitely in both directions, and from the point B having drawn the perpendicular AB, whose length is $\frac{1}{2}p$, in a separate plane we must describe a parabola such as CDF, whose principal right side is

$$\sqrt{\frac{t}{\sqrt{u}} + q - \frac{1}{4}p^2},$$

which I shall call n. After this, we must place the plane containing the parabola on that containing the lines AB and BK, so that its axis DE runs right along the straight line BK. And having made the section of this axis that is between the points E and D equal to $\dfrac{2\sqrt{u}}{pn}$, we must apply at this point E a long ruler, so that all the while that it is applied to point A of the lower plane, it always stays connected to these two points, while it is raised or lowered all along the line BK, on which its axis is applied. In this way the intersection of this parabola and this ruler, which will be at point C, will describe the curved line ACN, which is the point we must use in the construction of the proposed problem. Now after the curve is so described, let us take point L in the line BK, on the concave side of the parabola, and make BL equal to DC, that is, to $\dfrac{2\sqrt{u}}{pn}$; then, going from point L toward B, let us take, in the same line BK, the line LH equal to $\dfrac{t}{2n\sqrt{u}}$; and, from point H which we discovered thus, let us draw at right angles, on the same side as the curve ACN, the line HI, whose length is

$$\frac{r}{2n^2} + \frac{\sqrt{u}}{n^2} + \frac{pt}{4n^2\sqrt{u}},$$

which, for purposes of brevity, we will call $\dfrac{m}{n^2}$. And after this, having joined points L and I, let us describe the circle LPI, whose diameter is IL; and let us inscribe within this circle the line LP, whose length is

$$\sqrt{\frac{s + p\sqrt{u}}{n^2}}.$$

Then finally, from the center I and through point P, let us describe the circle PCN. This circle will intersect or touch the curved line ACN in as many points as the equation has roots. Thus the perpendicular drawn from these points on the line BK—such as CG, NR, QO, and the like—will be the required roots; and there are no exceptions to this rule, and no failures.

For, if the quantity *s* were so large in proportion to the others, *p*, *q*, *r*, *t*, and *u*, that the line *LP* was greater than *IL*, the diameter of the circle, so that is could not be inscribed in it, there would be only imaginary roots in the equation. The same would be true if the circle *IP* were so small that it did not intersect the curve *ACN* at any point. And *IP* can intersect *ACN* in six different points, so that there can be six different roots in the equation. But when it intersects it in fewer points, this signifies that some of these roots are equal to one another, or else are merely imaginary.

But if the method of tracing the line *ACN* by the movement of a parabola seems incommodious to you, it is easy to find many other ways of describing it. For example, if *AB* and *BL*

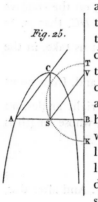

Fig. 25.

are the same quantities as before, and if *BK* is the same quantity as that we have posited for the principal right side of the parabola, we describe the half-circle *KST* whose center is taken at random on the line *BK*, so that it cuts some part of the line *AB*, as for example at point *S*; and then, from point *T* where the half-circle terminates, we take *TV*, going toward *K*, equal to *BL*. Then, having drawn the line *SV*, we draw through point *A* another line parallel to it, such as *AC*; and we also draw through *S* another line, parallel to *BK*, such as *SC*. The point *C* where these two parallels meet will be on the required curved line. And in the same way, we can find as many other points of the line as we wish.

Now the demonstration of all this is very easy. We apply the ruler *AE* and the parabola *FD* at point *C* (as it is certain that they can be applied there together, since *C* is in the curve *ACN*, which is described by their intersection); if *CG* is called *y*, *GD* will be $\frac{y^2}{n}$, because the right side, *n*, is to *CG* as *CG* is to *GD*. And subtracting *DE*, which is $\frac{2\sqrt{u}}{pn}$, from *GD*, we have GE equal to $\dfrac{y^2}{n} - \dfrac{2\sqrt{u}}{pn}$. Then, since AB is to BE as CG

is to GE, if AB is $\frac{1}{2}p$, then BE is $\dfrac{py}{2n} - \dfrac{\sqrt{u}}{ny}$.

And in the same way, let us suppose that point C of the curve has been discovered through the intersection of the straight lines SC, parallel to BK, and AC, parallel to SV; then SB, which is equal to CG, is y, and since BK is equal to the right side of the parabola, which I have called n, BT

equals $\dfrac{y^2}{n}$. For as KB is to BS, so BS is to BT. And since TV is

the same as BL, that is, $\dfrac{2\sqrt{u}}{pn}$, BV equals $\dfrac{y^2}{n} - \dfrac{2\sqrt{u}}{pn}$. And as SB

is to BV, so AB is to BE; consequently BE equals $\dfrac{py}{2n} - \dfrac{\sqrt{u}}{ny}$, as

before. From this we can see that the same curved line is described by these two methods.

After this, because BL and DE [6] are equal, DL and BE are

equal too; thus if we add LH, which is $\dfrac{t}{2n\sqrt{u}}$ to DL, which

is $\dfrac{py}{2n} - \dfrac{\sqrt{u}}{ny}$, we have the entire line DH, which is

$$\frac{py}{2n} - \frac{\sqrt{u}}{ny} + \frac{t}{2n\sqrt{u}} \, ;$$

and by subtracting GD, which is $\dfrac{y^2}{n}$, we have GH, which is

$$\frac{py}{2n} - \frac{\sqrt{u}}{ny} + \frac{t}{2n\sqrt{u}} - \frac{y^2}{n},$$

which I write in order as follows:

$$GH = \frac{-y^3 + \frac{1}{2}py^2 + \dfrac{ty}{2\sqrt{u}} - \sqrt{u}}{ny}.$$

[6] See Fig. 24, p. 252.

And the square of GH is

$$\frac{y^6 - py^5 + \left(\tfrac{1}{4}p^2 - \frac{t}{\sqrt{u}}\right)y^4 + \left(2\sqrt{u} + \frac{pt}{2\sqrt{u}}\right)y^3 + \left(\frac{t^2}{4u} - p\sqrt{u}\right)y^2 - ty + u}{n^2y^2}$$

And in whatever other part of this curved line we may imagine C to be—such as near N or Q—we will always find that the square of the straight line between point H and the point where the perpendicular from point C falls on BH can always be expressed in these same terms, and with the same plus and minus signs.

Moreover, since IH is $\dfrac{m}{n^2}$, and LH is $\dfrac{t}{2n\sqrt{u}}$, IL is

$$\sqrt{\frac{m^2}{n^4} + \frac{t^2}{4n^2u}},$$

because IHL is a right angle; and since LP is

$$\sqrt{\frac{s}{n^2} + \frac{p\sqrt{u}}{n^2}}.$$

IP or IC is

$$\sqrt{\frac{m^2}{n^4} + \frac{t^2}{4n^2u} - \frac{s}{n^2} - \frac{p\sqrt{u}}{n^2}},$$

because IPL is also a right angle. Then, having made CM perpendicular to IH, IM is the difference between IH and HM or CG, that is, between $\dfrac{m}{n^2}$ and y; therefore its square is always

$$\frac{m^2}{n^4} - \frac{2my}{n^2} + y^2.$$

And subtracting this from the square of IC, we get

$$\frac{t^2}{4n^2u} - \frac{s}{n^2} - \frac{p\sqrt{u}}{n^2} + \frac{2my}{n^2} - y^2,$$

as the square of CM, which is equal to the square of GH that we already found. Or else, dividing this sum by n^2y^2 as we did the other, we have

$$\frac{n^2y^4 + 2my^3 - p\sqrt{uy^2} - sy^2 + \dfrac{t^2}{4u}y^2}{n^2y^2}.$$

Then replacing n^2y^4 by

$$\frac{t}{\sqrt{u}}y^4 + qy^4 - \tfrac{1}{4}p^2y^4,$$

and $2my^3$ by

$$ry^3 + \sqrt{uy^3} + \frac{pt}{2\sqrt{u}}y^3,$$

and multiplying both sums by n^2y^2, we have

$$y^6 - py^5 + \left(\tfrac{1}{4}p^2 - \frac{t}{\sqrt{u}}\right)y^4 + \left(2\sqrt{u} + \frac{pt}{2\sqrt{u}}\right)y^3 + \left(\frac{t^2}{4u} - p\sqrt{u}\right)y^2 - ty + u$$

equal to

$$\left(\tfrac{1}{4}p^2 - q - \frac{t}{\sqrt{u}}\right)y^4 + \left(r + 2\sqrt{u} + \frac{pt}{2\sqrt{u}}\right)y^3 + \left(\frac{t^2}{4u} - s - p\sqrt{u}\right)y^2;$$

that is, we have

$$y^6 - py^5 + qy^4 - ry^3 + sy^2 - ty + u = 0.$$

From this it is apparent that the lines CG, NR, QO, and the like are the roots of this equation, which is what was to be demonstrated.

And so then if we wish to find four mean proportionals between the lines a and b, having posited x as the first line, the equation is

$$x^5 - a^4b = 0, \quad \text{or} \quad x^6 - a^4bx = 0.$$

And making $y - a = x$, we get:

$$y^6 - 6ay^5 + 15a^2y^4 - 20a^3y^3 + 15a^4y^2 - (6a^5 + a^4b)y + a^6 + a^5b = 0.$$

This is why we must take $3a$ as the line AB, and

$$\sqrt{\frac{6a^3 + a^2b}{\sqrt{a^2 + ab}}}$$

as BK, or the right side of the parabola, which I have called n. And for DE or BL we must take

$$\sqrt{\frac{a}{3n}\sqrt{a^2 + ab}}.$$

And after having described the curve ACN on the measure of these three, we must make

$$LH = \frac{6a^3 + a^2 b}{2n\sqrt{a^2 + ab}},$$

and

$$HI = \frac{10a^3}{n^2} + \frac{a^2}{n^2}\sqrt{a^2 + ab} + \frac{18a^4 + 3a^3 b}{2n^2\sqrt{a^2 + ab}},$$

and

$$LP = \sqrt{\frac{15a^4 + 6a^3\sqrt{a^2 + ab}}{n^2}}.$$

For the circle whose center is at point I and which passes through point P which is found thus, will intersect the curve at the two points C and N. If from these we draw the perpendiculars NR and CG, and subtract the smaller, NR, from the greater, CG, there will remain x, the first of the four required mean proportionals.

It is easy with this same method to divide an angle into five equal parts, or to inscribe a figure of eleven or thirteen equal sides in a circle, and to find an infinity of other examples of this rule.

Nevertheless we should note that in many of these examples, it can happen that the circle cuts the parabola of the second class so obliquely that it is difficult to recognize the point of their intersection. This construction, therefore, is not valuable in practice—which would be easy to remedy by inventing other rules like this, as can be done in a thousand ways.

But it is not my intention to write a thick book. Instead, I am trying rather to include much in a few words, as perhaps you will judge that I have done, if you consider that having reduced all the problems of a single class to a single construction, I have at the same time given the method of reducing them to an infinity of other different problems, and thus solving each of them in an infinity of ways. Then, besides this, I have constructed all plane problems by the intersection of a circle with a straight line, and all solid problems also by the intersection of a circle with a parabola, and finally in the same way all problems which are only one degree more complex, by making a circle intersect with a line which is only one degree more complex than the parabola; we have only to follow the same method in order to construct all problems to an infinite degree of complexity. For in the matter of mathematical progressions, once we have the first two or three terms, it is not difficult to find the others. And I hope that posterity will be grateful to me, not only for the things that I have explained, but also for those that I have voluntarily omitted, in order to leave the pleasure of inventing them to future generations.

METEOROLOGY

METEOROLOGY

First Discourse

Of the Nature of Terrestrial Bodies

It is our nature to have more admiration for the things above us than for those that are on our level, or below. And although the clouds are hardly any higher than the summits of some mountains, and often we even see some that are lower than the pinnacles of our steeples, nevertheless, because we must turn our eyes toward the sky to look at them, we fancy them to be so high that poets and painters even fashion them into God's throne, and picture Him there, using His own hands to open and close the doors of the winds, to sprinkle the dew upon the flowers, and to hurl the lightning against the rocks. This leads me to hope that if I here explain the nature of clouds, in such a way that we will no longer have occasion to wonder at anything that can be seen of them, or anything that descends from them, we will easily believe that it is similarly possible to find the causes of everything that is most admirable above the earth.

I shall speak, in this first discourse, of the nature of terrestrial bodies in general, so that, in the next one, I may better explain the nature of vapors and evaporations. Then, because these vapors rising up from the water of the sea sometimes form salt on its surface, I shall take the opportunity to pause a little and describe salt, and to see if in it we can ascertain the forms of these bodies that the philosophers hold to be composed of a perfect mixture of the elements, as well as those of meteors, which they say are composed of the elements in an imperfect mixture. After that, propelling the vapors through the air, I shall examine the origin of the winds; and making them gather together in certain places, I shall describe the nature of clouds. And by causing these clouds to dissolve, I shall say what causes rain, hail, and snow—nor shall I neglect that snow whose particles have the shape of very perfectly proportioned, small, six-pointed stars (although this was observed by the ancients, it is nevertheless one of the rarest marvels of nature). Nor shall I neglect storms, thunder, lightning, and the various fires that are kindled in the air, or the lights that may be seen there. But in particular, I shall try to portray the rainbow correctly, and to explain its colors in such a way that we can also understand the nature of all those which may be found in other objects. To this I shall add the cause of the colors we commonly see in the clouds and in the circles which surround the stars, and finally the cause of the suns, or moons, several of which sometimes appear together.

It is true that since the knowledge of these matters depends on general principles of nature which have not yet, to my knowledge, been accurately explained, I shall have to use certain hypotheses at the outset, as I did in the *Optics*. But I shall try to render them so simple and easy that perhaps you will have no difficulty in accepting them, even though I have not demonstrated them.

I assume, first, that water, earth, air, and all other such bodies that surround us are composed of many small particles of various shapes and sizes, which are never so well arranged, nor so exactly joined together, that there do not remain many spaces around them. And I assume that these spaces are not empty, but are filled with that very fine material by means of which (as I have explained above) [1] the action of light is communicated. Then, in particular, I assume that the small particles of which water is composed are long, smooth, and slippery, like little eels, which are such that however they join and interlace, they are never thereby so knotted or hooked together that they cannot easily be separated; and on the other hand, I assume that nearly all particles of earth, as well as of air

[1] *Optics*, p. 68.

and most other bodies, have very irregular and rough shapes, so that they need be only slightly intertwined in order to become hooked and bound to each other, as are the various branches of bushes that grow together in a hedgerow. And when they are bound together in this way, they compose hard bodies like earth, wood, or other such things; whereas if they are simply laid on one another without being interlaced at all (or only very slightly), and if in addition they are so small that they can be moved and separated by the agitation of the very fine material that surrounds them, they must occupy a great deal of space, and compose very rarefied and light liquid bodies such as oil and air. Moreover, we must consider that the very fine material which fills the spaces between the particles of these bodies is of such a nature that it never ceases to move here and there at great speed, but not exactly the same speed at all places and all times. Rather, it normally moves toward the surface of the earth with slightly greater speed than it does high in the air where the clouds are, and faster toward places near the equator than toward the poles, and even in the same place, it moves faster in summer than in winter, and during the day than at night. The reason for this becomes evident if we assume that light is nothing other than a certain movement or action by which luminous bodies impel this very fine material in straight lines, in all directions around them, as has been stated in the *Optics*. For it follows from this that the rays of the sun, direct as well as reflected, must agitate this material during the day more than at night, in summer more than in winter, under the equator more than under the poles, and near the earth more than toward the clouds. Then we must also consider that this very fine material is composed of various parts, and that although these are all very small, some of them are nevertheless much smaller than the others; and that the larger particles—or to speak more accurately, the less small ones—always have more force, just as all large bodies generally have more force than do smaller ones, when they are equally disturbed. This means that the less fine this matter is—that is, the more it is composed of these larger particles—the more it can agitate the particles of other bodies. And this is also why it is usually least fine in places and times where it is most agitated, such as toward the surface of the earth rather than toward the clouds, and under the equator rather than under the poles, and in summer rather than in winter, and during the day rather than at night. The reason for this is that because the heaviest of its parts have the most force, they can more easily go toward those places where, since the agitation is greater, it is easier for them to continue their movement. Nevertheless, there is always a quantity of the very small particles which slip in among these larger ones. And it is to be noted that all the terrestrial bodies have many pores through which these smaller particles can pass, yet there are many of these bodies whose pores are so narrow, or are located in such a way, that they do not receive the largest particles; it is usually these which feel the coldest when we touch them, or when we merely approach them. Thus, inasmuch as marbles and metals feel colder than wood, we must assume that their pores do not receive the very fine parts of this matter very easily, and, inasmuch as ice is even colder, that its pores receive them still less easily than those of marbles or metals. For I am assuming here that, as regards heat and cold, we need to consider nothing except that the small particles of the bodies we touch, being agitated more or less strongly than usual—either by the small particles of this very fine material or by whatever other cause there may be—also agitate more or less the small threads of those of our nerves which are the organs of touch. And when they agitate them more strongly than usual, this causes the sensation of heat in us; whereas when they agitate them less strongly, this causes the sensation of cold. And it is quite easy to understand that although this very fine material does not separate the parts of hard bodies, which are like intertwined branches, in the same way that it does those of water and all other liquid bodies, nevertheless it agitates and stirs them; more so or less, in proportion to the intensity of its movement and the size of its particles, just as the wind can shake all the branches of the bushes composing a hedge without removing them from their places in doing so. For the rest, we must assume that the ratio between the force of this very fine material and the resistance of the particles of other bodies is such that, when this material is agitated enough, and is no finer than it usually is in these places near the earth, it has the force to agitate these particles and cause them to move separately away from each other, and even to bend the majority of the small particles of the water among which it slides, and thus make it liquid. But when it is no more agitated, or no less fine, than it normally is in these places high in the air (or as it is sometimes in winter near the earth), it does not have enough force to bend and agitate them in this way; this is the reason they come to a stop, haphazardly joined to and lying upon one another, and thus form a hard body, namely ice. Thus you can picture the same difference between water and ice as between a group of small eels—either alive or dead—floating in a fishing boat full of holes through which the water of a river flows, agitating the eels; and a group of these same eels, quite dry and rigid with cold on the shore. And because water never freezes unless the material between its particles is finer than usual, it follows that the pores of the ice which is so formed are adapted only to the size of the particles of this finer material and are disposed in such a way that they cannot receive that which is less fine. Thus ice is always extremely cold, even if we keep it into the summer; and even then, it retains its hardness without growing gradually softer like wax, because heat penetrates to the inside only to the extent that the surface becomes liquid.

In addition it is to be noted here that among the long and smooth particles of which I have said water is composed, by far the majority of them bend, or cease to bend, according to whether the subtle material that surrounds them has slightly more or less force than normal, as I have just explained; but among these particles there are also larger ones which are not pliable in this way, and which compose salts; and in addition there are smaller ones which are always pliable, and these compose spirits or brandies, which never freeze.

When the particles of ordinary water entirely cease to bend, their most natural shape is not always as straight as saplings, but rather, in many cases, curved in various ways; from this it follows that they cannot then be ranged in as small a space as when the fine material, being sufficiently strong to bend them, causes them to accommodate their shapes to each other. But it is also true that when this force is stronger than is required for this effect, it causes the particles to expand anew, in a larger area. We can see this by experiment, if we fill a beaker —or some other such container having a rather long, straight neck—with hot water, and expose it to freezing cold air; for the water level will go down visibly, little by little, until the water reaches a certain degree of coldness, after which it will gradually swell and rise, until it is completely frozen. Thus the same cold which will have condensed or shrunk it in the beginning will rarefy it afterwards. And we can also see by experiment that water which has been kept hot for a long time freezes faster than any other sort, because those of its parts which can least cease to bend evaporate while it is being heated.

But in order that you may accept these hypotheses with less difficulty, know that I do not conceive the small particles of terrestrial bodies as atoms or indivisible particles; rather, judging them all to be made of the same material, I believe that each one could be redivided in an infinity of ways, and that they differ among themselves only as pebbles of many different shapes would differ, had they been cut from the same rock. Then, know also that in order to keep my peace with the philosophers, I have no desire to deny that which they imagine to be in bodies in addition to what I have given, such as their *substantial forms*, their *real qualities* and the like; but it seems to me that my explanations ought to be approved all the more because I shall make them depend on fewer things.

Second Discourse

Of Vapors and Exhalations

If you will consider that because the fine material in the pores of terrestrial bodies is more strongly agitated at some times than at others—either by the presence of the sun or by some such other cause—it correspondingly agitates the small particles of these bodies more strongly, you will easily understand that it causes those which are sufficiently small, and of such shape or situation that they can easily be separated from their neighbors, to scatter here and there from one another, and to rise into the air. This occurs not because of some particular inclination they have to rise upwards, nor because the sun has in itself some force which attracts them, but solely because they cannot find any other place in which it is as easy for them to continue their movement, just as the dust of a plain rises when it is merely pushed and agitated by the feet of some passerby. For although the grains of this dust are much larger and heavier than the small particles we are talking about, this does not keep them from taking their course toward the sky. And we even see that they climb much higher into the sky when a large plain is covered with people moving about, than when only a single man treads upon it. This should prevent anyone from being astonished that the action of the sun raises the small particles of the material composing vapors and exhalations so high, seeing that it extends over half the earth at once, and remains there for entire days. But notice that these small particles which are so lifted into the air by the sun must for the most part have the shape that I have attributed to those of water, because no other particles can so easily be separated from the bodies where they are located. And it will be these alone that I shall particularly call "vapors," in order to distinguish them from others which have more irregular shapes, and to which I shall confine the name "exhalations," because I know of no more appropriate one. Yet also in the class of exhalations I shall include the particles which have nearly the same shape as those of water, but are finer, composing spirits or brandies; for they can easily be set afire. And I shall exclude from this class those which, being divided into many branches, are so fine that they are only good for composing the bodies of the air. As for those which are slightly heavier, but also divided into branches, it is true that they can hardly free themselves from the hard bodies where they are to be found; but if occasionally fire occurs in these bodies, it forces them all out in smoke. Also, when water slips into the pores of these hard bodies, it can often disengage these particles from them, and carry the particles up with it-

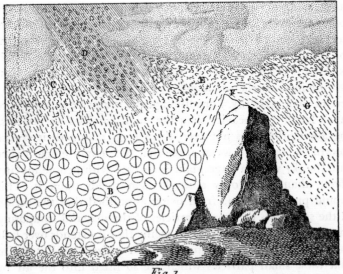

Fig. 1.

self—just as the wind, passing through a hedgerow, carries away the leaves or straws that are entangled among its branches; or rather, as water itself carries the small particles of those

oils that alchemists usually extract from dried plants to the
top of a beaker, when, having steeped them in a great deal
of water, they distill the whole together, and thus cause the
little oil that the plants contain to rise with the large quantity
of water which is among them. For in effect the majority of
these latter particles are the same as those which normally
make up the bodies of these oils.

Note also that vapors always occupy much more space than
water, although they are made of the same small particles.
The reason for this is that when these particles compose the
bodies of water, they move only strongly enough to bend and
interlace, by sliding against one another, as you see them represented here at *A;* whereas, when they have the form of a
vapor, their agitation is so great that they spin about very
rapidly in all directions, and for the same reason they are
stretched throughout their entire length, in such a way that
each has the force to drive away from around itself all its fel-
lows which try to enter into the small sphere that it describes, as
you can see them represented at *B*. In the same
manner, if you make the pivot *LM,* through
which the cord *NP* is passed, turn with sufficient speed, you will see that this cord will be
held stretched out quite level in the air, so
that it occupies in this way all the space included in the circle *NOPQ,* and you will not
be able to place any other body there without
the string immediately striking it with force,

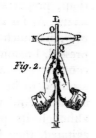

Fig. 2.

in order to drive it out. But if you make the cord move more
slowly, it will wrap itself around the pivot, and thus will not
occupy so much space.

Moreover, we must notice that these vapors can be more or
less compressed or expanded, hot or cold, transparent or
obscure, and moist or dry, at one time than at another. For
in the first place, when their particles are not agitated
strongly enough to hold them extended in a straight line, they
begin to bend and draw near to one another, as we see represented at *C* and *D*. Or else, when they are squeezed be-

tween mountains, or between currents of different winds
(which, being opposed, prevent each other from agitating the
air), or when they are under some clouds, they are incapable
of extending in as much space as their agitation requires, as
you see at *E*. Or finally, when the greatest part of their
agitation is being used to propel many of them together in a
single direction, they do not turn as strongly as usual, as they
are seen at *F*; or, leaving the space *E*, they engender a wind
which blows toward *G*. It is obvious that [in these cases] the
vapors composed of these particles are thicker or more condensed than when none of these three things happen. And it
is also evident that assuming the vapor at *E* to be as much
agitated as that at *B*, it must be much hotter, because its parts,
being more compressed, have more force—just as the heat of
a burning iron is much more intense than that of coal or of a
flame. And this is the reason why in the summer we often
feel that the heat is stronger and more stifling when the air,
being calm and compressed in equal degree from all directions, prepares for rain, than when it is clearer and more
serene. As far as the vapor at *C* is concerned, it is colder than
at *B*, inasmuch as, although its particles are slightly more compressed, I assume that they are much less agitated. And on the
contrary, the vapor at *D* is hotter, inasmuch as its particles are
assumed to be much more compressed, and only slightly less
agitated. And the vapor at *F* is colder than that at *E*; for,
although its particles are neither less compressed nor less
agitated, they lend themselves more to moving in the same
direction, which is why they cannot shake the small particles
of the other bodies so much—just as a wind which always
blows in the same way, even if very strongly, will not agitate
the leaves and branches of a forest as much as a more feeble
one which blows less evenly. And you can discover through experiment that heat consists of this agitation of the small
particles of terrestrial bodies: if you blow with sufficient
strength against your clasped fingers, you will observe that the
breath which leaves your mouth will seem cold to you above
your hand, where, passing very swiftly and with even force,
it will cause hardly any agitation; whereas it will feel hotter

to you in the spaces between your fingers, where, passing more unevenly and slowly, it will agitate their small particles more: In the same way, our breath will always feel hotter when we blow with our mouths wide open, than when we blow while keeping them nearly closed. And it is for this same reason that impetuous winds normally feel cold, and that there are hardly any warm winds which are not gentle.

Moreover, the vapors represented at *B, E,* and *F* are transparent, and cannot be distinguished from the rest of the air by sight; for since they move at the same speed and with the same oscillation as the subtle material which surrounds them, they cannot prevent this material from receiving the action of luminous bodies, but rather, they receive it with the material. The vapor at *C,* on the other hand, begins to become opaque or obscure, because its particles do not obey the fine matter so much that they can be moved by it in every way. And the vapor at *D* cannot be at all as obscure as that at *C,* because it is warmer. Thus you can see that in winter, the cold causes the breath or the sweat of overheated horses to appear in the form of a very dense, obscure, heavy smoke; whereas in the summer, when the air is warmer, it is invisible. And we must not doubt that the atmosphere often contains as many or more vapors when they are unseen as when they are seen. For how could it happen, short of a miracle, that in warm weather and in the middle of the day, the sun, shining on a lake or a swamp, would fail to raise many vapors from it, seeing that we notice that in that sort of weather the waters dry up and recede more than in cold and cloudy weather?

For the rest, the vapors at *E* are more humid—that is, more disposed to be converted into water and to moisten or dampen other bodies as does water—than those at *F*. For the vapors at *F,* on the contrary, are dry, seeing that when they strike with force against the humid bodies that they encounter, they can drive out, and carry away, the particles of water in these bodies and by this means dry them out. So also we know from experience that impetuous winds are always dry, and that there are no humid winds that are not weak. And it can be said that the same vapors at *E* are more humid than those at *D;* for because their particles are more agitated, they can more easily creep into the pores of other bodies in order to make them humid. But in another sense, it may be said that they are less humid, because the excessive agitation of their particles prevents them from taking the form of water as easily.

As for exhalations, they are capable of many more diverse qualities than vapors, because there can be more difference among their particles. But it will suffice here for us to note that their largest particles are hardly anything other than earth, such as we can see at the bottom of a container after having left snow or rain-water to settle in it; nor are their finest particles anything other than those spirits or brandies, which are always the first to rise up from the bodies which we distill; and among their medium-sized particles, some share the nature of volatile salts, and others that of oils, or rather the natures of the fumes which leave these salts and oils when we burn them. And although most of these exhalations rise into the air only when mixed with the vapors, this does not mean that they cannot easily be separated from them afterwards, either performing this separation of themselves, as oils disentangle themselves from the water with which we distill them, or with the help of the agitation of the winds which gather them together in one or many bodies, in the same way that womenfolk beating their cream separate butter from milk. Or often it also simply happens because, being more or less heavy and more or less agitated, they stop in a region that is lower or higher than are the vapors. And ordinarily oils do not rise as high as spirits, and those particles which are nothing other than earth do not rise as high as the oils. But there are no particles which stop at a level lower than do those that make up common salt; and although these are not, strictly speaking, either exhalations or vapors, because they never rise higher than immediately above the surface of the water, nevertheless, because it is through the evaporation of this water that they come to be there, and because there are many very remarkable things about them which can be conveniently explained here, I have no desire to omit them.

Third Discourse

Of Salt

The salinity of the sea consists only in those larger particles of its water which, as I have just said, are incapable of being bent like the others through the action of the fine material, or even of being agitated without the intervention of the smaller particles. For, first, if the water were not composed of certain particles as I have just assumed, it would be equally easy or difficult for it to be divided in every way and in all directions, so that it would not enter as easily as it does into bodies which have rather large pores, as do limestone and sand; or else it would also be able in some way to penetrate into those whose pores are narrower, such as glass and metals. And, if these particles did not have the shape I have attributed to them, when they are in the pores of other bodies, they could not so easily be driven from them solely by the agitation of winds, or by heat; you can prove this sufficiently by considering oils, or other slippery liquids, whose particles I have said have other shapes; for one can hardly ever make them leave a body completely once they have entered it. Finally, because we do not see bodies in nature which are so perfectly alike that there is not almost always some slight inequality in their size, we should have no difficulty in thinking that the particles of water are not all exactly equal, and particularly that in the sea, which is the receptacle of all waters, there are some particles so big that they cannot be bent, as are others, by the force which normally moves them. And I would like to try to show you here that this alone is sufficient to give them all the qualities that salt has.

First, it is not surprising that the particles of salt have a sharp and penetrating taste, which differs a great deal from that of fresh water: for because they cannot be bent by the fine material that surrounds them, they must always enter rigidly into the pores of the tongue, and thereby penetrate far enough into it to sting; whereas those which compose fresh water, because they are easily bent, merely flow softly over the surface of the tongue, and can hardly be tasted at all. And in the same way, when the particles of salt penetrate rigidly into the pores of the meat we want to preserve, not only do they remove the humidity from it, but they also act as small rods planted here and there among the particles of the meat; remaining firm and unbent there, they support these particles and prevent other more pliable ones among them from disarranging the meat particles by agitating them, and thus spoiling the bodies which they compose. This also is the reason why these meats become harder with the passage of time, whereas particles of fresh water, by bending and sliding here and there in the pores of the meats, could help to soften and spoil them. Moreover, it is not astonishing that salt water is heavier than fresh, since it is composed of particles which, being thicker and more massive, can arrange themselves in less space; for it is this upon which its weight depends. But it is necessary to consider why these more massive particles remain mingled with others that are less massive, when it would seem that they should naturally sink below them. And the reason for this, at least for the particles of common salt, is that they are of equal thickness at both ends, and completely straight, very much like tiny rods; for if there had ever been any of them in the sea that were thicker at one end than at the other, then having been made heavier by this means, they would have been quite free to fall to the bottom, ever since the beginning of the world. Or if there had been any of them that were curved, they would have been free to meet hard bodies, and be joined to them; for having once entered into their pores, they would not be able to get out again as easily as they would if they were uniform and straight. But because these particles of salt are laid down across one another, they allow those of fresh water, which are in perpetual agitation, to be rolled and entwined around them, arranging and dis-

posing themselves there in a certain order which allows them
to continue to move more easily, and at a faster rate, than if
they were all alone. For when they are thus rolled around the
others, the force of the fine material which agitates them is
used only to make them turn very rapidly around the particles
they embrace, and to cause them to pass here and there from
one of these particles onto the other, without thereby changing any of their curves. Whereas, when the particles are alone,
as they are when they compose soft water, they are necessarily
intertwined with one another in such a way that part of this
force of the subtle material must be used to bend them, in
order to disengage them from each other; thus this force
cannot move them either as easily or as quickly. Granting,
then, that it is true that these particles of fresh water can
move better when they are rolled around those of salt than
when they are alone, it is not surprising that they do roll
themselves about these particles when they are near enough
to them to do so, and that afterwards, remaining clasped to
them, they prevent the inequality of their weight from sep-
arating them. This is why salt dissolves easily in fresh water,
or when it is merely exposed to the air in humid weather, even
though only a determined amount of salt will be dissolved in
a determined quantity of water; namely, only in proportion
as the pliant particles of that water can surround the particles
of salt by rolling around them. And knowing that transparent
bodies are the more transparent the less they impede the
movement of the fine material in their pores, we may again
see from this that the water of the sea must be more transparent by nature, and cause slightly greater refractions, than
that of rivers. And we can also see that it must not freeze as
easily by noticing that water freezes only when the fine material among its particles does not have the force to agitate
them. We can even learn here the secret of making ice in
the summertime, which is one of the most marvelous secrets
known to inquiring minds, although it is not one of the
rarest. They place salt mixed with an equal quantity of snow
or crushed ice all around a vessel full of fresh water; and with-

out any other device, as this salt and snow melt together, the water contained in the vessel becomes ice. The explanation of this phenomenon is that the fine material which was around the particles of water—being thicker or less subtle, and as a result having more force than that which was around the particles of snow—will replace it in proportion as the particles of snow are rolled around those of the salt, as they melt; for the subtle material finds it easier to move in the pores of the salted water than in those of the fresh water, and it tends to pass unhesitatingly from one body into another, in order to enter those where its movement is the least hindered. In this way the more subtle material that was in the snow enters into the water, in order to take the place of that which leaves from it; and because it does not have enough force to undertake the agitation of that water, this is why the water freezes.

One of the principal qualities of the particles of salt is that they are very firmly fixed—that is, they cannot be turned into vapor as can those of fresh water. The reason for this is not only that they are thicker and consequently heavier, but also that because they are long and straight, they can hardly be suspended in the air for any length of time, be they in the action of rising higher or of descending, without one of their ends pointing downward, and thus being in a position perpendicular to the earth. For in climbing as well as in descending, it is much easier for them to divide the air when they are in this position than when they are in any other. This does not happen in the same way to the particles of fresh water because, being easily bent, they never stay completely straight unless they are rotating with great speed; whereas the particles of salt hardly ever turn in this way, for as they meet and strike against each other, and move about without being able to bend in order to absorb the shock, it is very difficult for them to stop. But when they are suspended in the air with one end down, as I have said, it is evident that they must go downward rather than climb, because the force which could push them upward is much less active upon them than it would be if they were laid crosswise. And it is less active exactly in proportion as the quantity of the air offering resistance to their points is less than that which would offer resistance to their length; while their weight, always remaining constant, exerts that much more force as the resistance of the air lessens. Add to this that sea water becomes soft when it crosses sand because the particles of salt, which lack pliability, cannot flow in the same way as do particles of fresh water through the tiny crooked paths surrounding the grains of this sand. Thus we shall see that fountains and rivers, which are composed only of water that has been evaporated into vapors, or else have passed through a lot of sand, must not be saline; and all this fresh water, returning into the sea, must render it neither more nor less saline, because as much other water is continually leaving it. Some of this rises into the air, is changed to vapors, and then falls as rain or snow upon the earth; but the largest part penetrates through subterranean tunnels underneath mountains where the heat in the earth also lifts the water in the form of vapor to the mountain peaks, where it replenishes the sources of fountains and rivers. And we shall also understand that the water of the sea must be more saline at the equator than near the poles, if we consider that the sun, having more force there, causes a large amount of vapor to leave the sea which does not afterwards fall back at the same places from which it came; instead, it usually falls at other places nearer the poles, as you will come to understand better later on in this treatise.

For the rest, if I had any desire to pause and explain the nature of fire in detail, I would here add the explanation of why the water of the sea is less useful for putting out blazes than that of rivers, and why it sparkles in the night when it is agitated; for you would understand that the particles of salt—which are quite easy to disturb because they are suspended among those of fresh water, and which have a great deal of force after being so shaken because they are straight and inflexible—can not only augment the flame when thrown into it, but can also cause flame themselves when rushing from the fresh water where they are suspended. So that if the sea at *A*, being strongly impelled toward *C*, encounters a bank of sand or some other obstacle there which forces it to climb toward *B*, the oscillation which this agitation imparts to the particles of salt can cause the first ones coming into the air to be disengaged from those of the fresh water which surround them, and so, finding themselves alone at *B*, at a certain distance from one another, they engender sparks similar to those which flints give off when we strike them together. It is true that for this effect it is requisite that these particles of salt be very straight and very slippery, so that they can more easily separate from those of fresh water; and from this it follows that neither brine, nor sea water which has been kept for a long time in a container, will have this effect. It is also requisite that the particles of the fresh water do not hold those of the salt too tightly, whence it follows that these sparks appear more often when it is hot than when it is cold; and the agitation of the sea must be sufficiently strong, whence it follows that the fire does not leave all its waves at the same time. And finally, it is necessary that the particles of the salt move point first, in the manner of arrows, and not crosswise; this is why all the drops spurting from the same body of water do not sparkle in the same way.

Fig. 3.

But now let us consider how, when salt forms, it floats on water, even though its particles are very fixed and heavy; and how it shapes itself there into small, square grains, somewhat similar to a table-cut diamond, except that the largest facet is slightly concave. First, it is essential for this effect that the water of the sea be retained in certain pools, to avoid both the continual agitation of the waves and the abundance of fresh water which the rains and rivers pour unceasingly into the ocean. Then warm, dry weather is also essential, so that the action of the sun has sufficient force to evaporate the particles of fresh water than are rolled around those of the salt.

And it must be observed that the surface of this water (like that of all other liquids as well) is always level and uniform. The explanation of this is that its parts move among themselves in a constant manner and with a constant oscillation, and that the particles of the air which touch it also move among themselves in a constant manner; but the latter do not move in the same manner, nor at the same speed as the former. And also, in particular, the fine material around the particles of air moves quite differently from that which is around the particles of water. This is the reason that their surfaces, rubbing against one another, polish each other just as if they were two hard bodies—except that this happens with much greater ease and almost instantaneously, for because their particles are not attached to each other in any way, they all arrange themselves at the first contact in the manner required for this effect. And this is also the reason that the surface of the water is much more difficult to divide than is the interior, as we can see by experience from the fact that all bodies that are sufficiently small, although they be of very heavy material as are small steel needles, can float and be supported on the surface when it is not yet divided; whereas when it is divided, the bodies sink right to the bottom without stopping. After this it must be considered that when the heat of the air is great enough to form salt, not only can it make some of the pliant particles in the sea leave it, and rise in vapor; it can also make them rise with such speed that before they have had time to spread out from around the particles of salt, they come to the surface of this water where they carry the salt particles with them, and do not succeed in spreading out from them until after the hole that they made in this surface to leave it is closed again. By this means, these particles of salt remain floating above all alone, as you see them represented at *D*. For, resting lengthwise on the surface there, they are not heavy enough to sink, any more than the steel needles of which I have just spoken; and they only cause the surface to bend and curve slightly under them because of their weight, in the same way as do these needles. Thus the first particles, scattered here and there on this surface, cause many small hollows or curvatures there; then the others that come afterwards,

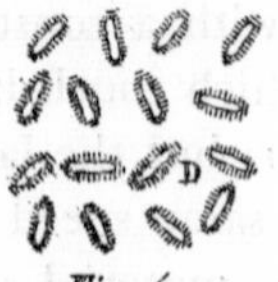

Fig. 4.

Fig. 5.

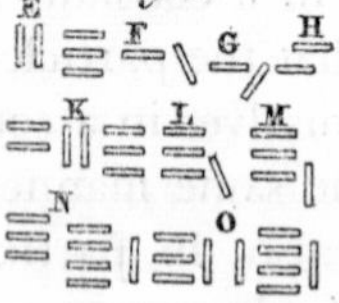

finding themselves on the slopes of these hollows, roll and slide toward the bottom, where they are joined against the first. And it is particularly important here to note that wherever they come from, these latter particles must be laid exactly side by side with the first ones, as you see them at *E;* at least this is so with the second ones and also often with the third, because by this means they go down slightly lower [in the hollow] than they could if they stayed in some other position, as we see them at *F,* or at *G* or *H.* And the movement of the heat which always agitates this surface slightly helps to arrange them in this way. Then, when there are two or three of them in each hole, side by side, those which come later can still be joined to them in the same way, if they are at all disposed to do so; but if it happens that they are inclined more toward the ends of the first particles than toward their sides, they will come to rest against them at right angles, as you can see at *K,* because in this way they also descend slightly lower than they would if they were arranged otherwise, such as are those at *L* or *M.* And because nearly as many of them come to rest against the ends of the first two or three as come to rest against their sides, it follows that, there being hundreds of particles so arranged together, they form a small tablet which to the eye appears very square, and which is like the base of the grain of salt that is beginning to form. And it must be noted that when there are only three or four of them laid in the same direction, such as at *N,* the ones in the middle sink slightly more than those at the edges; but when others arriving there are joined crosswise, such as at *O*, they help the others at the edges to sink almost as much as those in the middle, in such a way that the small square table which serves as the base of a grain of salt, normally being formed of many hundreds of particles joined together, can only appear to the eye as completely flat, even though it is always slightly curved. Thus, as this tablet increases in size, it sinks more and more, but so slowly that it can bend the surface of the water under it without breaking it. And when it has reached a certain size, it has sunk so much that the newly-arriving particles of salt coming toward it, instead of stopping against its edges, pass above it, and there they roll in the same direction and in the same way as the preceding ones rolled upon the water. This causes them to form a new squared tablet, which gradually sinks in the same way. Then the particles of salt coming toward it can again pass above it, and form a third tablet, and so on. But it must be noted that the particles of salt forming the second of these tablets do not roll as easily on the first one as those which formed that first tablet rolled upon the water; for the surface they encounter there is not at all as level, nor does it allow them to flow as freely. Thus it often happens that they do not roll right to the middle, and since the middle remains empty because of this, this second tablet does not sink proportionately as quickly as did the first, but rather becomes slightly larger before the third begins to form. And again, since the middle of the third one stays empty, it becomes slightly larger than the second, and so on, until the entire grain, which is composed of a great number of such small tablets placed upon one another, is completed—that is, until it cannot grow any larger because it is touching the neighboring grains at the edges.

As to the size of the first tablet which serves as the base of the grain, this depends on the degree of heat agitating the water in which it is being formed; for the more the water is agitated, the more the particles of salt swimming above cause its surface to bend. This causes this base to remain smaller, and the water can even be agitated so much that the particles of salt will go to the bottom before they have formed any grains.

As to the slope of the four facets which rise from the four sides of this base, it depends only upon causes already explained, when the heat is equal during the entire time that the grain is being formed. But if the heat increases, this slope will become less, and on the contrary, greater if it diminishes; so that if it increases and decreases at intervals, it will cause small steps along the length of these facets. And as for the four corners or sides which join these four facets, they are not usually very sharp or very uniform; for the particles which are joined to the sides of this grain are almost always applied lengthwise there, as I have said, but the ones which roll against its corners are more easily arranged there in another position, namely, as they are represented at *P*. This is why these corners are fairly blunt and rough, and why the grains of salt often split there more easily than in other places. It is also why the empty space that remains in the middle of the grain is almost round, rather than square. Besides this, because the particles which compose these grains are joined confusedly, and without any order other than the one I have just explained, it often happens that their ends, instead of touching, leave enough space between them for some fresh-water particles—which surround them and remain bent into circles—to lodge there, as you can see at *R*, when they are moving with only moderate speed. But when a very violent heat agitates them, they tend with a great deal of force to expand and unbend, just as they do when water expands into vapor, as has just been said; when this happens, they break their prisons at once, and with a sudden noise. And this is the reason why whole grains of salt shatter and leap and crackle when we throw them into the fire, and why they do not do the same thing when they are put there in

Fig.6.

Fig.7.

powdered form; for then these tiny prisons are already broken.

Moreover, the water of the sea cannot be so purely composed of the particles I have described that there are not also certain others among them whose shape is such that they are not prevented from remaining in the sea, even though they are much finer. And these particles, becoming entangled with the particles of salt while it is forming, can give it that very pleasant odor of violets which white salt has when it is freshly made, or the dirty color that black salt has, or any of the other variations which we can notice in salts, and which depend on the various waters in which they are formed.

Finally, you will not be surprised that salt is as crisp and brittle as it is, if you consider the way in which its particles are joined; nor will it surprise you that when pure, it is always white or transparent, if you consider the thickness of these particles and the nature of the color white, which will be explained hereinafter; nor that it melts easily enough on the fire when it is whole, considering that there are many particles of fresh water enclosed among its own. Nor will it surprise you that it melts with much more difficulty when it is well pulverized and very dry, so that there is no fresh water remaining in it, if you will notice that it cannot melt by itself if its particles do not bend, and its particles can be bent only with difficulty. For although we can imagine that in former times the particles of the sea have all been more or less pliant in some degree, we must consider that all those which were able to twist themselves around some others have since gradually been softened, and rendered very flexible, whereas those which are not so twisted have remained entirely rigid; so that there is now a great difference in this between the particles of salt and those of fresh water. But they both must be round: that is, those of fresh water are round like strings, and those of salt like cylinders or rods; for all bodies that move in different ways over a long period of time usually become rounded. And following this we can understand the nature of that extremely acrid and strong water which can corrode gold, and which the alchemists call the spirit or oil of salt. For inasmuch as it is extracted only by the violence of a very hot fire, either from pure salt, or from salt mixed with some other very fixed and dried body such as brick, which is used only to keep it from melting, it is evident that its particles are identical with those which formerly composed salt. But these particles could not be distilled through the distilling apparatus, and thus change from a fixed to a volatile condition, unless striking against one another by dint of being agitated by the fire, they changed from the rigid and inflexible particles that they were and became easy to bend. And in this same way they changed from round particles in the form of cylinders, into flat ones with sharp edges, like leaves of iris or of sword grass; for without this they would not have been able to bend. And consequently it is easy to judge the cause of their taste, which is very different from that of salt; for, lying lengthwise against the tongue, with their edges resting against the extremities of its nerves, and flowing along them and cutting them, they must agitate these nerves differently from the way they used to do before, and as a result cause a different taste, namely, the one we call acrid.

I could give the explanation of all the other properties of this water in this way, but it would go on to infinity; and it will be better if, returning to the consideration of vapors, I begin to examine how they move through the air, and how they cause winds there.

Fourth Discourse

Of Winds

Any agitation of the air that can be felt is called *wind,* and any invisible and impalpable body is called *air.* Thus, when water is greatly rarefied and changed into very fine vapor, we say that it has been converted into air, even though this vast air that we breathe is for the most part composed only of particles whose shapes are quite different from those of water, and which are much finer. And thus the air which is forced out of a bellows, or impelled by a fan, is called wind, although those more extensive winds which reign on the face of the sea and earth are normally nothing other than the movement of vapors which, by expanding, pass from their present location into some other, where they find it easier to expand. In the same way, we observe, in these hollow balls called Aeolipiles, that a little water being exhaled as vapor causes quite a large and strong wind, because of the small amount of material of which it is composed. And because this artificial wind can help us a great deal in understanding natural ones, it will be good for me to explain it here.

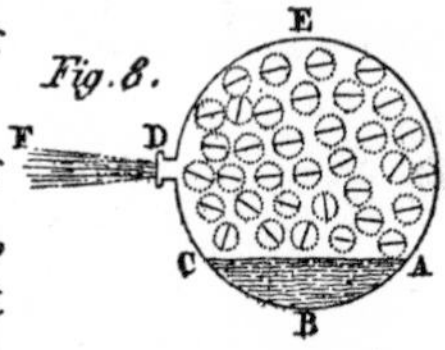

Fig. 8.

ABCDE is a ball of copper or some other such material, completely hollow and sealed, except that it has a very small opening at the place marked *D;* and with the section *ABC* of this ball full of water, and the other, *AEC,* empty— that is, containing only air—we place it on the fire; then the heat, agitating the small particles of water, causes many of them to rise above the surface *AC;* there they extend and are pushed against one another, turning at the same time, and make an effort to move apart in the manner explained above. And because they can move apart in this way only to the extent that some of them leave by the hole D, all the forces with which they push against each other conspire together to chase through the hole all the particles nearest to it; thus they cause a wind which blows from D toward F. And because there are always new particles of this water which, as they are raised by the heat above this surface AC, extend and separate from one another in proportion as some of them leave through the hole D, this wind never stops until all the water in this ball is evaporated, or else until the heat which causes it to evaporate stops.

Now the ordinary winds which occur in the air are caused in nearly the same way as this one, and there are only two principal fashions in which they differ. The first is that the vapors of which they are composed rise not only from the surface of the water, as in this ball, but also from humid earth and from the snows and clouds; normally they issue from these in greater abundance than from pure water, because in the former their particles are already nearly all disjointed and disunited, and thus are that much the easier to separate.

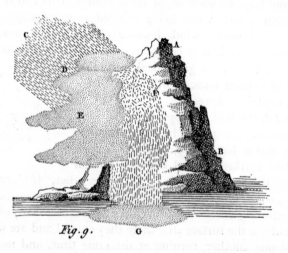

Fig. 9.

The second difference is that since these vapors cannot be enclosed in the air as they can in an Aeolipile, they are not prevented from expanding equally in all directions by anything but the resistance of some other vapors, or of some clouds or mountains, or finally of some wind which tends toward their location; but to compensate for this, there are often, in addition, other vapors which thicken, and compressing themselves at the same time that the others expand, cause them to take their course toward the space which the compressed ones leave to them. For example, if you imagine that there are now large vapors at the air space marked F, which expand and tend to occupy a space incomparably greater than the one containing them, and that at the same time there are other vapors at G which, compressing and changing into water or snow, leave the greatest part of the space they occupied empty, you will not doubt that the ones at F take their course toward G, and so compose a wind which blows there. This is especially true if you consider, also, that they are prevented from extending toward A and B by the high mountains there, or toward E because the air there is pressed and condensed by another wind which blows from C to D; and finally that there are clouds above them which prevent them from extending higher toward the sky. And notice that when the vapors pass in this way from one place to another, they bring along, or chase ahead, all the air that is in their way, and all the exhalations that are among them; so that although these vapors cause winds almost by themselves, they are nevertheless not the sole component of them. And note as well that the expansion and condensation of these exhalations and this air can help to produce these winds; but that [their influence] is so slight, compared to the expansion and condensation of the vapors, that they should almost not be taken into account. For when the air is expanded, it occupies only around two or three times more space than when it is moderately condensed, whereas the vapors occupy more than two or three thousand times as much space. And the exhalations do not expand—that is, they are not drawn from the terrestrial bodies, except with the help of a great heat; but once they have been so drawn, they can almost never, by any amount of cold, be condensed again as much as they had been previously. Whereas only a little heat is necessary to cause the water to expand into vapor, and again, very little cold is needed to cause the vapors to change into water.

But now let us see the particular properties and generation of the principal winds. First, we observe that all the air takes

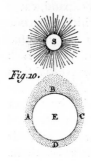

Fig. 10.

its course around the earth from east to west: we must necessarily assume this here, because the explanation of it cannot be conveniently derived except by explaining the entire fabric of the universe, which I do not intend to do here. But then we observe that east winds are normally drier, and make the air much cleaner and more serene, than the western ones. The explanation is that the western winds, being opposed to the normal course of vapors, arrest them and make them thicken into clouds; whereas the others chase and disperse them. In addition, we observe that east winds blow principally in the morning, and west winds at night. The reason for this will be evident to you if you will look at the earth $ABCD$, and at the sun S, which, lighting the half ABC and causing noon at B and midnight at D at the same time that it is setting for the people who live at A, and it is rising for those who live at C. For, because the vapors at B are very much expanded by the heat of the day, they take their course toward D, partly through A and partly through C, and at D they, re-place those which were condensed by the chill of the night. Thus they cause a west wind toward A, where the sun sets, and an east wind toward C, where it rises. And it must even be noted that this wind blowing toward C is normally stronger and faster than the one which blows toward A. This is so be-cause it follows the course of the entire mass of air, as well as because the part of the earth between C and D has gone longer without being lighted by the sun than the section be-tween D and A, and consequently the condensation of the vapors must have occurred sooner and to a greater extent there.

We also observe that the north winds blow primarily during the day, that they come from above to below, and that they are very violent, cold and dry. You can see the explanation of this by considering that the earth *EBFD* is covered with many clouds and mists near the poles *E* and *F*, where it is hardly heated by the sun at all; and that at *B*, where the sun is immediately overhead, it excites a quantity of vapors which are quite agitated by the action of its light and rise into the air very quickly, until they have risen so high that the resistance of their weight makes it easier for them to swerve, taking their courses on either side toward *I* and *M* above the clouds *G* and *K*, than it is for them to continue higher in a straight line. And these clouds *G* and *K*, which at the same time are also heated and rarefied by the sun, are converted into vapors that take their course from *G* toward *H* and from *K* toward *L*, rather than toward *E* and *F*; for the dense air around the poles resists them much more than do the vapors coming from the earth at noon, that is, at *B*; because these are very much agitated and ready to be moved in all directions, they can easily give up their place to them. Thus, taking *F* for the arctic pole, the course of these vapors from *K* toward *L* causes a wind from the north, which blows during the day in Europe. This wind blows downward, because it comes from the clouds toward the earth. And it is normally very violent, because it is excited by the strongest heat of all, namely that of midday; and it is made of the easiest material to dissolve into vapor, namely, clouds. Finally, this wind is very cold and dry—because of its force, in consequence of what was said above, and also because impetuous winds are always dry and cold. Thus, it is also dry, because it is normally composed only of the coarser particles of fresh water mixed with air, whereas humidity depends primarily upon the finer ones, and the latter are seldom found in the clouds from

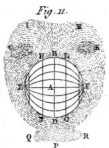

Fig. 21.

which this wind is engendered; for, as you shall presently see, their nature is more like that of ice than that of water. And the north wind is cold because it brings with it toward the south the very fine material that was in the north, on which cold primarily depends.

We observe, on the contrary, that the winds of the south usually blow more during the night, and travel upward, and are sluggish and humid. We can see the explanation for this, also, by looking again at the globe *EBFD*, and by considering that its section *D* at the equator, where I assume that it is now dark, still retains enough of the heat communicated to it during the day by the sun to cause many vapors to leave that region; but the air above, at *P*, does not retain proportionately as much heat. For thick and heavy bodies generally retain their heat for a longer time than do those which are light and fine; and also, those which are solid retain it for a longer time than those which are liquid. This is the reason that the vapors around *P*, instead of pursuing their course toward *Q* and *R*, stop and thicken into the shape of clouds; and these prevent the vapors issuing from *D* from climbing higher, and force them to take their course on either side toward *N* and *O*, so that they cause a southern wind there which blows principally during the night, and travels upward from the earth toward the atmosphere. Also, it cannot help but be a sluggish wind, because its course is retarded by the thickness of the night air and also because its material, coming only from earth or water, cannot expand as quickly or in such great quantity as that of other winds, which comes normally from clouds. And finally this wind is warm and humid, because of the tardiness of its progress; and it is humid, too, because it is composed of the finer particles of fresh water as well as the coarser ones, for they issue together from the earth. And it is warm, because it brings with it toward the north the subtle material that was in the south.

We also observe that in the month of March, and generally throughout the spring, the winds are drier and the changes of the atmosphere more sudden and frequent than in any other season of the year. The explanation can again be seen by looking at the globe *EBFD*, and considering that the sun—which I suppose to be opposite the circle *BAD* which represents the equator, and before this to have been for three months opposite the circle *HN*, which represents the Tropic of Capricorn—has heated half of the earth, *BFD*, where it is now spring, much less than the other half, *BED*, where it is autumn; and as a result, the half *BFD* is much more covered with snow, and all the atmosphere surrounding it is much thicker, and more full of clouds, than that which surrounds the other half *BED*. This is the reason why, during the day, many more vapors are expanded there, and on the other hand, why during the night many more of them are condensed. For because the mass of the earth is less heated there, and because the force of the sun is no less, there must be a greater inequality between the heat of the day and the cold of the night; and so these east winds which I have said blow primarily in the morning, and those from the north which blow during the middle of the day (both of which are very dry), must be much stronger and more abundant there than in any other season. And the west winds, which blow during the evening, must also be rather strong there, for the same reason that the east winds, which blow during the morning, are strong; for if the regular course of these winds is advanced, or retarded, or deflected ever so little by the particular causes which can more or less expand or thicken the atmosphere in each region, they meet one another and engender rains or storms; these normally cease soon afterwards, for the east and north winds, which chase the clouds away, remain the masters. And I believe that it is these winds of the east and north that the Greeks called the Ornithies, because they brought with them the birds that came in the springtime. But as to those they called the Etesies, which they observed after the summer solstice, it is probable that they proceed from vapors that the sun lifts from the earth and from the northern waters, after it has already stayed long enough around the Tropic of Cancer. For you know that the sun stays proportionately much longer in the Tropics than in the space between them; and we must think that during the months of March, April, and May, it dissolves the greater part of the clouds and snows about our pole into vapors and winds. But we should also know that—except for a few weeks afterwards, when that long day of six months' duration is slightly more than half over—it cannot heat the lands and seas to a degree sufficient to create the vapors that cause the winds.

For the rest, these general and regular winds would always be such as I have just explained them if the surface of the earth were covered all over evenly with water, or if it were equally barren of waters, so that there would not be the diversity of seas, lands, and mountains, nor any other cause but the presence of the sun capable of expanding vapors, nor any but its absence capable of condensing them. But it must be noted that when the sun shines it commonly causes more vapors to issue from the seas than from the land, because the land is dry in many places, and thus does not provide as much material for it; and on the other hand, when the sun is absent, the heat that it has caused makes more vapors leave the earth than the seas, because it is more deeply impressed there. This is why we often observe at the seashore that during the day the wind comes from the direction of the sea, and during the night from the land. And this is also why those fires called the Ardans guide travelers toward water at night, for they follow indiscriminately the course of the air which comes out toward the sea from neighboring lands, because the air which was there has condensed. We must also note that the air which touches the surface of the water follows its current in some way. From this it follows that winds often change along the seashores, as the see ebbs and flows, and that along great rivers we feel small winds in calm weather, which follow their course. Then it also must be noticed that the vapors coming from waters are much more humid and dense than

those that rise from the land, and that there are always
more air and exhalations among the former. Consequently
the same storms are normally more violent on the sea than
on land, and the same wind can be dry in one country
and humid in another; thus we say that the south winds
(which are humid almost everywhere) are dry in Egypt,
where there is nothing but the dry and burning land in
the rest of Africa to provide the material for them. And
without doubt this is the reason why it almost never rains
there: for although the north winds coming from the sea
are humid, still because they are also the coldest winds
that can be found there, they cannot easily cause rain, as
you shall hereinafter understand. Besides, it is essential to
consider that the light of the moon, which varies greatly
according to its proximity to the sun, contributes to the
expansion of the vapors, as does also the light of the other
stars. But this is only in the same proportion that we feel
this light acting against our eyes, for they are the most
certain judges that we can have for knowing the force of
light; as a result the light of the stars is insignificant compared with that of the moon, and the light of the moon is
insignificant compared with that of the sun. Finally, we
must consider that the vapors rise very unequally from the
diverse sections of the earth; for the heavenly bodies heat
the mountains differently from the plains, the forests differently from the prairies, cultivated fields differently from
deserts; and it is even the case that some lands are hotter
of themselves, or easier to heat, than others. And then,
when there form in the air vastly different clouds, which
can be transported from one region to another by the
slightest winds, and suspended at various distances from the
earth, even many together above each other, the heavenly
bodies again act against the highest differently than the way
they act against the lowest; and against the lowest clouds
differently than against the earth underneath it. They also
act differently against the same places on the earth when
there are no clouds covering them, and when there are; and

differently after it rains or snows, and before. This makes it nearly impossible to predict the particular winds which must occur each day in each area of the earth; and often, in fact, there are even many contrary winds which pass above one another. But we will be better able to determine in general what winds must be the most frequent and the strongest, and in what areas and seasons they must prevail, if we take precise notice of all the things which have been noted here. And we will be still better able to determine it for the great seas, especially in places far removed from land; for since the surface of water has none of the uneven-ness that we have just ascribed to land, irregular winds are generated much less often there. And winds coming from the shores can hardly reach there, as is sufficiently confirmed by the experience of our sailors, who for this reason have given the name Pacific to the largest of all the seas.

And I know of nothing worthy of further discussion here, except that all the sudden changes in the air (as when it becomes warmer, or rarer, or more humid than the season requires) depend on the winds—not only upon those in the same regions where these changes occur, but also upon those which are near them, and upon the various causes from which they proceed. For example, if we feel a south wind here which proceeds merely from some particular cause, and which originates quite close at hand and therefore does not carry very much heat, and at the same time there is also a north wind in a neighboring country which comes from rather far or a rather great height, the very fine ma-terial of the latter can easily reach us and cause an extra-ordinary chill. And this southern wind, coming only from a neighboring lake, can be very humid, whereas if it came from desert plains which were farther away it would be very dry. And because it is caused only by the expansion of the vapors of this lake, without the condensation of any others from the north contributing to it, it must necessarily make our air much denser and heavier than if it were caused only by this condensation, without there having been any expansion of the southern vapors. If we add to this that the fine material and the vapors in the pores of the earth, which take different courses, are also like winds there, carrying with them evaporations of all sorts according to the qualities of the earth through which they pass; and that apart from that, the clouds, by lowering, can cause a wind that chases the air downward—as I shall speak of later on—we will have, I believe, all the noteworthy causes of changes in the air.

Fifth Discourse

Of Clouds

After having considered how the vapors cause winds by
expanding, we must see how they form clouds and mists by
condensing and contracting: that is, as soon as they become
notably less transparent than pure air, if they extend to the
surface of the earth, we call them mists; but if they remain
suspended higher up, we call them clouds. And it must be
noted that what causes them thus to become less transparent
than pure air is that, when their movement is slowed and
their particles are close enough to touch each other, they
unite and gather in various small heaps which may be either
drops of water or pieces of ice. For while they remain completely separate and floating in the air, they can hardly impede the passage of light; whereas when they gather, even
though the drops of water or particles of ice which they
compose are transparent, nevertheless because each of their
surfaces reflects part of the rays that strike against them (as
was said of all surfaces of transparent bodies in the *Optics*),
the number of these surfaces is easily great enough to cause
all or nearly all of them to be reflected. And as to the drops
of water, they are formed when the fine matter around the
small particles of the vapors does not have enough force to
cause them to spread out and repel each other, and yet has
enough to cause them to bend, and then make all those that
encounter each other join and accumulate together in a ball.
And the surface of this ball immediately becomes uniform
and highly polished, because the particles of the air which
touch it move differently from the way it moves, and also
because the fine material in its pores moves differently from
that in the particles of the air (as has already been explained

in speaking about the surfaces of the water of the sea). And also, for the same reason, it becomes perfectly round: you may often have seen that the water of rivers whirls around and makes circles in places where something is preventing it from moving in a straight line as quickly as its agitation requires: in the same way, it is essential to think that the fine material, running through the pores of the other bodies as a river runs through the spaces between the grass growing in its bed, and passing more freely from one place in the air to another and also from one place in the water to another than it does from air into water or reciprocally from water into the air (as has been noted elsewhere), it must spin around inside of this drop. And it also spins outside, in the surrounding air, in a different direction from the way it does inside, and by this means it rounds off all the particles of its surface, for they cannot fail to follow its movements, inasmuch as water is a liquid body. And without doubt this is sufficient to understand why the drops of water must be perfectly round, because their sections are analogous to the surface of the earth, in that there is no reason why any of the sections of their circumference should be further from or closer to their centers than the others in this sense, given that they are neither more nor less pressed, on one side or on the other, by the air that surrounds them (at least if it is calm and tranquil, as we should assume here). But considering them in another sense, we can suspect that when they are so small that their weight does not have enough force to make them to divide the air and allow them to descend, they become flatter and thinner and more elliptical, as at T or V; therefore we must realize that they have air around their sides as well as underneath, and that if their weight is not sufficient to displace the air underneath, and allow them to descend, it is also not sufficient to allow the air around the sides to withdraw and permit them to grow wider. And because we can on the other hand suspect that, when their weight is sufficient to allow them to descend,

Fig. 12.

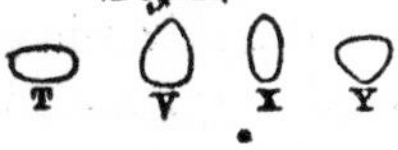

the air that they divide makes them longer and narrower, as at X or Y, we must realize that, since they are completely surrounded, the air they divide (whose space they will occupy as they descend), must rise above them at the same time to refill the space they leave immediately above them. And the air can do so by flowing all along their surface, where it finds the way shorter and easier than if they had a different shape; for everyone knows that of all shapes, the round has the greatest capacity, that is, the least surface area relative to the size of the body that it contains. And so however we look at it, these drops must always remain round, unless the force of some wind, or some other particular cause, prevents them from so doing.

As to their size, it depends on the distance between the particles of vapor when they begin to compose these drops, and also on the degree of their agitation afterwards, and on the quantity of other vapors which can come to unite with them. For each of them is at first composed of only two or three of the small particles of vapor, coming together, but immediately afterwards, if this vapor has been slightly thick, two or three of the drops formed from it join into one by meeting, and again two or three of these join into one, and so on, until they can no longer meet and come together. And while they are suspended in the air other vapors can come to join them and make them larger, until finally their weight causes them to fall as rain or as dew.

As for the small pieces of ice, they are formed when it is so cold that the particles of vapor cannot be bent by the fine material among them. And if this cold is not present until after the drops are already formed, it leaves them completely round as it freezes them, unless it is accompanied by a wind strong enough to cause them to become slightly flat on the side where it strikes them. If, on the other hand, the cold is present before the drops have begun to form, the particles of the vapor merely join lengthwise, and form only very slender fibers of ice. But if the cold occurs between these two times, which is usually the case, it freezes the particles of vapor as they bend and build up together, without giving them time to unite perfectly enough to form drops; and thus it makes small knots or lumps of ice from them which are completely white, because they are composed of many fibers which although they are bent upon one another, are nevertheless separate and have their own distinct surfaces. And these knots are, as it were, velvety, or covered all around with hairs, because there are always many particles of the vapor which cannot bend and amass together as quickly as the others, so that they press perpendicularly against them, and compose the tiny hairs which cover them. And according to whether this cold comes more slowly or all at once, and whether the vapor is thicker or finer, these lumps are bigger or smaller, and the hairs which surround them are stronger and shorter, or finer and longer.

You can see from this that there are always two things necessary for converting vapors into water or ice, namely, that their particles be close enough to touch each other, and that there be sufficient cold around them to cause them to unite and to halt one another when they touch. For it would not be enough for them to be very cold, if they were separated so far from one another in the air that they did not touch at all; nor for the particles to be very close to each other and very crowded if their heat—that is, their agitation—were strong enough to prevent them from joining. Thus we do not always see clouds being formed high in the air, even though the cold there is always great enough for this effect. It is necessary that there be, in addition, a western wind opposed to the normal course of the vapors to gather and condense them in the places where it ends; or else two or more other winds, coming from different directions, must press and accumulate the particles between them; or else one of these winds must impel them against an already formed cloud. Or else, finally, they must gather, of their own, against the underside of some cloud as they leave the earth.

Also, mists do not always form around us—neither in

winter, although the air is cold enough then, nor in summer, although the vapors are sufficiently abundant then; but only when the cold of the air and the abundance of the vapors concur, as often happens during the evening or at night after a rather hot day. This happens primarily in the springtime rather than in the other seasons, even autumn, because there is a greater inequality between the heat of the day and the cold of the night. And it also happens at the seashore or in marshlands more than in lands that are far from water, or water that is far from land; for the water loses its heat faster than the earth, and cools the air that condenses the vapors abundantly produced by the humid and warm lands. But the greatest mists are formed, like clouds, in places where the course of two or more winds terminates. For these winds impel many vapors toward these places, and these vapors thicken there, either in mists if the air near the earth is very cold, or in clouds if it is only cold enough to condense them higher up. And note that the drops of water or particles of ice of which the mists are composed can be only very tiny; for if they were ever so slightly heavier, their weight would make them go down to the earth very quickly, so that we would not say that this was a mist, but rather rain or snow. And, moreover, there can be no wind where these mists are without its dissipating them soon afterwards, especially when they are composed of drops of water: for the slightest agitation of the air causes many of these drops to join together, and to grow heavy and fall as rain or dew. Note also, concerning clouds, that they can be produced at various distances from the earth according to how much time the vapors have to climb before having condensed enough to compose the clouds. This is why we often see many of them above one another, and why we even see some which are agitated by different winds. And this happens principally in mountainous country, for the heat which lifts the vapors acts less uniformly there than in other places. It is essential to note, beyond this, that the highest of these clouds can hardly ever be composed of drops of water, but only of particles of ice; for it is certain that the air where they are is colder than, or at least as cold as, that at the summits of high mountains; and this is cold enough, even in the middle of summer, to prevent the snows there from melting. And because the higher the vapors rise, the more they encounter the cold that freezes them, and the less they can be pressed by winds, from this it follows that normally the highest parts of the clouds are composed only of very slender fibers of ice, very widely scattered from one another. Then slightly below are formed the knots or lumps of this ice, which are very tiny and covered with hairs; and by degrees, still others underneath, slightly larger; and finally, drops of water are sometimes formed at the lowest levels. And when the air containing them is entirely calm and tranquil, or else when it is all uniformly moved by some wind, these drops, as well as the particles of ice, can stay scattered rather far apart from one another and without any order, so that then the form of the clouds differs in no way from that of the mists. But the vapors are often impelled by winds which do not fill all the surrounding air evenly, and which, as a result, since they cannot make the vapors move in the same manner as this air, flow above and below the vapors, pressing them together and forcing them to assume a shape which can least impede their movement; therefore those surfaces along which these winds pass become quite flat and level. And what I want you

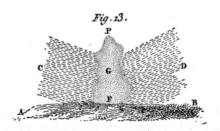

Fig. 13.

to note particularly here is that all the small knots or lumps of snow on these surfaces are arranged precisely in such a way that each of them has six other lumps around it, touching it or at least no further away from it than they are from each other. Let us suppose, for example, that above the earth *AB,* a wind comes from the western section *D,* and that this wind is opposed to the normal course of the air, or if you prefer, to another wind which comes from the eastern section *C;* and suppose that each of these two winds halts the other at the beginning, near the space *FGP,* where they have condensed some vapors of which they have made a confused mass; and at the same time, because their forces are balanced and equal in this location, they leave the air calm and tranquil there. It often happens that two winds are opposed in this way, for there are always many different ones about the earth at the same time, and each of them takes its normal path, without swerving, until the place where it encounters a contrary wind that resists it. But their forces can hardly remain balanced thus for long; and because their matter flows more and more into the mass, unless they both cease together (which is rare), and the strongest finally takes its course under or over the cloud, or even through the middle or all around it, according to its disposition. By this means, if the stronger does not deaden the other altogether, it at least forces it to change its direction. For example, I assume here that the western wind, having taken

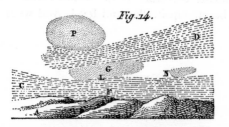

Fig. 14.

its course between *G* and *P,* has forced the eastern wind to pass below toward *F,* where it has caused the mist there to fall as dew, and has kept above itself the cloud *G,* which, finding itself pressed between these two winds, has become

very flat and spread out. And the small lumps of ice which
had been on its surface, both above and below, as well as on
the underside of the cloud *P*, must have been arranged there
in such a way that each of them had six others surrounding
it; for we cannot imagine any reason which would have prevented this, and all round and uniform bodies moved in the
same plane by a similar force naturally tend to be arranged
in this way, as you may see through experiment by randomly
throwing a row or two of unstrung round pearls on a plate,
and shaking them or blowing them slightly against each other
so that they come together. But note that I speak here only of
the upper and lower surfaces, not of those on the sides,
because the unequal quantity of material that the winds can
impel against them or remove from them at any given
moment usually gives their circumference a very irregular
and uneven shape. I also do not add the fact that the tiny
knots of ice which compose the inside of the cloud *G* must
be arranged in the same way as those of its surfaces, because
this is something which is not at all as obvious as the latter.
But I would like you to consider again the knots of ice that
can come to rest underneath the cloud after it is completely
formed; for if, while it remains suspended in the space *G*,
there are several vapors coming out of the places on earth
around *A*, and these vapors are gradually chilled in the air
and thereby converted into small knots of ice that the wind
pushes toward *L*, there is no doubt that these knots must be
arranged there in such a way that each of them is surrounded
by six others which are in the same plane and press against it
equally, and so form successive layers or sheets under the surface of this cloud, for as long as there is matter to make them.
And in addition it must be noted that the wind passing between the earth and this cloud acts with greater force against
the lowest of these sheets than against the one immediately
above it, and with more force against that one than against
the next above it, and so on; thus it can draw them off
and cause them to move separately, and in this way polish
their surfaces by smoothing down the tiny hairs around the

particles that make them up on two sides. And it can even cause a portion of these sheets to slide out from under this cloud G, and carry them away from there, for example toward N, where they compose a new cloud. And although I have only spoken here of the ice particles which are amassed in the form of small knots or lumps, the same can also be easily understood of drops of water, provided that the wind is not strong enough to cause them to interfere with one another; or else provided that there be certain exhalations around them or, as often happens, that they be separated by certain vapors not yet disposed to take the form of water. For otherwise as soon as they come in contact, many of them gather into one, and thus become so large and heavy that they are forced to fall as rain.

Moreover, what I have just said—that the shape of the circumference of each cloud is normally very irregular and uneven—must be understood only of those which occupy less space in height and width than the winds which surround them. For such a great abundance of vapors is sometimes found in the place where two or more winds meet, that they force these winds to swirl around them, and to form an extraordinarily large cloud which, because it is equally pressed on all sides by these winds, becomes completely round and uniform in its circumference. And even when these winds are slightly warm, or else exposed to the heat of the sun, such a cloud acquires a shell or crust of many particles of ice joined together, which can become quite large and thick without its weight causing it to fall, because the rest of the cloud supports it.

Sixth Discourse

Of Snow, Rain, and Hail

There are many things which together prevent clouds from descending immediately after they are formed. In the first place, because the pieces of ice or drops of water of which they are composed are very fine and consequently have a very large surface in proportion to the quantity of their matter, the resistance of the air that they would have to divide if they were to descend can easily have more force to prevent them from descending, than their weight has to compel them to do so. Then the winds are usually stronger near the earth, where their substance is thicker, than high in the air where it is finer; and for this reason they are more active from below to above than from above to below. Therefore, not only can they support the clouds, but often they can also cause these particles to climb above the region of the air where they are located. And the vapors can do the same thing; for, rising from the earth or coming from some other direction, they cause the air under them to expand. And again, the heat of that air can do so also, as it expands and repels these clouds, or the cold of the air above them, as it draws them to it by contracting them, or other similar things. And in particular, when the particles of ice are pushed against one another by the winds, they touch one another but nevertheless do not thereby completely unite, and they compose a body so rare, light and extended that if it were not for the heat which melts some of its particles and by this means condenses and increases its weight, it could almost never descend to the earth. But as has been said above, as water, when it is frozen, is in some way expanded by cold, so we must note that heat, which normally rarefies other bodies, usually condenses clouds. And this is easy to confirm by experiment in the case of snow, which is of the same material as clouds except that it is already more condensed; for we see that when it is put in a warm place it shrinks and diminishes a great deal in size before any water comes out of it and before it diminishes in weight. This happens to the extent that the extremities of the bits of ice which compose it, being finer than the rest, melt sooner; and once they are melted—that is, once they have become pliant and, as it were, alive and stirring—they slide toward the nearby bits of ice and attach themselves to them, without thereby becoming detached from the ones to which they are already joined, and thus the extremities cause the bits of ice to come closer to each other. But because the particles that make up the clouds are normally more distant from one another than those which compose snow on the earth, they cannot thus come closer to some of their neighbors without becoming more distant from others as a result; this is why, having been hithertofore evenly separated by the air, they afterwards divide into many small heaps or flakes, which become larger to the extent that the particles of the cloud have been compressed and the heat more diffused. And even when some wind, or expansion of all the air above the cloud, or some other such event, causes the highest of these flakes to descend first, they attach themselves to those below which they encounter in their path, and so make them larger. After this, heat can easily make them descend to the earth, by condensing them and making them heavier. And when they so descend, without being completely melted, they constitute snow; but if the air through which they pass is so warm that it melts them, as it always is during the summer, and very often is in other seasons in our climate, they are converted into rain. And it also sometimes happens that after having melted or almost melted, they come upon some cold wind which freezes them again and turns them into hail.

Now this hail can be of many kinds. First, if the cold wind

that causes it encounters drops of water which are already formed, it makes completely transparent and round grains of ice out of them, except that it sometimes makes them slightly flat on the side where it strikes them. And if it encounters flakes of snow which are nearly melted, but which are not yet rounded into drops of water, it makes that angular hail of various irregular shapes, whose grains are sometimes very large because they are formed by a cold wind, which in chasing the cloud downward, pushes many of its flakes against one another, and freezes them all in a mass. And it is to be noted here that when this wind approaches these melting flakes it causes the heat of the air around them—that is, the most agitated and coarsest of the fine material in this air—to be drawn into their pores, because the wind cannot penetrate them as quickly; the same way that sometimes when a wind or a rain comes up suddenly and cools the outside air on the earth, more heat than before comes into houses. And the heat in the pores of these flakes stays more toward their surfaces than at their centers, in proportion as the fine material which causes it can better continue its movements there; and near the surface the heat melts them more and more, just before they begin to freeze again; and even the most liquid flakes, that is, the most agitated ones which are found elsewhere, also tend toward the surface, whereas those that do not have time to be melted stay at the center. This is why the outside of each grain of this sleet is usually composed of continuous and transparent ice, yet it has a bit of snow inside, as you can see by breaking one of them. And because they hardly ever fall except in the summertime, this will assure you that the clouds can be composed of particles of ice then, as well as in the winter. The reason that prevents such hail—at least, hail whose grains are fairly large—from hardly ever falling in winter is that then the clouds almost never contain enough heat for this hail, unless they are so low that their matter, being melted or nearly so, would not have the time to be frozen again before falling to the earth. But if the snow is not yet so melted, but only slightly reheated and softened when the cold wind that converts it to hail comes on the scene, it is not made at all transparent, but remains white like sugar. And if the flakes of this snow are small enough, as about the size of a pea or smaller, each is converted into a grain of hail which is fairly round. But if they are bigger, they split and divide into grains which are all pointed in the form of pyramids. For the moment a cold wind begins to surround these flakes, the heat drawn into their pores condenses and shrinks all their particles by withdrawing from their circumference toward their center; this causes them to become fairly round, and the cold which penetrates and freezes them soon afterwards makes them much harder than snow. And because when they are fairly large, the heat inside them still continues to shrink and condense their interior particles by always withdrawing toward the center, after the exterior particles are so hardened and frozen by the cold that they cannot follow them, the flakes must split on the inside, following planes or straight lines which tend toward the center; and these splits increase more and more as the cold penetrates further, until finally they shatter and divide into many pointed pieces, which are so many grains of hail. I have not determined into how many such grains each of them can be divided; but it seems to me that normally it must be eight at the least, and that they may also perhaps divide into twelve, twenty, or twenty-four, but even better into thirty-two or even a much greater number, according to whether they are larger and whether they are made of a finer snow, and whether the cold that converts them into hail is more harsh, and arrives suddenly.

I have observed more than once of such hail that its grains had almost the shape of segments of a ball divided into eight equal parts through three sections which intersect at the center at right angles. Then I have also observed others which were longer and smaller, and seemed to be a quarter of the size of the others, although because their corners were blunted and rounded by contracting, they were almost of the shape of a lump of sugar. And I have also noticed that in front of, or behind, or even among these grains of hail there often fell some others which were round.

But there is nothing curious or remarkable about the diverse shapes of this hail, by comparison with those of snow, which is made from small knots or lumps of ice arranged by the wind in the form of layers, in the manner I described above. For when the heat begins to melt the small hairs of these layers, it first destroys the top and bottom ones, because they are the most exposed to its action; as a result, it causes the small quantity of liquid that comes out of them to spread out over their surfaces, where the liquid quickly fills the small unevennesses to be found there. Thus it makes them as flat and polished as are the surfaces of liquid bodies, even though it immediately refreezes there; for if the heat is no greater than is necessary to thaw these small hairs, surrounded with air, without melting anything further, it is not sufficient to prevent their matter from refreezing when it is on these surfaces of ice.

After that, this heat also softens and melts the tiny hairs that remain around the circumference of each knot, where it is surrounded with six others similar to it, and it causes those hairs which are the furthest away from the six neighboring knots to bend here and there indiscriminately, and to unite with those that are opposite them, on these six knots. For the latter ones, being cooled by the proximity of these knots, cannot melt; on the contrary, they cause the matter of the other hairs to be frozen again, as soon as this matter is mingled among its own. And in this way six points or radii around each knot are formed, which can have various shapes depending on the size and density of the knots, the strength and length of the hairs, and the intensity of the heat which assembles them; and also depending on the strength of the wind which accompanies this heat, if at least some wind does accompany it. And so the exterior face of the cloud, which was formerly as we see it at Z or M, afterwards becomes such as it may be seen at O or Q, and each of the pieces of ice of which it is composed has the shape of a tiny very carefully fashioned rose or star.

But so that you will not think that I speak of these matters only from opinion, I want to report to you an observation I made during the past winter of 1635. On the fourth of February, the air having previously been extremely cold, there fell in the evening in Amsterdam (where I was at that time) a little frost, that is, rain which froze upon striking the earth. And afterwards a very fine hail fell, whose particles, which were only slightly larger than those represented at *H*, I judged to be drops of the same rain, which were frozen high in the air. Nevertheless, instead of being exactly round, as doubtless these drops had been, they had one side notably flatter than the other, so that they almost resembled in shape the part of our eye called the crystalline humor. From this I understood that the wind, which was then quite strong and very cold, had the necessary force so to change the shape of the drops in freezing them. But what astonished me most of all was that among those grains which fell last, I noticed some which had six tiny teeth around them, similar to those in the wheels of clocks, such as you may see at *I*. And these teeth were very white, like sugar, whereas the grains, which were of transparent ice, seemed to be nearly black, and the teeth appeared obviously to be made of a very fine snow which attached itself around the grains after they were formed, as white frost attaches itself around plants. And I understood this all the more clearly because right at the end I ran across one or two of them which had innumerable tiny hairs about them, made of a paler and finer snow than that of the small teeth around the others, so that the one could be compared to the other as the uncrushed ash that covered coals while they were burning is compared to that which is burnt again

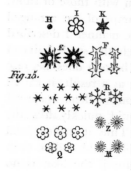

Fig.16.

and piled up in the grate. I was at great pains to imagine what could have formed and proportioned these six teeth around each grain so exactly, in the middle of the free air and during the agitation of a very great wind, until I finally considered that this wind had easily been able to carry some of the grains below or away from some cloud, and support them there because they were small enough; and there they must have been arranged in such a way that each of them was surrounded with six others in the same plane, following the normal order of nature. And I realized, moreover, that it was very likely that the heat which must have been in the air slightly beforehand, in order to cause the rain that I had observed, had also emitted certain vapors which this same wind had blown against these grains, where they were frozen in the form of very slender, tiny hairs; and perhaps these vapors had even helped to support them, so that they were easily able to remain suspended there, until more heat again came on the scene. And I realized that since this heat immediately melted all the hairs around each grain except those opposite the middle of some one of the six other grains which surrounded it (because their cold prevented its action), the matter of these melted hairs was immediately mixed among the six heaps of those that were left, and having by this means fortified them and rendered them much less penetrable by heat, it was frozen among them and so they had composed these six teeth. Whereas the innumerable hairs that I had seen around some of the last grains which had fallen had not been touched at all by this heat.

The next morning at approximately eight o'clock I again observed another kind of hail, or rather snow, of which I have never heard anyone speak. It was composed of small blades which were completely flat, highly polished and very transparent; they were about the thickness of a fairly heavy sheet of paper, and about the size of those seen at *K*, but so perfectly cut in hexagons with six sides that were so straight, and six angles so equal, that it is impossible for men to make anything so exact. I saw immediately that these blades must first have been small lumps of ice, arranged as I have just said, which were pressed by a very strong wind accompanied by enough heat to melt all their hairs, and to so fill all their pores with the humidity coming out of it that from being white, which they had been formerly, they became transparent. And I saw that at the same time this wind had so strongly pressed them against each other that no space remained between them, and that it had also planed their surface by passing above and below them, and so had given them the shape of these blades. There only remained the slight difficulty that these lumps of ice, having been thus half melted and at the same time pressed against one another, were not stuck together because of this pressure, but had remained completely separate; for although I expressly took great care in the attempt, I was never able to find two of them sticking to each other. But I soon satisfied myself about this by considering the way in which the wind continually agitates and successively bends all the particles of the surface of water by flowing over it, without making it rough or uneven by doing so. For I recognized from that that the wind infallibly causes the surfaces of clouds to bend and undulate in the same way, and that by continually stirring each particle of ice in a slightly different way from its neighbors, it does not allow them to stick entirely together, although it does not thereby disarrange them; and in the meantime it never ceases to smoothe and polish their tiny surfaces, in the same way that we sometimes see it polish that of the waves it makes in the dust of a field.

After this cloud, there came another one, which only produced small roses or wheels with six teeth rounded into semicircles, such as you can see at Q, which were quite flat and transparent, and approximately as thick as the blades which had preceded, and as well-shaped and well-proportioned as might possibly be imagined. I even perceived in the middle of some a very tiny white point, that one could have said was the mark of the leg of a compass someone used to round them. But it was easy for me to judge that they were formed in the same way as these blades, except that because the wind had pressed them much less, and perhaps because the heat had also been slightly less, their points were not completely melted, but only slightly shortened and rounded at the end in the form of teeth. And as for the white point which appeared in the center of some, I did not doubt that it came only from the heat, which had turned them from white to transparent, and had been so mild that it had not penetrated completely to their centers.

Afterwards there followed many other such wheels, joined two by two to an axis, or rather, because these axes were very large from the beginning, one could have said that they were so many small columns of crystal, of which each end was adorned with a rose with six petals that were slightly larger than their base. But afterwards, some more slender ones fell, and often the roses or stars at their extremities were unequal. Then there also fell more compressed ones, and gradually ones which were still more compressed, until finally these stars were completely joined; and there fell double ones having twelve points or radii which were rather long and perfectly proportioned, some quite equal and others alternately unequal, as you can see them at F and E. And all this gave me occasion to consider that particles of ice which are in two different planes or layers upon one another in the clouds can attach themselves together more easily than those of a single layer. For although the wind, which normally acts more strongly against the lowest of these layers than against the highest, can cause them to move slightly faster, as was noted a little while ago, nevertheless it can also sometimes act against them with equal force, and cause them to undulate in the same way. This happens especially when there are only two or three of them upon one another, and then, sifting between the lumps of ice of which they are composed, the wind causes the corresponding lumps of ice in different layers always to be held immobile against each other, despite the agitation and undulation of these layers, because in this way passage is easier for it. And meanwhile the heat—which is no less impeded by the proximity of the lumps of the two different layers from melting those of their hairs which face each other, than by the proximity of those of only one—merely melts other hairs around them; and these soon melt among the remaining ones and are refrozen there, and thus they make up the axes or columns which join these small lumps, at the same time that they are changed into roses or stars. And I was not astonished at the size of these columns that I had noticed in the beginning, although I well knew that the matter of the small hairs which had been around the two lumps could not have been sufficient to compose them: for I thought that there had perhaps been four or five layers upon one another, and that the heat, having acted more strongly against the two or three in the middle than against the first and last ones, because they were less exposed to the wind, had almost completely melted the lumps which composed them, and had formed these columns from them. Neither was I astonished to see two stars of unequal size often joined together; for, noticing that the radii of the largest were always longer and more pointed than those of the other, I judged that the cause of this was that the heat, having been stronger around the smaller one than around the other, had melted and softened its radii more; or else this smaller one could also have been composed of a smaller lump of ice. Finally, I was not surprised at those double stars having twelve radii, which fell afterwards; for I judged that each of them had been composed by the heat from a single one, with six radii. And because this heat was of a higher degree between the two layers where they were located than outside, it had completely melted the tiny fibers of ice that joined them together; thus it had stuck them together, as it had also shortened those fibers that joined the other stars which I had seen fall immediately before. Thus among the many thousands of these tiny stars which I considered that day, even though I took express care, I was never able to notice

a single one which had more or less than six radii, except
a very small number of these double ones which had twelve,
and four or five others which had eight. And these latter
were not perfectly round, as were all the others, but slightly
oval, and entirely similar to those you can see at *O*. From
this I judged that they were formed by the conjunction of
the extremities of two layers which the wind had pushed
against each other at the same time that the heat was
converting their tiny lumps into stars, for they had exactly
the shape that would have to be caused by this. And this
conjunction, occurring along a completely straight line, would
be hindered less by the undulation caused by the winds as
by that of the particles of a single layer. Besides, the heat
can also be greater between the edges of these layers, when
they approach each other, than in other places; and since
this heat has half melted the particles of ice which are
there, the subsequent cold can easily stick them together
at the moment they begin to touch.

For the rest, apart from the stars of which I spoke above,
which were transparent, there fell that day an infinity of others,
which were all white like sugar. Some of these had nearly the
same shape as the transparent ones. But most of them had
radii which were more pointed and slender, and were often
divided—sometimes into three branches, of which the two outside ones were twisted outward in different directions, and the
middle one remained straight, so that they represented a
fleur-de-lis, as you can see at *R*; and sometimes many of
them would represent feathers, or fern leaves, or other
similar things. And among these stars there also fell many
other pieces of ice in the form of fibers, without any other
definite shape.

All the causes of these are easy to understand. For as
to the whiteness of these stars, it proceeds merely from the
fact that the heat had not penetrated to the center of their
matter, as was clear from the fact that all the ones that
were very slender were transparent. And if sometimes the
radii of the white ones were longer and more blunted than

those of the transparent, this was not because they were melted as much by the heat, but because they had been previously pressed by the winds; and they were all longer and more pointed because they were less melted. And when these radii were divided into many branches, it was because the heat had abandoned the tiny hairs which composed them as soon as they began to draw close in order to gather together. And when they were divided into only three branches, it was because the heat had left them slightly later; and when this heat left, the two side branches were twisted toward either side, away from the middle one, because the proximity of the branch in the middle made them immediately colder and less flexible on its side; and this formed each radius into a fleur-de-lis.

The pieces of ice which had no definite shape assured me that all the clouds were not composed solely of tiny knots or lumps; but rather, there were also some of them that were made only of randomly intermixed fibers. As to the cause which made these stars descend, the violence of the wind which continued all that day made it obvious to me, for I judged that it could easily disarrange and break up the layers which composed these stars, after having formed them. And as soon as they were so disarranged, by inclining one of their sides toward the earth they could easily slice the air, for they were completely flat, and heavy enough to descend. But if these stars sometimes fell in calm weather, it is because the air underneath them, by contracting, drew the entire cloud to it, or because the air above, by expanding, pushed it down, and by this means disarranged them: whence it happens that in this event they are normally followed by more snow, which did not happen that day.

The following morning flakes of snow fell which seemed to be composed of an infinite number of very tiny stars joined together; nevertheless, upon looking very closely, I found that those inside were not as regularly formed as those above, and that they could easily have proceeded from the dissolution of a cloud similar to that which has been marked G above.[1]

Then, when this snow stopped, a sudden wind in the form of a storm caused a little white hail to fall; this hail was very long and slender, and each grain of it had the shape of a lump of sugar. And since the air became clear and serene immediately afterwards, I judged that this hail was formed from the highest part of the clouds, where the snow was very delicate, and composed of very fine fibers, in the way I have just described.

Finally, three days later, seeing snow composed completely of tiny knots or lumps surrounded with a great number of intermingled hairs, which did not have at all the shape of stars, I confirmed my belief in all that I had imagined concerning this matter.

As to clouds which are composed only of drops of water, it is easy to understand from what I have said how they come down in rain: namely, either through their own weight when their drops are large enough, or because the contraction of air under them, or the pressure of the air above, gives them cause to sink; or else because several of these causes concur. And it is when the air underneath contracts that there occurs the finest rain there can be; for then it is even sometimes so fine that we do not say that it is rain, but rather a mist, which falls. But on the other hand, the very heavy rain occurs when the cloud sinks only because it is pressed by the air above; for the highest of its drops, descending first, encounter others which make them larger. And in addition, I have sometimes seen in the summer, during calm weather accompanied by a heavy and stifling heat, that such a rain started to fall even before any cloud had appeared. The cause of this was that because there were very many vapors in the air, which doubtless were pressed by the winds from other places (as the calm and weight of the air attested), the drops into which these vapors

1 See Fig. 14, p. 304.

were converted became very large in falling, and fell as
they were being formed.

As for mists, when the cooling of earth, and the contraction of the air in its pores, causes them to sink, they are
converted into dew if they are composed of drops of water,
and into drizzling rain or white frost if they are composed
of vapors, which are already frozen, or rather, which freeze
as they touch the earth. And this happens especially at
night or in the morning, because that is the time when
the earth, being farthest from the sun, is cooled. But very
often, too, the wind lowers mists, by entering into the places
where they are; and it can even transport their matter
and make dew or frost from them in those places where
they have not been noticed; and that is why we see that
this frost is attached to plants only on the sides that the
wind touches.

As for evening damp, which falls only at night, and is
known only for the colds and headaches that it causes in
certain locales, it consists in nothing but certain fine and
penetrating exhalations which, being more fixed than the
vapor, are raised only in fairly warm areas on good days,
and fall again as soon as the heat of the sun abandons
them. This is why it has different characteristics in different
countries, and why it is even unknown in many, according
to the differences in the earths from which these exhalations
rise. And I do not deny that it is often accompanied by
the dew, which begins to fall as early as the evening, but
I do say that the dew is in no way the cause of the pains
of which we accuse it.

Manna is also composed of exhalations, as are other such
juices that descend from the air during the night; for as
to the vapors, they cannot change into anything but water
or ice. And these juices are not only different in different
countries, but also some of them attach themselves only to
certain bodies, because their particles are doubtless of such
a shape that they do not have sufficient purchase against
others to be arrested there.

But if the dew does not fall, and if in the morning we see mists rising on high and leaving the earth completely dry, this is a sign of rain. For this hardly ever happens except when the earth is not sufficiently cold during the night, or is extraordinarily overheated in the morning; then it produces a quantity of vapors which push these mists toward the sky, thus causing their drops, by colliding with each other, to grow large and be disposed to fall soon afterwards as rain. It is also a sign of rain to see that, when our air is very heavily laden with clouds, the sun nevertheless appears rather clearly in the morning. For this means that there are no other clouds toward the east, in the air adjacent to ours, which might prevent the heat of the sun from condensing those clouds above us, and even from also lifting new vapors from our section of the earth to augment them. But this set of conditions occurs only in the morning, and if it does not rain before noon, they give us nothing on which to judge what will happen toward evening.

I shall not say anything of many other signs of rain which we can observe, because they are for the most part very uncertain. And if you will consider that the same heat that is normally necessary in order to condense the clouds and draw rain from them can also, on the other hand, expand them and change them into vapors which sometimes lose themselves imperceptibly in the air and sometimes cause winds there (according to whether the particles of these clouds are slightly more pressed together or scattered, and whether this heat is a little more or a little less accompanied by humidity, and whether the air in the vicinity expands more or less, or is condensed), you will clearly see that all these things are too variable and uncertain to be accurately predicted by men.

Seventh Discourse

Of Storms, Lightning, and All Other Fires That Blaze in the Air

Moreover, it is not only when clouds are dissolved in vapors that they cause winds. They can also sometimes sink so suddenly that they propel all the air under them with great violence and turn it into a wind that is very strong but of short duration, which can be imitated by extending a sail a short distance up in the air, and then letting it fall flat out toward the earth. Strong rains are nearly always preceded by such a wind, which obviously acts in a downward direction, and whose coldness shows that it comes from the clouds, where the air is normally colder than it is around us. And it is because of this wind that the swallows' flying very low warns us of rain; for it brings down certain gnats on which they live, which normally buzz about and cavort high in the air when the weather is good. It is also this wind which sometimes—even though the cloud is very small or sinks only a little, and the wind is so feeble we can hardly feel it in the free air—blows down the chimney stacks and causes the ashes and straws in the fireplace to play, exciting them into small whirlwinds that are quite wonderful to those ignorant of the cause; and this is normally followed by some rain.

But if the descending cloud is very heavy and extensive (as it can be more easily on the great seas than in other places, because the vapors are very uniformly dispersed there, so that as soon as the least cloud is formed, it extends immediately into all the others around it), this infallibly causes a storm which is greater to the extent that the cloud is larger and heavier, and lasts all the longer when the cloud comes down from a greater height. And it is thus, I believe, that those typhoons occur that are so much feared by sailors in their great voyages, particularly a bit beyond the Cape of Good Hope; for there the vapors that rise from the Ethiopian Sea, which is very large and strongly heated by the sun, can easily cause a sudden, showery wind which, halting the natural course of the vapors coming from the Indian Sea, gathers them into a single cloud which, proceeding from the inequality which is between these two great seas and this land, must immediately become very much larger than those which are formed in the places where they depend on the several lesser inequalities existing between our plains and lakes and mountains. And because other clouds are almost never seen in these locations, as soon as the sailors perceive one beginning to form, even though it sometimes appears so small that the Flemish compared it to the eye of a bull (from which they gave it its name), and even though the rest of the air seems very calm and serene, they hasten to tie down their sails and prepare to receive a storm, which never fails to follow soon afterwards. And I even judge that it must be a greater storm, the smaller this cloud appeared at the outset. For since it cannot become thick enough to obscure the air and be visible, without also becoming fairly large, it can appear to be so small only because of its extreme distance; and you know that the more a heavy cloud descends from on high, the more violent is its fall. So this cloud, being very high, and becoming suddenly very large and heavy, descends all at once, propelling all the air under it with great violence, and causing by this means the wind of a storm.

It is even to be noted that the vapors mingled among this air are expanded by its agitation; and also, many other vapors emerge from the sea then, because of the agitation of its waves. This greatly increases the force of the wind, and by slowing the descent of the cloud, causes the storm to last that much longer. Then too, there are ordinarily exhalations mingled among these vapors, which—since the cloud cannot propel them as far away as it does the vapors, because their particles are less solid and have more irregular shapes—are separated from them by the agitation of the air in the same way that, as has been said above, we separate butter from skim milk by beating cream; and through this means they gather here and there in clusters which, floating as high as they can against the cloud, finally come to be attached to the ropes and masts of the ships, once the cloud succeeds in coming down. And there, being held by this violent agitation, they form what are called St. Elmo's fires, which console the sailors and make them hope for good weather. It is true that often these storms are at their greatest strength toward the end, and that there may be many clouds on top of one another, under each of which are found such fires. Perhaps this was the reason why, when the ancients saw but one of them, which they called the star of Helen, they considered it to be a bad sign, as if they had then still to wait for the worst of the storm; whereas when they saw two of them, which they named Castor and Pollux, they took them to be a good omen, for that was usually the greatest number of them that they saw, except perhaps when the storm was extraordinarily large, in which case they saw three and also considered them to bode ill because of that. Nevertheless, I daresay that our mariners sometimes see them in numbers up to four or five, perhaps because their ships are larger and have more masts than those of the ancients, or because they travel in places where the exhalations are more frequent. For in the end I can only speak from conjecture about things that happen on the high seas, since I have never seen them and have only very imperfect accounts of them.

But as for the storms that are accompanied by thunder, thunderbolts, whirlwinds, and lightning, of which I have been able to see some examples on land, I have no doubt that they are caused by the fact that there are many clouds on top of one another, so that it sometimes happens that the highest come down all at once upon the lowest. Thus, if the two clouds *A* and *B* are composed only of a very rare and extended snow, a warmer air will be found around the higher one, *A*, than around the lower, *B;* and it is clear that the heat of this air can condense it and increase its weight gradually, in such a way that the highest of its particles, beginning to fall first, will push or pull along with them a quantity of others, which will thus soon fall all together on the lower cloud with a great noise. In the same way, I remember formerly having

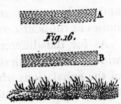

Fig. 16.

seen in the Alps, around the month of May, that when the snow was heated and made heavy by the sun, the least disturbance of the air was sufficient to cause some of it to fall in great heaps, which were called, it seems to me, avalanches; and these, resounding in the valleys, imitated the sound of thunder fairly closely. In consequence, we can understand why it thunders more rarely during the winter than the summer in these parts; for then it is not as easy for the highest clouds to absorb enough heat to dissolve. And we can understand why, when during the great heats after a southern wind of short duration, we again feel a damp and stifling heat, it is a sign that thunder will soon follow. For this means that this southern wind, having passed against the earth, has propelled the heat out of it toward the place in the atmosphere where the highest clouds are formed; and afterward, when it itself is propelled toward the place where the lowest clouds are formed, through the expansion of the lower air caused by the warm vapors that it contains, not only must the highest clouds be condensed and descend, but also the lowest ones, remaining very much rarefied, and even being blown and repelled by this expansion of the lower air, must resist these vapors in such a way that often they can prevent any particle of them from falling to earth. And notice that the noise which thus occurs above us must be more audible because of the resonance of the air, and be greater, because of the falling snow, than is that of avalanches. Then also notice that from the mere fact that the particles of the upper clouds fall all together, or one after the other, or faster or slower, and that the lower ones are more or less large and thick, and resist more or less strongly, all the different noises of thunder can easily be caused.

As for the differences between flashes of lightning, whirlwinds, and thunderbolts, they depend only on the nature of the exhalations which are in the space between two clouds, and on the way that the higher falls on the lower. For if it is preceded by great heat and dryness, so that this space contains a quantity of very fine, highly inflammable exhalations, the higher cloud can hardly be so small, nor descend so slowly, that by propelling the air between it and the lower cloud, it cannot cause a flash of lightning to leave it—that is, a light flame which is instantaneously dissipated. So that we can then see such flashes of lightning without hearing the noise of thunder at all; and sometimes this even happens without the clouds being thick enough to be visible.

On the other hand, if there are no exhalations in the air suitable for becoming inflamed, we can hear the thunder without any flashes of lightning appearing because of it.

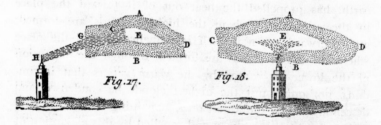

Fig. 17.   Fig. 18.

And when the highest cloud falls only in sections following each other, it causes hardly any lightning and thunder; but when it falls all at once and fast enough, it can cause whirlwinds and thunderbolts in addition. For it must be noted that its extremities, such as *C* and *D*, must sink slightly faster than the middle, inasmuch as the air underneath them, having less distance to go in order to escape from the cloud, gives way to them more easily; thus, because it comes to touch the lower cloud sooner than the middle, a great deal of air is enclosed between the two, as you see at *E*. Then, because this air is pressed and propelled with great force by the middle of the higher cloud, which is still continuing to descend, it must necessarily break the lower one to escape, as you see at *F*; or else it must split open one of its extremities, as you see at *G*. And when it has thus broken this cloud, it descends with great force toward the earth, and then from there it reascends by turning around, because the resistance that it finds on all sides prevents it from continuing its movement in a straight line as quickly as its agitation requires. And so it makes a whirlwind, which cannot be accompanied by either lightning or thunderbolts, if no exhalations in this air are ready to be ignited; but when some of them are, they are all gathered in a heap, and are propelled with this air very tumultuously toward the earth, and so form thunderbolts. And these thunderbolts can burn the clothes and singe the hair without injuring the body, if these exhalations, which normally have the odor of sulphur, are only slippery and oily, so that they compose a light flame which only attaches itself to bodies that are easy to burn. On the other hand, it can break bones without damaging flesh, or melt a sword without marring the scabbard, if these exhalations, being very fine and penetrating, partake only of the nature of volatile salts or acids; by this means they do not exert any effort against bodies that give way to them, yet they scorch and dissolve all those that offer them great resistance, as we see that acid dissolves the hardest metals, but does not act against wax. Finally, a thunderbolt can sometimes change into a very hard rock, which breaks and fractures everything it encounters, if among these very penetrating exhalations there exist a quantity of those others which are slippery and sulphurous; and especially if there are any of them like that earth which we find at the bottom of rainwater, when we leave it to settle in some container. As you can see by experiment, if you mix certain portions of that earth, salt-peter, and sulphur, and set fire to this composition, it will suddenly form a rock.

But if the cloud is opened at the side, as at *G*, the thunderbolt, being thrown sideways, encounters the peaks of towers or rocks rather than low places, as we see at *H*. But even when the cloud is broken underneath, there is a reason why the thunderbolt falls on high and prominent places rather than on others: because if, for example, the cloud *B* is no more disposed to break in one place than in another, it is certain that it must break in that which is marked *F*, because of the resistance of the steeple that is underneath. There is also a reason why each clap of thunder is ordinarily followed by a shower of rain, and why when this rain becomes very abundant, it hardly thunders any more. For if the force with which the higher cloud, in falling from above, shakes the lower one, is sufficient to cause the whole thing to descend, it is clear that the thunder must cease; and if it is not sufficient, it can nevertheless often bring many flakes of snow out of it, and these, melting in the air, cause rain.

Finally, it is not unreasonable for people to hold that loud noise, such as bells or cannons, can diminish the effect of thunderbolts; for it helps to dissipate the lower cloud, and make it fall, by shaking the snow of which it is composed. This is known well by those who normally travel in valleys where avalanches are to be feared; for they even abstain from talking and coughing when passing, out of fear that the noise of their voice will move the snow.

But as we have already noticed that there is sometimes lightning without thunder, so in places in the air where there are very many exhalations and few vapors to be encountered, there can be formed clouds which are so slim and light that when they fall from a rather great height, they cause no thunder to be heard, nor do they excite any storm in the air, even though they envelop and join together many exhalations; from these they form not only these smaller flames which we would call falling stars, or others that go across the sky, but also fairly large balls of fire, which, coming right to us, are like miniature thunderbolts.

And to the extent that there are exhalations of many diverse natures, I do not even judge it to be impossible that the clouds, by pressing them, sometimes form from them a material which seems, according to its color and consistency, like milk, or blood, or flesh; or else in being burned, becomes such that we take it for iron, or for rocks; or finally, in becoming corrupted, engenders certain small animals in very little time; thus we often read, among the miracles, that it rained iron, or blood, or locusts, or similar things. In addition, without there being any cloud in the air, the exhalations can be piled up and ignited by a single puff of the winds, especially when there are two or more contrary ones which meet one another. And finally, without winds and without clouds, simply by a fine and penetrating exhalation alone, which shares the nature of the salts, insinuating itself into the pores of another which is slippery and sulphurous, there can be light flames formed high as well as low in the air: for example, we see these stars which cross the sky high in the air, and lower down, many of those burning or frolicsome fires, as well as those others which lodge in certain bodies, such as the hair of children, or the manes of horses, or on the points of pikes which have been rubbed with oil in order to clean them, or similar things. For it is certain that not only a violent agitation, but often also simply the mingling of two different bodies, is sufficient to set them afire: as we see by pouring water on lime, or storing hay before it is dry, or by an infinity of other examples which we encounter every day in chemistry. But all these fires have very little force in comparison with lightning; the reason for this is that they are composed only of the softer and stickier particles of the oils, even though the liveliest and most penetrating particles of the salts also normally concur in producing them. For the latter are not thereby halted among the others, but instead they scatter promptly in the free air, after having set [the softer particles] afire; whereas lightning is principally composed of these more lively and penetrating ones which, being very violently pressed and propelled by the clouds, carry the others with them right to the earth. And those who know how strong and swift the fire of saltpeter and sulphur, mixed together, is—whereas the slippery part of sulphur, being separated from its spirits, would have little force or speed—will not find anything to doubt in this.

As for the duration of the fires which fly or lodge around us, it can be longer or shorter according as their flame is slower or faster, and their matter more or less thick and condensed. But as for the duration of the fires which are seen only high in the air, this could be but very short; for if their matter were not very much rarefied, their weight would cause them to descend. And I find that the philosophers were right in comparing them to that flame which we see run all along the smoke coming from a torch we have just extinguished, when, being brought near another torch, it ignites. But I am quite amazed that after this they were able to imagine that the comets and the columns or stripes of fire that we sometimes see in the sky were composed of exhalations; for they last incomparably longer.

And because I have tried to give a detailed explanation of their production and their nature in another treatise, and because I do not believe that they belong to the study of meteorology, any more than do the earthquakes and the minerals which many writers include there, I shall speak in addition here only of certain lights which, appearing in the night during calm and serene weather, give idle people cause to imagine squadrons of ghosts who battle in the air, to whom they prophesy loss or victory for a particular group they admire, according to whether fear or hope predominates in their fancy. And because I have never seen such sights,

and because I know how the accounts we give of them are
usually falsified and augmented by superstition and ignorance, I shall content myself to deal in a few words with
all the causes which seem to me capable of producing them.
The first is that there are many clouds in the air, sufficiently
small to be taken for so many soldiers; and falling onto one
another, these enclose enough exhalations to cause a quantity
of small flashes, and to throw small fires, and perhaps to
cause small noises to be heard, by which means these soldiers
seem to do battle. The second cause is also that there are
such clouds in the air; but instead of falling on one another,
they receive their light from the fires and lightning flashes
of some large storm, which occurs so far away that it cannot
be perceived in that location. And the third cause is that
these clouds, or some other more southern ones, from which
they receive their light, are so high that the rays of the
sun reach right to them; for if we notice the refractions
and reflections that two or three such clouds can cause,
we will find that they have no need to be very high in
order to cause such lights to appear toward the south, after
the hour of twilight has passed, and sometimes also after
sundown. But this does not seem to belong so much to this
discourse as to the following one, where I intend to speak
of all the things that we may see in the air without their
actually being there, after here having concluded the explanation of all those which are seen in the same way as
they actually are.

Eighth Discourse

Of the Rainbow

The rainbow is such a remarkable phenomenon of nature, and its cause has been so meticulously sought after by inquiring minds throughout the ages, that I could not choose a more appropriate subject for demonstrating how, with the method I am using, we can arrive at knowledge not possessed at all by those whose writings are available to us. First, I considered that this arc can appear not only in the sky, but also in the air near us, whenever there are many drops of water in the air illuminated by the sun, as experience shows us in certain fountains; thus it was easy for me to judge that it came merely from the way that the rays of light act against those drops, and from there tend toward our eyes. Then, knowing that these drops are round, as has been proven above, and seeing that their being larger or smaller does not change the appearance of the arc, I then took it into my head to make a very large one, the better to examine it. And for this purpose I filled a perfectly round and transparent large flask with water, and I discovered that, for example, when the sun came from the section of the sky marked *AFZ,* and my eye was at point *E,* then when I put this ball in the location *BCD,* its part *D* appeared to me completely red and incomparably more brilliant than the rest; and I discovered that whether I approached it or drew back from it, and whether I placed it to the right or left, or even made it turn around my head, provided that the line *DE* always had an angle of approximately 42° with the line *EM,* which must be imagined to extend from the center of the eye toward that of the sun, this part *D* always appeared equally red. But as soon as I caused this angle *DEM* to become ever so slightly bigger, this red color disappeared. And if I made the angle slightly smaller, the color did not disappear all at once, but rather it first

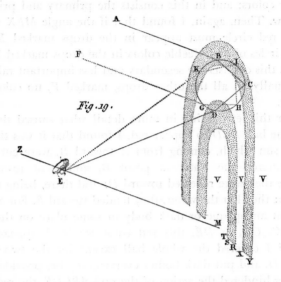

Fig. 19.

divided into two less brilliant parts, in which one saw yellow, blue, and other colors. Then, also looking at the part of this ball which is marked *K*, I perceived that if I made the angle *KEM* around 52°, this part *K* would appear red too, but not as brilliant as at *D;* and that if I made it slightly larger, other weaker colors would appear. But I found that if I made it ever so slightly smaller, or very much larger, no colors would appear. I understood clearly from this that if all the air toward *M* were filled with such balls, or in their place drops of water, there must appear a very red and brilliant point in each of those drops from which the lines drawn toward the eye *E* make an angle of around 42° with *EM*, as I assume in the case of those marked *R;* and that if these points are looked at all together, without our noting anything about their position except the angle under which they are seen, they must appear as a continuous circle of the color red. In the same way there must be points in those drops marked *S* and

T from which the lines drawn toward *E* make slightly more acute angles with *EM*, and these points compose circles of weaker colors; and in this consists the primary and principal rainbow. Then, again, I found that if the angle *MEX* was of 52°, a red circle must appear in the drops marked *X*, and other circles of more feeble colors in the drops marked *Y*, and that in this consists the secondary and less important rainbow. And finally, in all the other drops, marked *V*, no colors can appear.

After this, examining in more detail what caused the part *D* of the ball *BCD* to appear red, I found that it was the rays of the sun which, coming from *A* toward *B*, were curved as they entered the water at point *B*, and went toward *C*, whence they were reflected toward *D*; and there, being curved again as they left the water, they tended toward *E*. For as soon as I put an opaque or dark body in some place on the lines *AB*, *BC*, *CD*, or *DE*, this red color would disappear. And even if I covered the whole ball except for the two points *B* and *D*, and put dark bodies everywhere else, provided that nothing hindered the action of the rays *ABCDE*, the red color nevertheless appeared. Then I was also searching for the cause of the red which appeared at *K*; and I discovered that it was the rays which came from *F* toward *G*, where they curved toward *H*, and in *H* were reflected toward *I*, and in *I* reflected again toward *K*, and then finally they curved at point *K* and tended toward *E*. Therefore the primary rainbow is caused by the rays which reach the eye after two refractions and one reflection, and the secondary by other rays which reach it only after two refractions and two reflections; which is what prevents the second from appearing as clearly as the first.

But the principal difficulty still remained, which was to understand why, since there were many other rays there which, after two refractions and one or two reflections, can tend toward the eye when this ball is in another position, it is nonetheless only those of which I have spoken that cause certain colors to appear. And in order to resolve this difficulty, I looked to see if there were some other subject where they appeared in the same way, so that by comparing them with each other I could better judge their cause. Then, remembering that a prism or triangle of crystal causes similar colors to be seen, I considered one of them which was such as *MNP* is here, with its two surfaces, *MN* and *NP,* completely flat, and inclined to one another at an angle of around 30° or 40°, so that if the rays of the sun *ABC* cross *MN* at right angles, or nearly so, so that they do not undergo any noticeable refraction there, they must suffer a fairly great refraction in coming

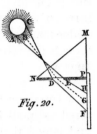

Fig. 20.

out through *NP.* And when I covered one of these two surfaces with a dark body, in which there was a rather narrow opening such as *DE,* I observed that the rays, passing through this opening and from there going to contact the cloth or white paper *FGH,* paint all the colors of the rainbow there, and that they always paint the color red at *F,* and the blue or violet at *H.* From this I learned, first, that the surfaces of the drops of water need not be curved in order to produce these colors, for those of this crystal are completely flat; nor does the angle under which they appear need to be of any particular size, for it can be changed here without their changing. And although we can cause the rays going toward *F* to curve sometimes more or sometimes less than those going toward *H,* they nevertheless always paint red, and those going toward *H* always paint blue; neither is reflection necessary, for there is none of it here; nor finally do we need a plurality of refractions, for there is only one of them here. But I judged that there must be at least one refraction, and even one such that its effect was not destroyed by another, for experiment shows that if the surfaces *MN* and *NP* were parallel, the rays, being straightened as much in the one as they were curved in the other, would not produce these colors. Also, I had no doubt that light was necessary, for without it we would see nothing. And I observed, moreover, that shadow, or the limitation of this light, was necessary; for if we remove the dark body on *NP,* the colors *FGH* cease to appear; and if we make the opening *DE* large enough, the red, orange, and yellow at *F* extend no further because of that than do the green, blue, and violet at *H*—instead, all the extra space between the two at *G* remains white. After this, I tried to understand why these colors are different at *H* and at *F,* even though the refraction, shadow, and light concur there in the same way. And conceiving the nature of light to be as I described it in the *Optics,* namely as the action or movement of a certain very fine material whose particles must be pictured as small balls rolling in the pores of earthly bodies, I understood that these balls can roll in various ways according to the various causes which determine them; and in particular that all the refractions that occur on the same side cause them to turn in the same direction. But when they have no neighboring balls which are moved notably faster or slower than they, their turning motion is nearly equal to their motion in a straight line; whereas when they have some on one side that move more slowly, and others on the other side that move as fast or faster (as happens in the confines of shadow and light), then if they meet those that move more slowly on the side toward which they are rolling, as do those which make up the ray *EH,* this causes them to turn less quickly than if they were moving in a straight line. And it is just the opposite when they meet them on the other side, as do those of the ray *DF.* In order to understand this better, consider that the ball *1234* is propelled from *V* toward *X,* in such a way that it travels only in a straight line, and that its two sides *1* and *3* descend at equal speed to the surface of the water *YY,* where the movement of the side marked *3,* which encounters it first, is retarded, while that of side *1* still continues; this causes the whole ball to turn infallibly following the numbers *123.* Then imagine that it is surrounded with four other balls, *Q, R, S,* and *T,* of which *Q* and *R* tend to move with more force toward *X* than does *1234,* and the other two, *S* and *T,* tend toward there, but with less force. It is clear from this that

Q, pressing the part of the ball marked *1*, and *S*, retaining the one marked *3*, increase its spin; and that *R* and *T* do not hinder it, because *R* is disposed to move toward *X* faster than *1234*

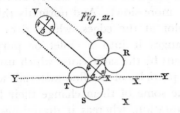

Fig. 21.

follows it, and *T* is not disposed to follow *1234* as quickly as *1234* precedes it. This explains the action of the ray *DF*. Then, on the contrary, if *Q* and *R* tend more slowly than *1234* toward *X*, and *S* and *T* tend more quickly toward there, *R* hinders the rotation of the part marked *1*, and *T* that of the part *3*, without the two others, *Q* and *S*, doing anything. This explains the action of the ray *EH*.

But it must be noted that since this ball *1234* is perfectly round, it can easily happen that when it is pressed fairly hard by the two balls *R* and *T*, it is turned about, and spins around the axis *42*, instead of stopping its rotation because of them; thus, changing its position in an instant, it afterwards rotates according to the numbers *321;* for the two balls *R* and *I*, which caused it to begin to rotate, force it to continue until it has achieved a half-turn in this direction, and then they can augment its rotation instead of retarding it. This enabled me to resolve the most important of all the difficulties that I had in this matter. And it is demonstrated quite clearly from all this, it seems to me, that the nature of the colors appearing at *F* [1] consists only in the fact that the particles of the fine substance that transmits the action of the light have a stronger tendency to rotate than to move in a straight line; so that those which have a much stronger tendency to rotate cause the color red, and those which have only a slightly stronger tendency cause yellow. As on the contrary, the nature of those that are visible

[1] See Fig. 20, p. 335.

at *H* consists only in the fact that these small particles do not rotate as quickly as they usually do, when there is no particular cause which hinders them from it; so that green appears where they turn just a little more slowly, and blue where they turn very much more slowly. And normally this blue is mixed with a rosy color at the edges, which gives it vivacity and glitter and changes it into a violet or purple color. This doubtless happens by the same cause which usually retards the rotation of the particles of the fine material, when it is strong enough to make some of them change their location, and to increase their rotation, whereas it diminishes that of others. And in all of this, the explanation accords so perfectly with experience that I do not believe it possible, after one has studied both carefully, to doubt that the matter is as I have just explained it. For if it is true that the sensation that we have of light is caused by the movement or inclination to movement of some material that touches our eyes—as many other things witness—it is certain that the different movements of this material must cause different sensations in us. And as there can be no variation in these movements other than the one I have mentioned, so we do not find any variation through experience, in the sensations we have of them, other than that of colors. And it is not possible to find a single thing in the crystal *MNP* which can produce colors, except the way in which it sends the small particles of the fine material toward the line *FGH,* and from there toward our eyes. From this, it seems to me, it is quite obvious that we should not look for anything else in the colors displayed by the other objects; for ordinary experience shows that light or white, and shadow or black, together with the colors of the rainbow which have been explained here, suffice to compose all others. And I cannot approve the distinction made by the philosophers when they say that there are some true colors, and others which are only false or apparent. For because the entire true nature of colors consists only in their appearance, it seems to me to be a contradiction to say that they are false, and that they appear. But I do acknowledge that shadow and refraction are not always necessary to produce them; and that instead of these the size, shape, situation, and movement of the particles of bodies we call colored can variously compete with light, in order to increase or diminish the rotation of the particles of the fine material. So that even in the rainbow, I doubted at first whether the colors were produced there quite in the same way as in the crystal *MNP;* for I did not notice any shadow which cut off the light, nor did I yet understand why they appeared only under certain angles, until having taken my pen and calculated in detail all the rays which fall on the various points of a drop of water, in order to see under what angles they could come toward our eyes after two refractions and one or two reflections, I found that after one reflection and two refractions, very many more of them can be seen under the angle of 41° to 42° than under any lesser one; and that none of them can be seen under a larger angle. Then I also found that after two reflections and two refractions, very many more of them come toward the eye under a 51° to 52° angle, than under any larger one; and no such rays come under a lesser. So that there is a shadow on both sides, cutting off the light which, after having passed through an infinity of raindrops illuminated by the sun, comes toward the eye under the angle of 42° or slightly less, and thus causes the primary and most important rainbow. And there is also a shadow cutting off the light coming under the angle of 51° or slightly more, which causes the exterior rainbow; for not receiving rays of light in your eyes, or receiving notably fewer of them from one object than from another that is near it, is the same thing as seeing shadow. This clearly shows that the colors of these arcs are produced by the same cause as are those which appear with the aid of the crystal *MNP,* and that the radius of the interior arc must not be greater than 42°, nor that of the exterior one smaller than 51°. And finally, it shows that the exterior surface of the primary rainbow must be much more limited than the interior one, and vice versa for the secondary, as can be seen through experiment. But in order that those who know mathematics

can see whether the calculation I have made of these rays is
sufficiently exact, it is necessary that I explain it here.

Let *AFD* be a drop of water whose radius *CD* or *AB* I
divide into as many equal parts as I wish to calculate rays, in

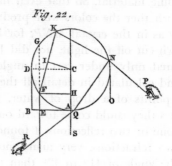

Fig. 22.

order to attribute an equal amount of light to all of them.
Then I consider one of these rays in detail, for example *EF*,
which, instead of passing directly through toward *G*, is deflected toward *K*, and reflected from *K* toward *N*, from which
it goes toward the eye *P*; or else it is reflected once more from
N to *Q*, and from there is turned toward the eye *R*. And having drawn *CI* at right angles on *FK*, I know from that which
was said in the *Optics* that *AE*, or *HF*, and *CI* have between them the ratio by which the refraction of the water is
measured. So that if *HF* contains 8,000 parts, inasmuch as
AB contains 10,000, *CI* will contain about 5,984, because the
refraction of the water is slightly greater than 3 to 4; as exactly as I have been able to measure it, it is 187 to 250. Thus
because I had the two lines *HF* and *CI*, I easily understood
the two arcs, *FG* which was 73° 44′, and *FK* which was 106° 30′.
Then, subtracting double the arc *FK* from the arc *FG* added to
180°, I have 40° 44′ as the size of the angle *ONP*, for I assume
that *ON* is parallel to *EF*. By subtracting 40° 44′ from *FK*, I
have 65° 46′ for the angle *SQR*, for I assume that *SQ* is parallel to *EF*. And calculating all the other rays parallel to *EF*
which pass through the divisions of the diameter *AB* in the
same way, I compose the following table:

line HF	line CI	arc FG	arc FK	angle ONP	angle SQR
1,000	748	168°30′	171°25′	5°40′	165°45′
2,000	1,496	156°55′	162°48′	11°19′	151°29′
3,000	2,244	145°4′	154°4′	17°56′	136°8′
4,000	2,992	132°50′	145°10′	22°30′	122°4′
5,000	3,740	120°	136°4′	27°52′	108°12′
6,000	4,488	106°16′	126°40′	32°56′	93°44′
7,000	5,236	91°8′	116°51′	37°26′	79°25′
8,000	5,984	73°44′	106°30′	40°44′	65°46′
9,000	6,732	51°41′	95°22′	40°57′	54°25′
10,000	7,480	0	83°10′	13°40′	69°30′

It is easy to see, in this table, that there are many more rays which make the angle ONP around 40°, than there are those which make it less; and also more of them which make SQR around 54° than make it greater. Then, in order to make it still more precise, I do the following:

line HF	line CI	arc FG	arc FK	angle ONP	angle SQR
8,000	5,984	73°44′	106°30′	40°44′	65°46′
8,100	6,058	71°48′	105°25′	40°58′	64°37′
8,200	6,133	69°50′	104°20′	41°10′	63°10′
8,300	6,208	67°48′	103°14′	41°20′	62°54′
8,400	6,283	65°44′	102°9′	41°26′	61°43′
8,500	6,358	63°34′	101°2′	41°30′	60°32′
8,600	6,432	61°22′	99°56′	41°30′	58°26′
8,700	6,507	59°4′	98°48′	41°28′	57°20′
8,800	6,582	56°42′	97°40′	41°22′	56°18′
8,900	6,657	54°16′	96°32′	41°12′	55°20′
9,000	6,732	51°41′	95°22′	40°57′	54°25′
9,100	6,806	49°	94°12′	40°36′	53°36′
9,200	6,881	46°8′	93°2′	40°4′	52°58′
9,300	6,956	43°8′	91°51′	39°26′	52°25′
9,400	7,031	39°54′	90°38′	38°38′	52°
9,500	7,106	36°24′	89°26′	37°32′	51°54′
9,600	7,180	32°30′	88°12′	36°6′	52°6′
9,700	7,255	28°8′	86°58′	34°12′	52°46′
9,800	7,330	22°57′	85°43′	31°31′	54°12′

And I see here that the largest angle, ONP, can be 41° 30′, and the smallest, SQR, 51° 54′, to which, adding or subtracting around 17 minutes for the radius of the sun, I have 41° 47′ for the greatest radius of the interior rainbow, and 51° 37′ for the smallest radius of the exterior one.

It is true that if the water is warm, its refraction is slightly less than when it is cold, which can change certain things in this calculation. Nevertheless, it will only increase the radius of the interior rainbow by one or two degrees, at the most; and then that of the exterior rainbow will be nearly twice that much smaller. This is worth noting because through this we can demonstrate that the refraction of water can hardly be less or more than I assume. For if it were slightly larger, it would make the radius of the interior rainbow less than 41°, whereas by common belief we give it 45°; and if we assume it small enough to make it truly 45°, we will find that the radius of the exterior arc is also hardly more than 45°, whereas to the eye it appears much larger than the interior one. And Maurolicus, who is, I believe, the first who determined the one of 45°, determines the other to be around 56°, which shows how little faith we must have in observations which are not accompanied by true reason. For the rest, I have not had any trouble understanding why the red is on the outside of the interior arc, nor why it is on the inside in the exterior; for the same factor which causes it to be near F [2] rather than H, when it appears through the crystal MNP, also brings it about that if we look at this crystal when the eye is in the location of the white screen FGH, we will see the red toward its thicker part MP, and the blue toward N, because the ray tinted red which goes toward F comes from C, the part of the sun that is closest to MP. And this same factor also makes it happen that when the center of the drops of water (and as a result their thickest part) are on the outside, with respect to the colored points forming the interior rainbow, the red must appear on the outside there; and that when they are on the inside with respect to those which form the exterior rainbow, the red must also appear on the inside.

[2] See Fig. 20, p. 335.

Thus, I believe that no difficulty remains in this matter, unless it perhaps concerns the irregularities which are encountered; for example, when the arc is not exactly round, or when its center is not in the straight line passing through the eye and the sun, which can happen if the winds change the shape of the raindrops; for they may not lose the smallest part of their roundness without this making a notable difference in the angle under which the colors must appear. There has sometimes also been seen, so I have been told, a rainbow so reversed that its ends were turned upward, as is here represented at *FF*. I can only explain how this happens

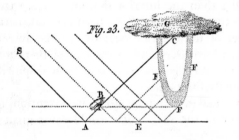

Fig. 23.

through the reflection of the rays of the sun falling on the water of the sea, or of some lake. For example, if coming from the section of the sky *SS*, they fall on the water *DAE*, and from there are reflected toward the rim *CF*, the eye *B* will see the arc *FF*, whose center is at point *C*, so that if *CB* is projected right to *A*, and *AS* passes through the center of the sun, the angles *SAD* and *BAE* are equal, and so the angle *CBF* is around 42°. Nevertheless, for this effect it is also necessary that there be no wind at all to trouble the surface of the water at *E*, and moreover, perhaps, that there be some cloud, such as *G*, which prevents the light of the sun, going in a straight line toward the rain, from blotting out the light that this water *E* sends there: whence this happens but rarely. Besides this, the eye can be in such a situation, with respect to the sun and rain, that we can see the lower part which terminates the rainbow, without seeing the higher part; and so we will take it to be an inverted arc, even though we do not see it near the sky, but near the water or the earth.

I am also told that sometimes a third kind of rainbow above the two usual ones has sometimes been seen, but that it was much feebler, and approximately as much removed from the secondary one as that is from the primary. I judge that this could not have happened unless there had been many very round and transparent grains of hail mingled among the rain; since the refraction in these is notably greater than in water, the exterior rainbow was necessarily very much larger there, and so appears above the other. And as for the interior one, which for the same reason would necessarily have to have been smaller than the interior rainbow [we see with] rain, it is possible that it will not have been noticed, because of the great luster of the exterior one; or else, because their edges are joined, we will have taken the two of them for only one, but for one whose colors will have been disposed otherwise than is usually the case.

And this makes me remember an invention for making signs appear in the sky, which would cause great wonder in

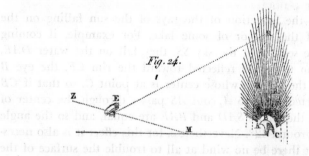

Fig. 24.

those who were ignorant of the causes. I suppose that you already know the method of making a rainbow visible by the use of a fountain. For example, if the water coming out of the small holes ABC leaps high enough and expands in the air in all directions toward R, and if the sun is toward Z, so that, since ZEM is a straight line, the angle MER can be around

42°, the eye E will not fail to see near R a rainbow exactly like the one which appears in the sky. To this it is now necessary to add that there are oils, spirits, and other liquids, in which refraction is notably greater or lesser than in common water, and which are no less clear and transparent because of that. So that we would be able to dispose many fountains in order, in which, having various of these liquids there, we would see through their means a great part of the sky full of the colors of the rainbow: this would be accomplished by causing the liquids whose refraction was the greatest to be the nearest to the spectators, and by not letting them rise so high that they hinder the view of the ones which would be behind them. Then, because by closing a section of the holes ABC we can make any part of the rainbow RR that we wish disappear without removing the others, it is easy to understand that in the same way, by appropriately opening and closing the holes of these various fountains, we would be able to cause that which will appear colored to have the shape of a cross, or a column, or some other such thing which gives cause for wonder. But I admit that skill and much work would be necessary in order to proportion these fountains, and to cause the liquids there to leap so high that these figures could be seen from afar by a whole nation, without the trick being discovered.

Ninth Discourse

Of the Color of Clouds, and the Circles or Coronas That We Sometimes See Around the Heavenly Bodies

After what I have said about the nature of colors, I do not believe I have to add very many things concerning the colors that we see in the clouds. For firstly, as to whether they are white, or else dark or black, this comes only from their being either more or less exposed to the light of the heavenly bodies, or else to shadow, their own as well as that of their neighbors. And there are only two things to note here. One is that the surfaces of transparent bodies cause part of the rays which come toward them to be reflected, as I have said above.[1] This is the reason that light can more easily penetrate fifty feet of water than it can a bit of foam which, although it is nothing other than water, contains many surfaces; the first of these reflects a part of this light, the second another part, and so on, until there soon remains none at all, or nearly none, which passes through. And thus it is that neither crushed glass, nor snow, nor the clouds when they are fairly thick, can be transparent. The other matter to be noted here is that although the action of luminous bodies consists only in propelling the fine material that touches our eyes in a straight line, nevertheless the normal movement of the small particles of this material—of those in the air around us, at least—is to roll in the same way that a ball rolls on the ground, when it is propelled only in a straight line. And it is the bodies that make them roll in this way which we properly call white, as doubtless

[1] See p. 298.

do all those bodies which fail to be transparent only because of the multitude of their surfaces, such as foam, crushed glass, snow, and clouds. From this we can understand why the sky appears blue when it is very clear and free of haze, provided we know that of itself, it yields no light, and would appear extremely black if there were no exhalations or vapors above us. But there are always more or fewer of them which reflect some rays toward our eyes, that is to say, which drive back toward us the small particles of fine material propelled against them by the sun or the other stars. And when these vapors are in sufficiently large number, the fine material, being driven back toward us by the first vapors, meets others afterwards, which cause its small particles to roll and turn before they reach us. This then causes the sky to look white, whereas if the fine material does not encounter enough other particles to cause its small particles to turn in this way, it can only appear as blue, following what has just been said of the nature of the color blue. And it is the same cause which also makes the water of the sea seem to be blue in places where it is very pure and very deep; for only a few rays are reflected from its surface and none of those which penetrate it return. In addition, we can here understand why often when the sun is setting or rising, the whole part of the sky where it is appears red; this happens when there are not so many clouds, or rather mists, between it and us that its light cannot come through them, yet this light does not come through them as easily right against the earth as when the sun is a bit higher, nor as easily at a slight height as when it is very much higher. For it is evident that this light, undergoing refraction in these mists, causes the particles of the fine material which transmit it to turn in the same direction that a ball would, coming from the same direction while rolling on the earth; so that the turning of the lowest particles is always augmented by the action of the higher ones, because it is supposedly stronger than theirs. And you know that this is sufficient to cause the color red to appear, which, being afterwards reflected in the clouds, can be extended in all directions in the sky. And it is to be noted that when this color appears in the morning, it presages wind or rain, because it testifies that there are few clouds toward the east, so that the sun will be able to raise very many vapors before midday, and before the mists which cause it to appear begin to ascend. Whereas in the evening it testifies to good weather, because when there are only a few, or no, clouds toward the setting sun, the eastern winds must prevail and the mists descend during the night.

I shall not stop to speak in more detail of the other colors that we see in the clouds; for I believe their causes are all sufficiently included in what I have said. But around the heavenly bodies there sometimes appear certain circles, whose explanation I should not omit. They are like the rainbow, in that they are round, or nearly round, and always surround the sun or some other heavenly body; this shows that they are caused by some reflection or refraction whose angles are all nearly equal. And they are also like the rainbow in that they are colored, which shows that there is refraction, and in the shadow which limits the light which produces them. But they differ in the fact that the rainbow is never seen except when it is actually raining in the location near which we see it, although often it does not rain where the spectator is; but the circles are never seen where it rains, which shows that they are not caused by the refraction which occurs in drops of water or in hail, but by that which is caused in those small stars of transparent ice of which I spoke above. For there is no other imaginable cause in the clouds which would be capable of such an effect; and although we never see such stars fall except when it is cold, reason nevertheless assures us that they are formed in all seasons. It is even the case that because some heat is necessary to cause them to turn transparent from their original whiteness, as is required for this effect, it is likely that the summer is a more appropriate season for this than the winter. And although the majority of the stars that fall appear to the eye to be extremely flat and uniform, it is still certain that they are all slightly thicker in the middle than at the edges, as, in certain ones, can also be seen by the eye. And according as they are thicker or less thick in the middle, they cause these circles to appear larger or smaller; for there are doubtless many sizes of them. And if those that we have observed most often have had their diameters at around 45°, as certain people have written, I wish to believe that the particles of ice that cause them to be of this size have the convexity which is most normal to them, and which is also perhaps the greatest that they are in the habit of acquiring, without melting completely. For example, let ABC be the sun, D the eye, and E, F, G many small particles of transparent ice arranged side by side, as they are when they are formed, and of such a convexity that the ray coming, for example, from point A on the edge of the particle marked G, and from point C on the edge of the one marked F, turns back toward D; and that there come toward D many other rays which go through the other particles of ice

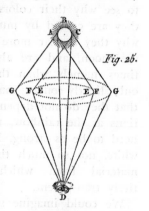

Fig. 26.

near E, but not a single one of those which go through the particles beyond the circle GG. It is manifest that, besides the rays AD, CD, and the like, which pass in a straight line and cause the sun to appear in its accustomed size, the others, which undergo refraction toward EE, must render all the air included in the circle FF quite brilliant, and cause its circumference between the circles FF and GG to be like a corona painted with the colors of the rainbow; and they must even insure that the red be inside toward F, and the blue outside toward G, in the same way that we are accustomed to observing it. And if there are two or many rows of particles of ice upon each other, provided that this does not prevent the rays of the sun from traversing them, those rays which will pass through two of them through their edges will be curved nearly twice as much as the others, and will produce yet another colored circle, very much larger in circumference, but less apparent than the first; so that we will then see two coronas, one inside the other, of which the inner one will be the more brightly colored, as has also sometimes been observed. Besides this, you can well see why these coronas do not usually form around stars which are very low on the horizon, for the rays then encounter the particles of ice too obliquely to pass through them. And it is easy to see why their colors are not as vivid as the other; for they are caused by much smaller refractions. And you see why they appear more frequently than the corona around the moon, and are also even noticed around stars sometimes, namely when the interposed particles of ice, being only slightly convex, make them very small; for to the extent that they do not depend on so many reflections and refractions as the rainbow, the light that causes them does not need to be as strong. But often they merely appear to be white, not so much through lack of light as because the material from which they are formed is not entirely transparent.

We could imagine still others of them which could be formed in imitation of the rainbow in drops of water, namely, primarily by two refractions without any reflections; but then there is nothing that determines their diameter, and the light is not limited by shadow, as is required for the production of the colors. Then they can also be formed by two refractions and three or four reflections; but their light, being then extremely weak, can easily be blotted out by that which is reflected from the surface of the same drops—which makes me doubt if they ever appear; and calculation shows that their diameter should be very much greater than we find in those we usually observe.

Finally, as to those we sometimes see around lamps and torches, their cause must be sought, not in the air, but only in the eye which looks at them. And I experienced this very clearly during the past summer. It was while traveling at night in a ship, when—after having been leaning my head all evening on one hand, with which I shut my right eye, while I looked toward the sky with the other—a candle was brought to where I was; and then, opening both eyes, I saw around the flame two coronas whose colors were as vivid as any I have ever seen in the rainbow. *AB* is the larger, which was red at *A*, and blue at *B; CD* is the smaller,

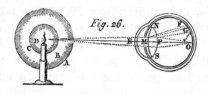

Fig. 26.

which was also red at *C*, but white at *D*, and which extended right to the flame. After this, closing the right eye, I perceived that these coronas disappeared, and that on the contrary, by opening it and closing the left eye, they continued to appear, which assured me that they proceeded only from some disposition that my right eye had acquired while I kept it shut. And this was the reason that, besides the majority of the rays from the flame that it received (represented at *O* where they converged together), there were also some of them which were so deflected that they extended throughout the space *fO*, where they colored the corona *CD*, and certain other rays extended in the space *FG*, where they colored the corona *AB*. I do not determine what this disposition was, for many different ones can cause the same effect: for example, if there are merely one or two small wrinkles in some one of the surfaces *E, M, P*, which, because of the shape of the eye, extend there in the form of a circle whose center is in the line *EO*, as there often are completely straight ones which intersect on this line *EO*, they cause us to see large rays scattered here and there around the flames; or else if there is something opaque between *E* and *P*, or even somewhere off to the side, provided that it extends there in a circle. Or finally, this can happen if the humors or membranes of the eye have in some way changed in temper or shape; for it is very common in those who have a disease of the eyes to see such coronas, and they do not appear alike to everyone. It is only necessary to note that the outer portion, such as *A* and *C*, of these coronas is usually red, quite the opposite to the ones we see around the heavenly bodies. The reason for this will be clear to you if you will consider that in producing their colors, it is the crystalline humor *PNM* that takes the place of the crystal prism of which I spoke earlier, and the base of the eye *FGf* which takes the place of the white screen which was behind it. But perhaps you will wonder why, since the crystalline humor has this power, it does not color all the objects we see in the same way, unless you consider that the rays coming from each point of these objects toward each point on the base of the eye—some passing through the side marked *N*, and the others through the one marked *S*— have completely contrary actions, and destroy one another, at least as far as concerns the production of colors; whereas here the rays going toward *FGf* pass only through *N*.

And all of this can, it seems to me, be very useful in confirming the truth of what I have said about the nature of colors, so closely are the two related.

Tenth Discourse

Of the Apparition of Several Suns

Sometimes we see still other circles in the clouds, different from those of which I have spoken in that they never appear as anything but completely white; and instead of having some heavenly body in their center, they normally go across the center of the sun or moon, and seem parallel, or nearly parallel, to the horizon. But because they appear only in those large, completely round clouds of which we spoke above, and because we also sometimes see several suns or moons in the same clouds, it is necessary that I explain both together. For example, let *A* be the south, where the sun is, accompanied by a warm wind tending toward *B;* and let *C* be the north, from which comes a cold wind, also tending toward *B*. And there I assume that these two winds encounter, or form, a cloud made of pieces of snow; and this cloud is so extensive, in depth and in width, that the winds cannot pass one above and the other below, or else between two of them, as they usually do. Instead, they are forced to take their course around it. By this means, not only do the winds make the cloud round, but also, because the wind coming from the south is warm, it slightly melts the snow around the cloud's circumference; and because this snow is immediately refrozen—by the cold north wind as well as by the proximity of the interior snow, which is not yet melted—it can form, as it were, a large ring of ice which is completely continuous and transparent, whose surface will not fail to be quite polished, for the winds which round it off are very uniform. And in addition, this ice

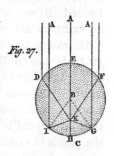

Fig. 27.

is thicker on the side *DEF,* which I assume to be exposed to the warm wind and the sun, than on the other side, *GHI,* where the snow was not able to melt so easily. And finally, it must be noted that in a mass of air of this composition, free of turbulence, there cannot be enough heat around the cloud *B* to form ice there, unless there is also enough of it in the earth below to stimulate vapors supporting it, by lifting and propelling skyward all the bodies of the cloud that it surrounds. Consequently, it is evident that the brightness of the sun, which I assume to be fairly high toward the south, falling all around on the ice *DEFGHI,* and from there being reflected on the whiteness of the neighboring snow, must make this snow appear, to those underneath it, in the shape of a large, completely white circle; and it is also evident that it is sufficient for this effect that the cloud be round, and slightly denser at the edge than in the middle, without it being necessary for the ring of ice to be formed. But when the ring is formed, if we are underneath, near point *K,* we can see as many as six suns, which seem to be set into the white circle much as diamonds are set into a ring. Thus the first, at *E,* is caused by the rays coming directly from the sun, which I assume to be at *A;* the two following ones, at *D* and *F,* by the refraction of the rays going through the ice in these places, where, since the thickness of the ice is diminishing, they are curved inward on both sides, as they are in traversing the prism of crystal of which I have just spoken. And for this reason, these two suns have their edges colored red, on their side near *E,* where the ice is the thickest; and the other edge is blue, where it is less thick. The fourth sun appears through reflection at point *H,* and the two last ones, also through reflection, at *G* and *I,* by means of which I assume that we can describe a circle whose center is at point *K,* and which passes through *B,* the center of the cloud, so that the angles *KGB* and *KBG,* or *BGA,* are equal; and the same is true of *KIB* and *KBI,* or *BIA.* For you know that reflection always takes place at equal angles, and that because ice is a polished body, it must represent the sun in all the locations from which its rays can be reflected toward the eye. But because rays coming directly [from their source] are always stronger than those which come by refraction, and because the latter are stronger than reflected ones, the sun must appear more brilliant at *E* than at *D* or *F*, and here again more brilliant than at *G*, *H*, or *I*. And these three—*G*, *H*, and *I*—must not have any colors around their edges, as do the two *D* and *F*, but be only white. But if the observers are not at *K*, but some place further toward *B*, so that the circle of which their eyes are the center, and which passes through *B*, does not cut the circumference of the cloud, they will not be able to see the two suns *G* and *I*, but only the four others. And if, on the other hand, they are quite far back toward *H*, or beyond toward *C*, they will be able to see only the five suns *D*, *E*, *F*, *G*, and *I*. And also if they are sufficiently far beyond, they will only see the three *D*, *E*,

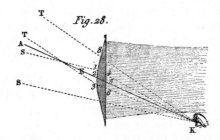

Fig. 28.

and *F*, which will no longer be in a white circle, but as if crossed by a white band. So also, when the sun has risen so slightly above the horizon that it cannot illuminate the part of the cloud *GHI*, or else when this cloud is not yet formed, it is evident that we must only see the three suns *D*, *E*, and *F*.

For the rest, I have only had you consider up until now the plane of this cloud, and there are still various things to be noted, which will be better seen in its side view. First, even if the sun is not in the straight line going from *E* toward the eye *K*, but higher or lower, it must nevertheless appear there, especially if the ice there is not too extensive in height or depth; for then the surface of this ice will be so curved that wherever it is, it will almost always be able to send the sun's rays back toward *K*. Thus if in its thickness it has the shape comprised between the lines *123* and *456*, it is evident that not only when the sun is in the straight line *A2* will its rays crossing this ice surface be able to go toward the eye *K*, but also when it is much lower, as in the line *S1*, or very much higher, as in the line *T3*. Thus they will always make it appear as if it were near *E*; for if we do not assume the ring of ice to be very large, the difference between the lines *4K*, *5K*, and *6K* is not considerable. And notice that this can cause the sun to be visible even after it has set, and that it can also make the shadow of sundials go forward or back, and cause them to mark an hour quite different from the one it actually is. Nevertheless, if the sun is very much lower than it appears at *E*, so that its rays also pass through the bottom of the ice in a straight line to the eye *K*, as in the line *S7K* (which I assume to be parallel to the line *S1*), then besides the six preceding suns, we will see yet a seventh underneath them, which, having the most light, will efface the shadow that the others could cause on the sundials. In the same way, if it is so high that its rays can pass in a straight line toward *K* through the top of the ice, as in the line *T8K* (which is parallel to *T3*), and if the interposed cloud is not so opaque as to hinder them, we will be able to see a seventh sun above the six others. But if the ice *123*, *456* is extended higher and lower—as far as the points *8* and *7*, for example—then if the sun is at *A*, we will be able to see three suns on top of one another around *E*, namely at the points *8*, *5*, and *7*; and then we will also be able to see three of them on top of one another at *D*, and three at *F*, so that there will appear to be up to twelve of them, enclosed in the white circle *DEFGHI*. And if the sun is slightly lower than at *S*, or higher than at *T*, there could again appear to be three of them at *E*, that is, two in the white circle, and another below or above; and then again there could appear two toward *D*, and two toward *F*. But I do not know that anyone has ever observed so many of them at once; or even if, when three of them have been seen on top of one another, as has happened many times, anyone has noticed any others at their sides; or else if, when three of them have been seen side by side, as has also happened many times, anyone has noticed any others above or below them. The reason for this is doubtless that the breadth of the ice marked between points 7 and 8 normally has no [set] ratio to the size of the circumference of the whole cloud. Thus the eye must be very close to point E when the ice appears broad enough for it to distinguish there three suns on top of one another; and on the other hand, it must be very far away in order for the rays which are curved toward D and F, where the thickness of the ice is the most diminished, to reach right to it.

And it rarely happens that the cloud is so complete that we see more than three suns at the same time. Nevertheless, it is said that in the year 1625 the king of Poland saw as many as six of them. And it is only three years since the mathematician of Tübingen observed the four designated here by the letters D, E, F, and H; he even noted particularly, in what he wrote of them, that the two at D and F were red on the side near the middle one, E, which he called the true sun, and that they were blue on the other side; and he wrote that the fourth one, H, was very pale, and was only slightly visible, which quite confirms what I have said. But the most elegant and most remarkable observation that I have seen concerning this matter is that of the five suns which appeared at Rome on the twentieth of March in the two or three hours after noon, in the year 1629. And in order that you can see whether it accords with my discourse, I wish to give it here in the same terms in which it was divulged at that time:

A is a Roman observer. B is a vertex over the location of the observer. C is the sun observed overhead in that direction. AB is a vertical plane, in which are found the observer's eye and the sun which was observed, and in which the vertex B also lies; and so all these are represented by the vertical line AB, and thus the entire vertical plane falls along this line. Around the sun C appeared two imperfect coronas, concentric with the sun, of various colors. The smaller or inner one, *DEF,* was fuller and more perfect, although it was imperfect, or rather, open, from D to F, and it ballooned itself out in a constant attempt to close itself; and sometimes it did close, but soon it opened once more. The other corona, always dimmer and hardly visible, was *GHI,* which was exterior and secondary; nevertheless, it was variegated and showed colors unique to itself, but it was always unstable. A third corona, which was of one color and was indeed very large, was *KLMN.* It was completely white, like the coronas which are often seen near and around the moon. This was an eccentric arc, which was perfect in the beginning part, which intersected the middle of the sun. Toward the end part, however, from M to N, it was dim and deformed, and at the bottom it was almost nonexistent. Moreover, in the intersections common to the circle and the exterior corona *GHI,* there appeared two parahelia N and K, of which the latter was less visible. N, however, shone more brightly and luminously. The gleaming center of both was like the sun, but the sides were tinged with the colors of the rainbow. The circles of these were observed not to be spherical or sharply defined, but uneven and full of gaps. N, an unstable apparition, was emitting a dense and incandescent tail *NOP,* with continuous variation in length. L and M, which were across the zenith B, were less intense than the former, N and K, but rounder and white, similar to their own circle, to which they cleaved, emitting a milky or pure silver color, although M, the middle third, even now had almost disappeared, and immediately afterwards left only dim traces of itself; in fact, the circle had disappeared from that part. The sun N waned before the sun K, and when N grew dim and disappeared, K grew brighter; and K disappeared last of all.

CKLMN was a white circle in which five suns were seen, and it is necessary to picture it such that if the spectator

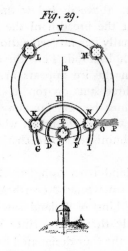

Fig. 29.

they are formed above or below; therefore it can happen that we see two coronas together, one within the other, which are nearly of the same size, but which do not have precisely the same center.

In addition it can happen that besides the winds which surround this cloud, there is a wind that passes above or below, and this again forms some surface of ice there, causing other varieties of this phenomenon; and the surrounding clouds can do this too, if rain is falling from the cloud. For the rays, reflecting from the ice of one of these clouds toward these drops, will represent the sections of the rainbow there, and their positions will be quite diverse. So also the observers, under not only one such cloud, but in the midst of several, can see other circles and other suns. Concerning this, I do not believe it is necessary for me to converse further with you; for I hope that those who have understood all that has been said in this treatise will, in future, see nothing in the clouds whose cause they cannot easily understand, nor anything which gives them any reason to marvel.

The Library of Liberal Arts

Below is a representative selection from The Library of Liberal Arts. This partial listing—taken from the more than 200 scholarly editions of the world's finest literature and philosophy—indicates the scope, nature, and concept of this distinguished series.